282-285

SO-BLA-282

THE BASIS
OF HUMAN
EVOLUTION

THE BASIS OF

HUMAN EVOLUTION

Withdrawn from UF. Surveyed to Internet Archive

Withdrawn from UF. Surveyed to Internet Archive

BERTRAM S. KRAUS, Ph.D.

*Director, Cleft Palate Research Center, Professor of Anatomy,
School of Dentistry, and Professor of Physical Anthropology,
Division of Social Sciences, University of Pittsburgh*

Illustrated by Virginia E. Brooks

HARPER & ROW, Publishers, New York, Evanston, and London

THE BASIS OF HUMAN EVOLUTION   Copyright © 1964 by Bertram S. Kraus. Printed in the United States of America. All rights reserved. No part of this book may be used or reproduced in any manner whatsoever without written permission except in the case of brief quotations embodied in critical articles and reviews. For information address Harper & Row, Publishers, Incorporated, 49 East 33rd Street, New York 16, N.Y.

Library of Congress Catalog Card Number: 64–18489

TO   *My wife, Dorothy*
My friend, Irwin P. Pohl
My teacher, Wilton Marion Krogman

CONTENTS

ACKNOWLEDGMENTS OF FIGURES

THE BASIS
OF HUMAN
EVOLUTION

INTRODUCTION

Ah, tell me, tell me now what fate awaits me . . .
Is all that I can hope this brief existence,
In which, like wine, my struggling soul, when strain'd,
Will be pour'd out and swallow'd in the dust?
Or is this spirit meant for something higher?
And shall those who come after me progress,
Becoming worthier to draw near Thy throne?

ADAM, in *The Tragedy of Man,* Imre Madach.

If one of the goals of education is to instill into the younger members of each generation a knowledge of the history and nature of the world in which they must function efficiently as adults, it is deplorable that one of the most fascinating and meaningful facets of this subject has been largely neglected—even at the college level. Most college graduates today are either uninformed or misinformed about the evolution of life forms and particularly about the genesis of their own species. The few courses offered on college campuses in biological evolution or specifically human evolution are either elective or are taken primarily by majors in zoology and anthropology or by graduate students. To the best of my knowledge neither textbook nor course in the evolution of man is available at the high school level.

In the past few years several excellent works on evolution in general or on human evolution have appeared. While they have doubtless been adopted into the curricula of anthropology and zoology departments, they are not well suited for the general college student who is not a major in these subjects or for the adult who wishes to become generally informed about the sub-

1

ject. There are several reasons why this is so. Some of these texts are heavily weighted in favor of the author's special field of knowledge or interest. This results in a book that strongly stresses genetics and underplays the importance of culture and paleontology, or that emphasizes the anatomical and anthropometric minutiae of the many hominid fossils while slighting the genetic and biological principles that help to interpret them. In any case, the student or reader who wishes merely to gain a general comprehensive understanding of the present status of our knowledge and interpretation of man's evolution is quickly "snowed" by a plethora of technical terms. As an anthropologist who has been teaching undergraduate and graduate students for almost twenty years, I am convinced that there must be a simpler way to lead the college undergraduate as well as the general reader into both an adequate comprehension of, and a quickened interest in, the events and processes that led to our presence on this earth. It is partly my purpose to attempt, with this book, to provide a simpler way.

The newcomer to the subject of human evolution can quite easily be overwhelmed by both the immensity of the subject and the vast amount of specialized knowledge that must be brought to bear upon the subject to gain our present understanding. Let him be reassured on two counts. First, no one of us who teaches or writes about the evolution of man possesses more than a small fraction of this total body of knowledge; and second, what we know about evolution is but a small fraction of what we would like to know and eventually will know. In fact, the reader must approach this subject with an attitude quite different from that with which he might enter upon the study of physics, chemistry, or geology. In the latter he can feel a certain basic security, confident that what are presented to him in both course and textbook are facts, time-tested and true. It may be many courses and many books later before he begins to enter upon fields where knowledge becomes scanty and questions are asked that have not yet been answered. This is not so in a subject like evolution which draws not only upon the physical sciences, but also upon the biological and social sciences for enlightenment. Almost with the first page, or the first day of class, we must make frequent use of such words as "maybe," "probably," "indicative of," "an alternative interpretation," and the classic "more investigation is necessary."

This incompleteness of our knowledge and the fact that we perforce ask more questions than we can yet answer are reflected in the organization of this book into "Problems" rather than the conventional "Chapters." It is perhaps as important to know what questions one should ask as to know what questions have been answered. As an anatomist friend, Harry Sicher, is wont to say, "the sign of true scholarship is to discover what important questions have not yet been asked." One should emerge from an introductory course in human evolution with a "sense of problem," that is, he should be aware not only of what we know but also of what we do not know but need to know. His level of understanding should preclude such questions as "Has the Missing Link been found?" and foster such questions as "What are the significant effects of the Industrial Revolution upon the role of Natural Selection in human evolution?"

I have indicated that many disciplines contribute to our understanding of evolution. These include: anatomy, physiology, sociology, embryology, paleontology, geology, geochronology, zoology, genetics, anthropology, archaeology, biochemistry, and psychology. The many divisions of each of these general areas of knowledge are also involved to a greater or lesser degree. It is readily apparent, therefore, that the student of evolution can only "skim the cream" off most of these fields as they pertain to his area of interest. The task of writing about evolution is primarily one of integration and interpretation. Since integration involves selection of what one regards as pertinent facts, laws, principles, and hypotheses from many areas of learning, and since interpretation is based upon the writer's own training, experience, and attitudes about science and life in general, it follows that there is much that is arbitrary and subjective in a book about human evolution. It is important, therefore, that facts and fancy be labeled as such. This is an obligation that I shall carefully attempt to fulfill in what follows. We might compare this book with what the physical anthropologist does when he attempts to reconstruct from the skeleton the physical appearance of the once-living man. The bones are "facts" but the addition of the soft tissues which cloak them and the modeling of the facial features into specific forms, like a "pug nose," full lips, and large brown eyes—these are educated guesses and are susceptible to alterations and modifications by "experts."

The study of human evolution is a very worthwhile exercise in patience. In the modern world of technical know-how, a high premium is placed upon the acquisition of facts and the ability to provide ready answers. There is little time for contemplation or audience for him who suggests there may be an alternate explanation of the existing facts. The present state of the evidence may not warrant any interpretation or conclusion, but the tempo of our times often demands conclusions which are premature and eventually prove to be fallacious. This unfortunate tendency is often carried into the field of scholarship. In the case of human evolution it can and does wreak significant harm to society. We must learn to be chary of judgments, based on insufficient or even no evidence, that touch upon socially inflammatory subjects. We must be willing, in the absence of decisive proof, to hold any definitive pronouncements or conclusions in abeyance. This is particularly true with regard to such subjects as the origin of races or the evaluation of racial differences. I do not mean to imply that these matters should not be discussed. Far from it. If anything, the study of man's evolution should provide one with a deeper perspective and a more profound background from which modern man in his complex world might be reassessed.

This brings us to a question that is too seldom asked. Why study human evolution? Since I am of the firm belief that every citizen, to be truly educated, should be at least generally informed about man's emergence from lower forms of animals, it is obvious that my purpose is not to make everybody a specialist or scholar. It is not important that one remembers that *Pithecanthropus erectus* was found on the banks of the Trinil River, or that Günz, Mindel, Riss, and Würm are names given to the successive glaciations in Europe in Pleistocene times. What is extremely important is that one emerges from his study of human evolution in possession of a series of concepts about the nature and principles of biological evolution, the nature and role of heredity in the evolutionary process, the special characteristics of human evolution, the relative recency of Man's arrival on the scene, the role of culture in shaping Man's evolutionary past and probable future, and the biological meaning of sex.

Every college professor knows that when he touches upon any facet of sex in his lecture he attains a remarkably high degree of attention in his class. It is quite understandable that young adults have a deep and abiding interest in sex. Their basic knowledge about the biological significance of sex, however, is in inverse ratio to their interest. I have repeatedly asked my classes to write down on an unsigned piece of paper their ideas of what the role of sex is in any bisexual species. The answers are invariably either "reproduction" or "fun." The majority of college students receive their degrees with no further comprehension of the important function that sex plays in the evolutionary process.

We are continuously alerted, in recent years, by radio, newspapers, magazines, and television about the dangers of radiation to the human species. The arguments pro and con have spread beyond the scientific halls of ivy to the political and religious arenas where they have become emotionally charged. A public that is largely uninformed has been driven to opposite extremes of attitude, each equally unjustified. Indifference to the increasing exposure to radiation from radioactive fallout is foolhardy, but hysteria also serves no real purpose. The latter has led many patients to refuse to submit to roentgenographic examination for diagnostic dental or medical purposes. What do we really know about the effect of radiation on the present generation, and can we assess the genetic damage that might be inflicted on future generations? Any real understanding of this problem requires that we be familiar with the role of mutations in the evolution of life on earth.

Since I am primarily concerned with presenting concepts rather than details, and with providing the reader with general understanding rather than attempting to make him a specialist in anthropometry, population genetics, or geochronology, I will make minimum use of details and nomenclature except as a means to facilitate comprehension. At the end of the book, suggested readings will be listed for the various topics discussed, problem by problem. The list, of course, is by no means intended to be complete. My experience as both student and teacher has led me to believe that a long list of references will "scare off" all but the specialist or major. My goal is to lead the reader gently into a difficult field. If this book succeeds in stirring his imagination and interest, the references that are provided will, in turn, guide him to additional reading.

This little volume is not written for my colleagues upon whose erudition and published works I have leaned so heavily. After years of reading, thinking, and teaching human evolution, it is now impossible to identify the many sources from whence I have acquired certain points of view or particular ways of interpreting the available evidence. Although the views expressed herein are peculiarly my own, I have no wish to assert their ultimate worth or superiority. Indeed, they should be regarded merely as one way of looking at life from the perspective afforded by familiarity with the history of life on earth. Each reader will doubtless construct his own philosophy and frame his own questions in accordance with his experience, his intellectual capacities, and his acquired interests. This is the goal I seek; not that one differs from me in his interpretation, but that he *does* interpret, on a basis of new and deeper understanding.

PROBLEM I

MAN'S KINSHIP WITH THE ANIMAL KINGDOM

When I view all beings not as special creations, but as the lineal descendants of some few beings which lived long before the first bed of the Cambrian system was deposited, they seem to me to become ennobled.

CHARLES DARWIN, *The Origin of Species*, 1859

Introduction

Increasing numbers of our young people are struggling through 16 years of secondary and higher educational institutions in order to achieve the distinction of adding the letters A.B. after their names. If they persist another year or two they may supplement this with the letters M.A. or M.S. Another three years of successful effort in graduate school will bring them to the pinnacle of educational recognition—the bestowal of another three letters—the Ph.D. Twenty-one years of dedicated study and self-denial in order to put on a calling card: Thomas Jones, A.B., M.A., Ph.D. These degrees, however, shrink into insignificance when we realize that Mr. Jones, without attending even one year of school, could legitimately have printed a card with the following legend:

Thomas Jones, A.K., S.K.M., P.C., S.P.V., C.M., O.P., S.O.A., S.F.H., F.H., G.H., S.S., S.S.C., (or S.S.M. or S.S.N.)

These degrees have been conferred upon each of us by virtue of the fact that we have been born as members of the human species. Not twenty-one years but perhaps half a billion years of struggle have gone into the attainment of these honors. They

7

tell us who we are more completely and more specifically than do the more transitory labels we earn in our brief span of life. For we are, each of us, members in good standing of the:

Animal Kingdom
Subkingdom Metazoa
Phylum Chordata
Subphylum Vertebrata
Class Mammalia
Order Primates
Suborder Anthropoidea
Superfamily Hominoidea
Family Hominidae
Genus Homo
Species sapiens
Subspecies Caucasoideus
(or Mongoloideus,
or Negroideus)

Although it is obvious that Man is an animal rather than a plant, there are simpler forms of life that are exceedingly difficult to classify as belonging either to the Plant or Animal Kingdom. What are the characteristics of animals that distinguish them from plants? For one thing, animals are heterotrophic, that is, they must acquire the food they need by eating other organisms. Most plants can manufacture their essential food requirements from the elements. Plants never stop growing throughout their lifetime, but animals generally have a definite and limited period of growth (if we define growth as increase in size). Animals propel themselves through their environment while plants remain sedentary. Plants are dependent in part on the environment for successful reproduction and propagation, but animals are generally able to reproduce without significant assistance from environmental factors. There are notable exceptions to these distinctions, particularly as we examine the simpler forms of life. Man, then, is a *bona fide* member of the Animal Kingdom.

The Divisions of the Animal Kingdom

Zoologists divide the Animal Kingdom into two parts, one comprising those animals consisting of but a single cell—the Protozoans—and those which are multicellular—the Metazoans. Man clearly belongs to the latter group. He is a Metazoan rather than a Protozoan.

The Metazoans, in turn, are divided into major groupings or Phyla. Whereas in Protozoans the single cell performs all of the essential functions of life, in Metazoans there are specialized cells, some of which accomplish digestion, some locomotion, and some reproduction, etc. The various Metazoan Phyla include the following:

Phylum Porifera—such as sponges

Phylum Coelenterata—such as jellyfishes and hydra

Phylum Ctenophora—such as sea-walnuts and comb-jellies

Phylum Platyhelminthes—flatworms

Phylum Nemertina (Rhynchocoela)—ribbon or round worms

Phylum Aschelminthes—rotifers, hookworms, pinworms, etc.

Phylum Acanthocephala—intestinal spiny-headed worm of pigs

Phylum Annelida—earthworms, clamworms, medicinal leeches

Phylum Arthropoda—such as spiders, crabs, scorpions, crayfish, shrimp, barnacles, centipedes, millipeds, insects, etc.

Phylum Mollusca—such as oysters, clams, mussels, conchs, chitons, snails, squids, octopi, etc.

Phylum Echinodermata—starfish, sea urchins, sea cucumbers, sea lilies, etc.

Phylum Chordata—birds, reptiles, amphibians, fish, and mammals

Among the phyla the chordates are generally distinguished by a ventrally located heart, a closed blood system, a notochord (or axial stiffening), a dorsally located nerve cord that is tubular and terminates in an enlarged area forming a brain, a segmented body, a complete digestive system, a cartilaginous or bony skeleton inside the body, a caudal appendage (or tail), and the appearance of pharyngeal gill slits at some stage of development. Man is therefore a member of the Phylum Chordata.

Four divisions of the chordates are recognized, called subphyla. Three of these are together called Acrania, since its members lack a bony cranium. They include such forms as the tunicates, *Amphioxus*, and worm-like creatures such as *Balano-*

glossus. The fourth division is called the subphylum Vertebrata, and consists of animals possessing the following structures:

A bony or cartilaginous vertebral column
Two pairs of jointed appendages
Girdles to which the appendages are attached
A brain formed from three primary brain vesicles
An endocrine system
Separate sexes, each with paired gonads and ducts
An endoskeleton
A covering of skin consisting of an outer and inner layer
A locomotor system consisting of appendages with attached
    muscles
Paired kidneys and ducts to form an excretory system
An autonomic nervous system
Ten or twelve cranial nerves with motor and sensory func-
    tions
A large body cavity, containing the visceral organs

Of these four divisions, man clearly belongs to the subphylum Vertebrata.

In turn, the vertebrates have been sorted into various classes. These are:

Cyclostomata—lampreys and hagfishes
Chondrichthyes (Elasmobranchii)—sharks and rays
Osteichthyes (Pisces)—bony fish
Amphibia—frogs and salamanders
Reptilia—lizards, crocodiles, turtles, snakes
Aves—birds
Mammalia—(see below)

Man is the type of vertebrate known as a mammal. Mammals have the following characteristics that distinguish them from other vertebrates:

Body hair
Nails, claws, or hoofs on digits
Warm bloodedness
Occipital condyles for articulation of cranium with verte-
    bral column
Four-chambered heart
Lungs

Diaphragm separating body cavity into pleural and abdominal cavities

Two sets of teeth—deciduous and permanent (diphyodon-
tia)

Mammary glands for suckling young

Fetal membranes and placenta

Non-nucleated red blood corpuscles

Constant temperature

Teeth of different types (heterodontia)

Integumental glands—sweat, sebaceous, scent, and tear

There are many kinds of mammals, most of which are placed
in the subclass Eutheria ("true mammals"). The egg-laying
mammals, such as the duck-billed platypus and the spiny ant-
eater, are assigned to a separate subclass Prototheria ("first animals") and to a special order—Monotremata. Pouched animals,
like the kangaroo and opossum, belong to the subclass Metatheria and the special order Marsupialia. The number of divisions into which the Eutheria should be partitioned is not
generally agreed upon by zoologists but we shall consider the following 16 orders:

Insectivora—shrews, moles, hedgehogs

Dermoptera—"flying lemurs"

Chiroptera—bats

Edentata—anteaters, sloths, armadillos

Pholidota—scaly anteaters, pangolins

Lagomorpha—rabbits

Rodentia—squirrels, porcupines, beavers, rats, guinea pigs

Cetacea—whales, dolphins, porpoises

Carnivora—cats, dogs, bears, weasels, otters, seals, walrus,
sea lions, etc.

Tubulidentata—aardvark

Proboscidea—elephants

Hyracoidea—coneys

Sirenia—dugongs, sea cows

Perissodactyla—horses, rhinoceros, tapirs

Artiodactyla—pigs, camels, deer, giraffes, goats, cattle, sheep,
antelopes, hippopotami, buffaloes

Primates—lemurs, tarsiers, monkeys, apes, man

We notice, as we narrow down the list of animals with which

man has characteristics in common, that these characteristics become less and less fundamental. For example, the traits that separate the higher divisions, such as the phyla, involve whole structures or systems. Rotifers and Porifera (sponges) differ in many basic ways; Rotifers have well-developed digestive systems while in sponges digestion occurs within individual cells; Rotifers have a distinct nervous system but sponges do not.

The Primates

The differences among the orders of Mammals are easily detected but of far less fundamental nature. The Primates are Mammals in that they possess the common characteristics of all Mammals, but they are a special kind or order of Mammals exhibiting characteristics which, though relatively superficial, are not held by other Mammals. In general, the Primates have:

Nails on digits instead of claws
A completely enclosed bony orbit
Prehensile hands and feet
Opposability of at least one first digit to remaining digits
Orbits directed forward instead of to the side
Enlarged cerebral hemispheres of the brain
Only one pair (except in certain prosimians) of mammary
glands, thoracically placed
Well-developed clavicles

These criteria definitely bring Man into that division of Mammals known as Primates. Thus far in the process of partitioning the Animal Kingdom into more and more specific categories only a general understanding of anatomy is necessary to grasp the nature of the traits which characterize the various groups into which we have placed Man. When we try to define Man's position among the Primates we find the differences that distinguish the several types of Primates are less obvious and require more detailed consideration. We shall attempt to expound upon these characteristics with the aid of illustrations. Primarily we shall focus upon the hard parts of the body—the skeleton and the teeth—since they alone survive as fossils.

The living members of the order Primates are found in all parts of the world. Certain groups, however, live in extremely restricted areas of the earth. Taxonomists—those scholars whose chief concern is the arrangement of living animals into appropriate and meaningful categories of presumed relationship—are in considerable disagreement over the classification of the Primates. For the most part we shall follow Simpson's[1] arrangement as presented in his monograph *The Principles of Classification and a Classification of Mammals*. He divides the order into two suborders—Prosimii and Anthropoidea. The suborder Prosimii is further divided into three infraorders—Lemuriformes, Lorisiformes, and Tarsiiformes. The many species and genera of prosimians are subsumed under six groupings called Families. They are: the *Tupaiidae* (tree shrews) found in the East Indies, Malaya, the Philippines, Borneo, and Sumatra; the *Lorisidae* (lorises, pottos, bush babies) found in Africa, Southeast Asia, and the Philippines; the *Tarsiidae* (tarsiers) in the East Indies and the Philippines; and the *Indridae* (indris, sifakas, avahis), the *Daubentoniidae* (aye-aye), and the *Lemuridae* (lemurs)— all three of which are restricted to Madagascar and the Comoro Islands off the southeast coast of Africa. In contrast to the Lemuridae, of which there may be over 85 existing species confined mainly to one island, the Tarsiidae are represented by only one living species, *Tarsius spectrum*, found throughout Malaysia.

The Tupaiidae have until recently been classified as Insectivores rather than Primates. As Simpson has pointed out, either they are "the most primate-like insectivores or the most insectivore-like primates." A brief description of the tree shrew, the lemur, and the tarsier is essential at this point since all three forms have important implications for human evolution.

The Prosimians

The tree shrews are small, agile, arboreal animals that somewhat resemble squirrels. Unlike the other Primates the digits of fore and hind paws are equipped with long curved claws. The tail is not prehensile but is used for balancing, and is generally very bushy. The orbits are directed somewhat laterally, unlike

[1] Simpson, G. 1945. The Principles of Classification and a Classification of Mammals. *Bulletin of the American Museum of Natural History*, vol. 85.

the lemurs whom they most resemble in the Primate family. Like the latter they have a naked moist nasal tip, provided with mucous and serous glands. Their brain is less complex than that of other Primates but less primitive than other insectivores. They may have as many as three pair of mammary glands. They have the same four types of teeth as other Primates; but the number of each type in each upper quadrant is like that of the New World monkeys—2 incisors, 1 canine, 3 premolars, and 3 molars, whereas there are 3–1–3–3 in each lower quadrant. Tree shrews primarily subsist on insects but will also eat fruit, seeds, and small mammals. Most of them are diurnal, only the pen-tailed tree shrew being nocturnal. Like the lemurs, they comb their fur with their long lower incisor teeth. Generally two young are born at one time.

The lemurs have flat nails on the second digit of the hind paw which bears a sharp claw. In length of the body they range from 4 inches (mouse lemur) to 24 inches (indri). Their eyes are very large, perhaps as an adaptation to the nocturnal life they lead. The lower incisor and canine teeth are unusually thin and elongated to form a sort of comb with which the animals preen their fur. In most of the lemurs the dental formula (that

is, the number of each kind of tooth) is $\frac{2-1-3-3}{2-1-3-3}$. The tail is

used entirely as a balancing organ. Hands and feet are extremely prehensile and are characterized by great mobility of the thumb and big toe. The upper lip is not free but is attached to the underlying gingiva so that the lemur laps water instead of suck-ing. The eyes look forward. Lemurs are primarily frugivorous. They do not menstruate. As in the tree shrews they have a preg-nancy of four months, after which usually one young is born. Lemurs are almost entirely arboreal.

The tarsier is also a nocturnal arboreal Primate. It has un-usually large eyes for its body which is only about eight inches in length. Its ears are also very large and the tail is long and de-void of hair except at its tip. The digits bear nails except for the second and third digits of the foot which are equipped with claws. The two long bones of the lower half of the leg are fused at the distal end, while the foot itself is greatly elongated. The latter feature is associated with the tarsier's method of locomotion which is by tremendous lightning-like leaps from tree to tree. Unlike the lemur the lip is unattached and mobile, yet the tarsier, too, drinks by lapping. His snout is less protrusive than either shrew or lemur and the nose, except for a small strip, is covered with skin. The dental formula is like that of the lemur except that there is but one incisor in each of the lower quadrants. The eyes and orbits are directed completely forward. Tarsiers have a monthly estrous cycle and vaginal bleeding occurs, but not of the menstrual type. Generally one offspring is produced at birth.

New and Old World Monkeys

That Man more closely resembles the members of the suborder Anthropoidea than those of the suborder Prosimii will be obvious as we now turn our attention to the former.

The rest of the Primates have a more widespread distribution than the Prosimii. The living Anthropoidea are classified into three superfamilies and five families as follows:

Superfamily Ceboidea
    Family Cebidae
    Family Callithricidae
Superfamily Cercopithecoidea
    Family Cercopithecidae
Superfamily Hominoidea
    Family Pongidae
    Family Hominidae

The Ceboidea include all the living Primates of North, Central, and South America, among which are the howler monkeys, capuchins, woolly monkeys, spider monkeys, squirrel monkeys, and marmosets. The Cercopithecoidea are the monkeys of Europe, Africa, and Asia, such as the macaques, Barbary apes, baboons, mandrills, drills, langurs, and guenons. The Hominoidea contains two families, the Pongidae or anthropoid apes, and the Hominidae or Man. Two of the anthropoid apes are found in Africa—the chimpanzee and the gorilla. The other two, the orang-utan and the gibbon, are found in southeast Asia and the East Indies.

Since Man is considered to be a member of the superfamily Hominoidea rather than of the Ceboidea or Cercopithecoidea, let us review briefly some of the special characteristics of each of these groups. The New World monkeys differ from the Old World monkeys in a number of ways. Their dental formula is $\frac{2-1-3-3(2)}{2-1-3-3(2)}$ while that of the Old World monkeys as well as the apes and Man is $\frac{2-1-2-3}{2-1-2-3}$. The finger and toe nails of the New World monkeys are compressed laterally and appear arched. The septum between the two nostrils is very broad, while the nostrils themselves are directed lateralwards rather than forward and downward. For this reason the New World monkeys are referred to as "platyrrhines" while the Old World monkeys are called "catarrhines." Many of the latter have well-developed cheek pouches which enable them to store quantities of food for later mastication. This feature is absent in the Ceboidea. Generally the snout protrudes farther forward in the Old World monkeys, a trait that is referred to as "prognathism." Grasping tails are found only among certain New World monkeys, where they attain their maximum degree of prehensility in the spider monkey. Ischial callosities—naked pads of skin over the lower portion of the buttocks—are characteristic of the Cercopithecoidea only. In Old World females, during menstruation, the skin of the perineal region (anus and genitalia) swells and becomes highly colored. This characteristic is absent in all New World monkeys. In both groups the big toe can be opposed to the rest of the digits, but only in the Old World monkeys is the thumb also opposable. In the New World monkeys the thumb is often much reduced in size and in the spider monkeys it has disappeared or become vestigial, as is the case with Colobus, an African monkey.

Man's Place Among the Primates: the Anatomical Evidence

We have succeeded in differentiating the Ceboidea from the Cercopithecoidea. Our next task, to consider the characteristics that distinguish Cercopithecoidea, Pongidae, and Hominidae, is not as easy as the system of nomenclature would appear to imply. Not all scholars, by any means, wish to include Man with the anthropoid apes as a superfamily Hominoidea distinct from the superfamily Cercopithecoidea. There is an increasing number of primatologists who claim that Man has more characteristics in common with the Old World monkeys than with the anthropoid apes. The precise taxonomic scheme that is applied to this part of the Primate order is of profound significance to the whole problem of human evolution, since, as we shall see later, taxonomy has important implications for the interpretation of evolutionary lines of ascent. At this point, however, we shall merely attempt to enumerate some of the characteristics which seem to unite and others which appear to separate anthropoid apes, Man, and the Old World monkeys.

Man differs from apes and monkeys in the following traits:

Teeth

    Lack of sex difference in size of canine teeth
    Reduction of canine tooth to the occlusal level of the other teeth
    Absence of diastema (gap) in the upper and lower dental arches

Head

    Largest relative brain size
    Curly or wavy head hair
    Prominent chin
    Large mastoid processes
    Prominent anterior nasal spine
    Greatest reduction in prognathism
    Presence of mental ossicles at birth
    Everted mucous membrane to form lips
    Acute angle of nasal bones to form nasal bridge
    Greatest reduction of brow ridges
    Foramen magnum placed near center of base of skull

Trunk (Thorax and Abdomen)

    Relative absence of body hair
    True inguinal ligament
    Lack of a penis bone
    Enlargement of sacral surface of ilium
    Curvature of sacrum
    Unique structure of kidney
    Anterior curvature of ilium

Lowest placed nipples
Lowest placed shoulders

Extremities
Short upper limbs relative to lower limbs
Complete erect posture and bipedal gait
Complete extensibility of fingers and palm
Greatest relative length of thumb
Complete opposability of thumb to other fingers
Loss of opposability and abductability of big toe

Growth
Greater length of the postnatal period of growth
Prenatal closure of suture between maxilla and premaxilla
Very late fusion or lack of fusion of nasal bones

Behavior
Articulate speech
Capacity for abstract thought
Ability to produce culture

There are, of course, many other special characteristics of human anatomy but the above list will suffice to indicate the nature of the differences which separate Man from his fellow Primates. Physiological, serological, and biochemical traits will be dealt with later.

It would be an interesting and revealing exercise if we could make a clay representation of a spider monkey, chimpanzee, or rhesus monkey skull and then remodel it to form a human skull, ignoring absolute size but observing true proportions. After scrutinizing the drawings of these skulls in Figure 1, which skull, in your opinion, would require the least amount of remodeling?

Man resembles the anthropoid apes and differs from the Old World monkeys in the following respects:

Head
Increase in size of head and brain relative to body size
Longer neck

Trunk
Absence of an external bony tail
Attenuation and disappearance of ischial callosities
Reduction in the total number of vertebrae
Increased number of sacral vertebrae

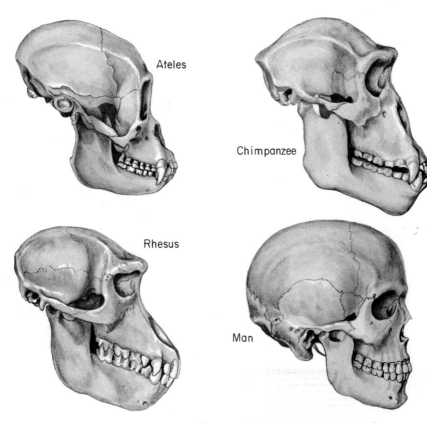

FIGURE 1. *Lateral Views of Skulls of Anthropoidea*

Reduced length of abdomen compared with length of thorax
Increased width of the shoulders and sternum
Greater breadth of the pelvis, shoulders, and chest

Extremities

Greater length of hands and thumbs relative to body size
Longer limbs, particularly the arms
Longer tarsus (the seven bones making up the posterior half of the foot)

Growth

Protracted periods of pregnancy and postnatal growth
Later fusion of the nasal bones

On the other hand, some authorities stress the many ways in which Man resembles Old and New World monkeys and the gibbon and differs from the remaining three anthropoid apes. These so-called "generalized" or "primitive" traits include:

Teeth
Eruption of the deciduous canine before the second molar
Parabolic shape of the dental arch
Relatively small permanent canine teeth

Head
Juncture of the sphenoid and parietal bones
Absence of a "simian shelf" (inwardly projecting bony plates at the base of the lower jaw)
Absence of laryngeal sacs or pouches

Trunk
Lack of a female sexual skin
Presence of a Pyramidalis muscle overlying the lower end of the Rectus abdominus muscle.

Extremities
Fully extended hands in the quadrupedal posture
Length of the thumbs relative to the rest of the hand
Presence of the Quadratus plantae, a muscle which assists and also partly inhibits the long flexor muscles of the toes
Short arms relative to length of the legs
The sequence of union of the epiphyses to the shafts of the long bones
Arrangement of skin fold or ridge pattern of the fingers (dermatoglyphics)

Growth
Late closure of the cranial sutures

It can be seen, then, that Man resembles the Ceboidea or Cercopithecoidea and differs from the Pongidae in a number of anatomical characters but that he resembles the latter and differs from the former in many others. A judgment about which group of Primates Man is akin to in terms of morphological and anatomical similarities is really dependent upon the weight one places on each trait. The question of weighing the significance of such traits is an extremely complicated one and it is doubtful if complete agreement could ever be reached by any two students of the problem. The truth is that we are still too ignorant of

the genetic basis and adaptive value and history of anatomic structures to make any judgment at all. Furthermore, we
have too scanty a knowledge of comparative primate anatomy
to place much reliance upon any listing of such traits, many of
which have been observed in only one representative of a particular genus or family. Perhaps the best statement we can make
at present is that Man has certain morphological and anatomical
similarities with each of the various groups of Primates, but in
certain structures is clearly unique among the Primates.

In terms of evolution, as we shall see, the most significant of
Man's peculiarly human traits are: (1) his completely erect
posture and habitual bipedal gait, (2) articulate speech, (3)
capacity for abstract and symbolic thought, and (4) immense
potentialities for learning and producing a cultural way of life.
The last three of these characteristics are products of the high
degree of development of Man's brain. Hence, in reality, we are
confronted with two fundamentally anatomic achievements that
set him apart from the rest of the Animal Kingdom—his erect
posture and his complex brain. The presumed relationship between these two entities in the course of human evolution will
be discussed in a subsequent Problem.

The Evidence of Biochemistry and Genetics

Anatomy, morphology, and behavior were once the chief clues
to Man's relationships within the Animal Kingdom. Now, however, there is increasing attention being paid to biochemical,
genetical, serological, and physiological traits as new techniques
and understandings develop. As with the more gross aspects of
the body, the results of these comparative studies are as yet in-
conclusive but appear to suggest that Man is more similar to
the anthropoid apes than to the monkeys. Coon has summarized
the results and cited the recent pertinent literature on this subject.[2] Man apparently resembles the apes rather than other Primates in the following biochemical, genetic, and physiological
traits:

[2] Coon, C. 1962. *The Origin of Races*. New York: Alfred A. Knopf,
Inc.

1. The metabolism of the crystalline compound purine
   (Many Primates tested. Man is closer to the apes.)
2. The ABO blood groups
   (Many Primates tested. Man is closer to the apes, excluding
   the gorilla.)
3. The MN blood groups
   (Many Primates tested. Man is closer to the chimpanzee.)
4. The precipitin test
   (Many Primates tested. Man is identical to the chimpanzee.)
5. Hemoglobins, haptoglobins, and serum transferrins
   (Many Primates tested. Man is similar to the apes.)
6. Whole globulin molecules
   (Only chimpanzee, gorilla, and orang were tested. Man is
   almost identical to the chimpanzee and gorilla.)
7. Serum albumin and serum gamma globulin
   (Gibbon, macaque, mandrill, and marmoset were tested.
   Man is closer to the gibbon.)
8. Gamma globulin, Gm group
   (Chimpanzees, gibbons, baboons, and rhesus, spider, and red
   monkeys were tested. Man is closer to the chimpanzee.)
9. Rate of excretion of amino acids in the urine
   (Only the four anthropoid apes were tested. The apes are
   quite different from man but resemble each other.)

The Evidence of Genetics

One of the more promising new approaches to the study of
primatology is the analysis of chromosomes, the gene-bearing
bodies which reside within the nucleus of each cell. It is known
that each species has a characteristic diploid, or somatic, number of chromosomes per cell. In Man there are 23 pairs of
chromosomes to produce the diploid number of 46. Chromosome counts have been made of many different species of Primates. In lemurs there is a range from 44 (black lemur) to 66
(mouse lemur). Among the lorises one species (slow loris) has a
count of 50 while another (potto) a count of 62. The various
marmosets thus far examined have diploid numbers of 46 and
48. Other New World monkeys range from 34 to 62. Old
World monkeys have diploid numbers from 42 to 72 but the
various species of macaques seem stabilized at 42, as do mandrills, drills, and baboons. Among the anthropoid apes, the gibbons all have the diploid number 44, and the gorilla, chimpanzee, and orang-utan show 48 chromosomes.

Although a difference in chromosome count is a clear indication of specific difference, the converse is not necessarily true. Thus, Man and the common marmoset have the same diploid number, 46, but we would hardly argue that the two are members of the same species.

While chromosome counts, in themselves, are not reliable indicators of degrees of affinity among animals, the analysis of the proportional characteristics of individual chromosomes to produce a pattern or karyotype may hold great promise for the future. Chromosomes vary not only in length but in the position of the centromere along its length. The centromere thus divides each chromosome into two arms of differing relative lengths depending on the position of the centromere. If the latter is located at the extreme end of a chromosome, the chromosome is then termed *telocentric*; if in the middle, *metacentric*; and if somewhere between end and middle, *subterminal*. It may be extremely significant that Man has no telocentric chromosomes in his karyotype, since it has been suggested that early Primates had a diploid number of 70 chromosomes all of which were telocentric. In the evolution of anthropoid apes and Man, according to this theory, the number was reduced by a process of combination or fusion of telocentric chromosomes into metacentric or subterminal chromosomes. The further study of what might be called "comparative Primate karyology" should throw additional light on this interesting speculation.

The Evidence of Embryology and Growth

Ordinarily, when we have occasion to describe the differences between two kinds of tree, or two types of animal, or even two people, we are most wont to visualize the characteristics possessed by each in the *adult* form. This is entirely natural since we see and interact with most plants and animals at some time in their mature stages of development. Equally characteristic of each species is the way in which its members arrive at the fully adult trait. In other words, the various developmental stages in the ontogeny of the individual are, within the bounds of normal variation, typical of each species. The study of the prenatal aspects of development is called embryology, while the subsequent stages of maturation are often referred to, in less formal terms, as the period of postnatal growth.

In Man the prenatal period has been divided into two stages, embryonic and fetal. The former encompasses a period of about two lunar months following conception, at the end of which time the embryo has, in general, achieved morphological differentiation of organs and external body form that is recognizable as human.

In the subsequent eight lunar months until birth, there is continued growth whereby changes in proportions of various parts of the body take place and the organs and systems are readied to take over when the new individual must leave the protective womb of the mother and begin to function more or less independently. The rate of growth during the prenatal period is so tremendous that by the time of birth the organism, which started out as a single-celled entity weighing .0000005 grams and measuring 0.1 millimeters in length, has attained 5 percent of its eventual adult weight or 3200 grams, and 30 percent of its adult length or 500 millimeters! An anatomist, Robert Bean, once calculated that if the rate of growth of the first month of embryonic life were to be maintained until adulthood, the resultant individual would be $128,350^{1100}$ light years in length![3]

Consequently, the rate of growth in the postnatal period is far less dramatic. It is a period when the "brakes" are being applied to growth, at least in terms of rate of increase in size. Growth eventually ceases in Man somewhere between 17 and 21 years of age. The postnatal stages in human development are given terms which are often more characteristic of cultural maturation than of anatomic or physiologic changes. The classification varies and is dependent upon the objectives and point of view of the classifier. For example, one way of labeling the postnatal aspects of human development is as follows:

Birth

Neonatal period	first two weeks after birth
Infancy	the first year of life
Preschool Childhood	from 1 to 6 years

[3] Robert Bean, cited in Krogman, W. 1943. Principles of Human Growth, *Ciba Symposia*, 5:1458–1466.

Childhood	from 6 to about 12
Puberty	variable, a 2 year period somewhere between 10 and 14
Adolescence	from puberty to about 18
Young Adulthood	from 18 to 35
Adulthood	35 to about 60
Old Age	over 60

Obviously this classification is purely arbitrary after puberty, a physiologic phenomenon, and is dependent upon social and cultural values. Certainly it would not apply to other Primates.

Unfortunately our knowledge of human embryology is confined for the most part to the White (or Caucasoid) branch of mankind, so that at the subspecific, sub-subspecific, or racial level we can say very little about the appearance of racial differences in the embryo or fetus. One anatomist (Schultz, 1926) has claimed to have detected numerous such differences between Negroes and Whites but his methodology in arriving at such observations leaves much to be desired in the light of modern statistical techniques. In my opinion it was decidedly premature and unquestionably a poor choice of language to make such pronouncements as: ". . . it can be stated that the white race has deviated farther from the simian condition of this proportion (face height relative to brain height) than has the negro."[4] This is precisely the type of judgment against which I cautioned the reader in the Introduction. It may or *may not* be true that the Negro fetus has a proportionately higher face than the White fetus. If so, it can only be statistically evident, with considerable overlap of the two populations. Furthermore, to draw conclusions about the evolutionary pathway of a trait without paleontological documentation is extremely hazardous. It might further be surmised that racial differences which are present at birth can be detected at some stage of fetal development.

At this point it may be well to ask: How can the study of comparative embryology give us any clues as to the relationship of Man to other animals and particularly to the Primates? Before we consider this question, let us first turn to a related but more comprehensive problem, namely, the interpretation

[4] Schultz, A. 1926. Fetal Growth of Man and Other Primates. *Quarterly Review of Biology*, 1:465–521.

that should be placed upon similarities and differences in morphological, anatomical, and physiological characteristics as we compare Man with other members of the Animal Kingdom.

Phylogenetic Reconstruction

The arrangement of living animals into various phyla and a series of subdivisions of phyla, such as we have done in the preceding pages, is based upon both quantitative and qualitative similarities and differences in morphology, anatomy, physiology, and embryology. Classification (or taxonomy) has been an intellectual activity of Man probably since he first began to survey the world about him. The system we now use is basically that of Carolus Linnaeus (1707–1778), who was a Swedish botanist. It was Charles Darwin, however, who, in his *The Origin of Species,* first asked the question "But what is meant by this system?" To Darwin, classification had a deeper meaning than merely to provide a convenient way of dividing the Animal Kingdom or to "reveal the plan of the Creator." He formulated his understanding in the following words:

I believe . . . that community of descent—the one known cause of close similarity in organic beings—is the bond, which though observed by various degrees of modification, is partially revealed to us by our classifications.[5]

The implication, then, is that the more similar two kinds of animals are, the more recent in time was the common ancestor of the two, while the more dissimilar are two types of animals, the more distant in time did the common ancestor of both exist. The degree of resemblance, therefore, is a general indication of the degree of kinship. We might call the classification of living animals a "horizontal" approach while the depiction of ancestral ties might be labeled a "vertical" approach. The reconstruction of lines of descent (phylogenetic lines) among the Primates and particularly that of Man, is a primary aim of the study of human evolution. Historically, the horizontal approach, utilizing at first the evidence of comparative anatomy, and only more recently the clues afforded by physiology, embryology, and

[5] Darwin C. 1928. *The Origin of Species.* Great Britain: The Temple Press Letchworth.

genetics, constituted the sole basis for reconstructing the story of evolution. Later, as more and more the systematic search for the fossil remnants of early animal life developed, and techniques for determining both absolute and relative chronology became more refined and precise, the vertical approach was combined with the horizontal to produce our present knowledge and concepts about evolution.

In Darwin's time, however, almost the sole evidence for deductions about animal evolution came from the horizontal approach based upon comparative anatomy and embryology. Perhaps this method can best be illustrated by drawings on a two-dimensional plane in which the horizontal dimension represents degree of resemblance or morphological similarity and the vertical dimension represents time. A horizontal line drawn across the top of the paper includes all the living forms of animals, whereas another horizontal line drawn across the middle of the page would include all the forms living, say, 50 million years ago. The farther down the page we place the horizontal line (or fragments of it) the earlier in time did the forms we wish, or are able, to describe exist. Vertical lines indicate lines of descent and imply that the forms at the top of such a line are the ultimate descendants of those at the bottom. The divergence of two lines leading from a common ancestor to a more recent descendant implies in a general way the progressive increase in differences between the two descending lines as the number of generations increase.

Let us now examine the meaning of the various hypothetical examples presented in Figure 2. In A the two living forms are represented as Gorilla and Man. They are connected to a common ancestor, X, by lines which converge downward to this common ancestor. In other words, X broke into two groups each of which, with the passing of time, pursued its own evolutionary destiny, becoming more and more different in morphology and anatomy. In B three Primates, Rhesus, Gorilla, and Man, are shown ultimately to be derived from a common ancestor, but Gorilla and Man are more closely related since their common ancestor, X, is more recent than the common ancestor of all three, Y. The line leading from Y to X may be looked upon as the common line of descent of both Gorilla and Man and might

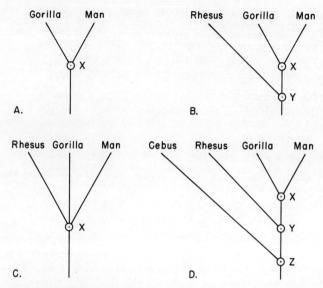

FIGURE 2. *Hypothetical Examples of Phylogenetic "trees"*

be labeled the "gorilla-hominid" line. Y is therefore the common ancestor of Rhesus and the "gorilla-hominid" forms. In C a different interpretation must be sought. Here the lines of descent of all three living forms are shown to spring "simultaneously" from a common ancestor. The line leading up to X could then be considered the common "rhesus-gorilla-hominid" line of ascent. In D a New World monkey, Cebus, is added and the resultant diagram gives one concept of the vertical relationship of these four Primates. Gorilla and Man, according to this representation, have a common ancestor X, which in turn shares a common ancestor Y with Rhesus. Y and Cebus have a common ancestor Z. The line leading up to Z is therefore the common ancestral stem of the living forms Cebus, Rhesus, Gorilla, and Man.

Interpretations of Primate Phylogeny

We are now ready to analyze the various interpretations of Man's kinship, first with the anthropoid apes, and then with the

other members of the order Primates. We eliminate the aspect
of chronology since this would introduce a complicating factor
for which we are not yet prepared. These interpretations are
presented in Figure 3, together with the names of the men who
proposed them. It is clear that, mathematically, there are a great
many possible arrangements and one is given the impression
from just the six arrangements presented that there is wide-

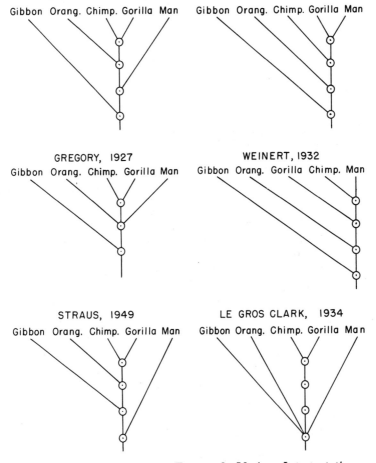

FIGURE 3. *Various Interpretations
of Primate Phylogeny*

spread disagreement among foremost students of the subject. By many, the chimpanzee and gorilla are considered to be most closely allied, that is, to have the most recent common ancestor.[6] Generally the gibbon is thought to be the most distant relative of Man among the Pongidae, but Le Gros Clark and Straus think otherwise.[7] Clearly the evidence is not conclusive and a reliable judgment must await additional fossil finds as well as more detailed genetical and biochemical analyses.

There is growing number of scholars who are coming to feel that the two-dimensional representation of phylogenetic relationships is not only an inadequate way of conveying the story of evolution but is quite apt to be misleading in that it, perforce, neglects the very nature of evolution. With this point of view I am in hearty agreement. Nevertheless, before we can propose other methods of representation we must first become acquainted with the many facets of the subject which enter into such consideration.

Although arguments still center upon the phylogenetic relationships among the various Pongidae and Man, an even more intense dispute rages over the broader problem of whether, indeed, Man is not more closely related to the Cercopithecoidea than to the Pongidae. On the one hand there is the school initiated by Thomas Huxley, who, in his essay "Man's Place in Nature" (1863) stated:

Thus, whatever system of organs be studied, the comparison of their modifications in the ape series leads to one and the same result—that the structural differences which separate Man from the the the Gorilla and the Chimpanzee are not so great as those which separate the Gorilla from the lower apes . . . there would be no rational ground for doubting that man might have originated, in the one case, by the gradual modification of a man-like ape; or, in the other case, as a ramification of the same primitive stock as those apes.[8]

His more recent adherents include Sir Arthur Keith and William King Gregory. The latter has concluded, in his paper "The

[6] Schultz, A. 1936. Characters Common to Higher Primates and Characters Specific for Man. *Quarterly Review of Biology*, 11:259–283, 425–455.

[7] Le Gros Clark, W. 1934. *Early Forerunners of Man*. London: Balliere, Tindall, and Cox.

[8] Huxley, T. 1890. *Man's Place in Nature*. New York: The Wheeler Publishing Company.

Origin of Man from a Brachiating Anthropoid Stock" (1930), that:

. . . in all the bones of his limbs, hands, feet, pectoral and pelvic girdles man is demonstrably nearer to the brachiating gorilla and the chimpanzee than to the primitive Eocene quadrupeds.[9]

The foremost spokesman for the opposing school of thought is William Straus who, in a paper entitled "The Riddle of Man's Ancestry" (1949), stated:

Making due allowance for the fact that a considerable part of the disagreement between the various theories of human ancestry is undoubtedly one of semantics, it is suggested that a non-anthropoid concept of man's ancestry is in closer agreement with known facts than is the orthodox theory. The presumed earliest representatives of the hominid line would consequently be visualized as essentially unspecialized monkey-like quadrupeds who, in their evolution, avoided the brachiating (arm-swinging) and other peculiar specializations characteristic of the anthropoid apes, and therefore never passed through an actual anthropoid-ape stage.[10]

Diagrams illustrating the two main schools of thought are presented in Figure 4. The common ancestries designated by capital letters in Figure 5 indicate the points of controversy with which we are most concerned. Letters V and R (in Figure 5) represent a third phylogenetic problem that has perplexed the students of Primate evolution—the question of which Prosimian line, lemuriform or tarsiiform, led to the higher forms of Primates. According to one famous anatomist, Wood Jones, monkeys, apes, and Man evolved from a primitive tarsier form. He went even farther in claiming that Man developed directly and independently from the early tarsiers (*Man's Place Among the Mammals*).[11] William King Gregory[12] and Ashley Montagu,

[9] Gregory, W. 1930. The Origin of Man From a Brachiating Anthropoid Stock. *Science*, 71:645–650.

[10] Straus, W. Jr., 1948. Riddle of Man's Ancestry. *Yearbook of Physical Anthropology*, 4:134–157.

[11] Wood Jones, F. 1929. *Man's Place Among the Mammals*. New York: Longmans, Green, and Company.

[12] Gregory, W. 1934. *Man's Place Among the Anthropoids*. Oxford: Clarendon Press.

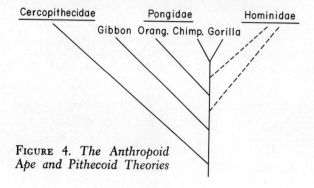

THE ANTHROPOID APE THEORY

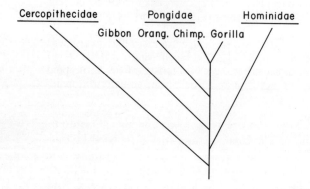

FIGURE 4. *The Anthropoid Ape and Pithecoid Theories*

THE PITHECOID THEORY

among others, have vigorously attacked Wood Jones' thesis. Probably the most prevalent view regarding the phylogenetic position of the tarsiers among the Primates is given in Figure 5.[13]

A further point of controversy is indicated by the letter T (Figure 5) representing the common ancestor of the modern varieties or races of Man. The question most frequently raised here is a temporal rather than a phylogenetic one. There is general agreement that the modern races are descended from a common hominid ancestor, but how long ago the various lines began to diverge from this ancestor is a moot point.

[13] Keith, A. 1934. *The Construction of Man's Family Tree*. London: Watts and Company.

Let us now briefly recapitulate the four basic problems in the phylogenesis of the Primates as they particularly affect Man. At the same time let us keep in mind that historically the various hypotheses that have been advanced have been based in large part upon the comparative study of bones, teeth, soft parts, and, to a lesser extent, embryology. We may list the problems as follows:

1. From which of the early Prosimian stocks have the Anthropoidea evolved?
2. Has Man an ancestor in common with all the anthropoid apes or with only particular ones?
3. Has Man evolved independently from an early Old World monkey like line without passing through an anthropoid ape stage?
4. How far back in time is the common ancestor of the modern races of Man to be found?

Finally, it should be mentioned that the ancestors of the modern tree shrew, whether the latter is to be placed in the order Primates or the order Insectivora, are generally accepted

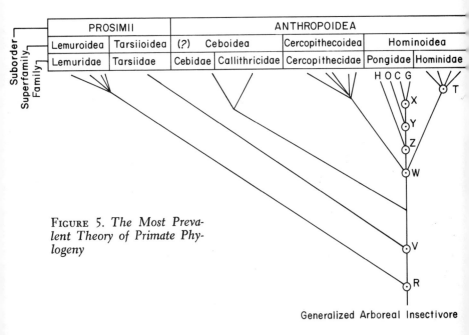

FIGURE 5. *The Most Prevalent Theory of Primate Phylogeny*

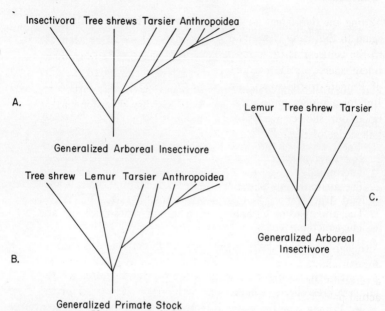

FIGURE 6. *The Phylogenetic Position of the Tupaiids in Primate Evolution: Three Interpretations*

as representing the sort of generalized arboreal mammal from which the Primates evolved. Simpson, however, on the basis of "the many definite and special lemuroid characters of the tupaiids" feels that the line leading to the living tree shrews should come off the line leading to the primates "after this line had become distinct and had acquired the most basic of primate characters."[14] The only known fossil form that can be surely considered tupaioid is *Anagale,* found in the Oligocene of Mongolia. This fossil, according to Simpson, would seem to support a theory of primitive lemuroid ancestry for the tupaiids. At any rate, it seems probable that the primitive tree shrews were the closest link between the Primates and the ancestral mammalian stem. Possible interpretations of the phylogenetic position of the tupaiids are presented in Figure 6.

As we proceed to take into account other kinds of evidence

[14] Simpson, G. *Op. cit.*

bearing on the evolution of Man, we shall be forced to turn again to the many charts which depict one or another theory as to the course this evolution took. One very important and pertinent source of information is the fast growing accumulation of Primate fossils which provide tangible links with the past. But for a proper understanding of how these fossils shed light upon our subject we must first acquire some more detailed knowledge of the following topics:

1. The ways in which time is measured and the age of fossils determined.
2. The anatomy of the skeleton and teeth of Man, since these hard structures are all that remain of past forms.
3. The principles of biological evolution.
4. The genetic mechanism of evolution.

Although the comparative anatomy and physiology of living animals allows us to hypothesize about evolution and to attempt a vertical delineation of probable phylogenetic lines, without the actual paleontological landmarks (the fossils), the chronological signposts, and the theoretical guideposts of principles of biological evolution, there would be no real advance beyond the stages of speculation. We turn, therefore, to a consideration of space and time.

PROBLEM II

PERSPECTIVES IN SPACE AND TIME

All things that live, endure for the same span;
The century-old tree, the one-day beetle,
Grow conscious, joy and love, and pass away
When they have reached their own appointed aims.
Time does not move. 'Tis only we who change.
A hundred years are but as one brief day.

LUCIFER, in The Tragedy of Man, Imre Madach.

Introduction

In this Problem we shall concern ourselves with the temporal and spatial relationships of life forms on earth. Inevitably, as we contemplate the immense stretch of time that has elapsed since the earth itself was formed and since the earliest animate beings made their appearance, we shall see our own life-span shrink into insignificance. This may be a somewhat depressing experience since we have been imbued from the time of infancy with a sense of the individual's importance. When we study the complex culture and society in which we find ourselves and realize that in the "three score years and ten" that is our expected longevity, each of us is capable of assimilating much of this culture and may contribute something to it, we understandably become convinced of Man's overwhelming superiority in the Animal Kingdom. It is perhaps paradoxical that in scanning the past we become dismayed at the transitoriness of Man and the

37

relative insignificance of a human life, but when we learn about the biological inheritance from the incredibly remote past that each of us as individuals receives and passes on to our children, then we take heart and again feel impressed with the importance of each of us. This time, however, our pride is based upon a foundation of knowledge about ourselves as part of a great stream of life, and not upon self-imposed and egocentric values.

The Time Perspective

In the previous Problem we found that each of us is a *bona fide* member of a number of animal societies, but we neglected to indicate how long an indoctrination period preceded each new membership. Most of us can comprehend figures in the hundreds and even thousands, but unless we are Congressmen dealing with the national budget it is difficult to grasp the meaning of hundreds of thousands or millions. In order to gain a proper perspective of time it is necessary to convert years to some scale that is familiar to all of us. Many people have crossed the United States either by car, train, or plane, and those who have not have at least become familiar with the mileage and geography through study of a map. Let us therefore open an atlas to a map of the United States and draw a straight line from San Francisco to New York City. If a superhighway were built along this line it would extend about 2460 miles from Union Square in San Francisco to the very entrance to Grand Central station in New York City. Let this highway represent the passage of time from the beginning of the formation of the earth (in San Francisco) to the present moment (at Grand Central Station). In other words, about 5 billion years is represented by these 2460 miles, so that each mile we traverse will be equivalent to the passage of almost 2,000,000 years. As we leave Union Square on our journey across the United States we shall depict important events in the history of the earth and of life itself in terms of cities, towns, and geographical features.

As we leave Union Square the earth is just beginning to form its molten inner core. We travel eastward at a steady rate through Yosemite National Park and into Nevada. Continuing through Nevada we pass through the town of Ely and thence into Utah. Without stopping we traverse the entire state of Utah, entering Dinosaur National Monument on its northeastern border. As we leave the Monument in northwestern Colorado we pause briefly to note that there is no sign of life in any form but that the earth itself exhibits many active volcanoes. We continue through northern Colorado, cross the southeast tip of Wyoming near Cheyenne and then enter Nebraska. Without pausing we cross central Nebraska and enter Iowa, making our second stop of the trip at Ames, a town about 40 miles north of Des Moines. Here, for the first time, we can distinguish tiny single-cell marine animals, algae, and fungi. [1]

Continuing eastward through Iowa, northern Illinois and Indiana, we enter Ohio and stop briefly in Cleveland, where we see, in addition to the marine protozoans, some molluscs and simple marine invertebrates. These are the only signs of life until we cross into Pennsylvania north of the town of Sharon and make our next stop at the line separating Forest from Elk County. Here we see an abundance of such arthropods as trilobites, branchiopods, and eurypterids as well as brachiopods (bryozoans). We proceed another 39 miles to Benezett where the first fishes and land plants appear. For the next 32 miles we continue to observe these primitive fishes and plants until we reach South Renovo, Pennsylvania, where we find wingless insects crawling about the ground. After a short drive of 17 miles we halt at a place about five miles east of Glen Union where we see the first forests, amphibians, and many sharks. Twenty-two more miles takes us to Williamsport, Pennsylvania, where reptiles make their first appearance. There are increasing numbers of amphibians and sharks. A short 25 mile drive brings us to the town of Millville where we get our first glimpse of mammal-like reptiles and modern-type insects. In 12 more miles, at Beach Haven, Pennsylvania, the primitive amphibians, once so numerous, have disappeared and the first egg-laying mammals and dinosaurs may be viewed. When we proceed another 19 miles to the little town of Whitehaven, we see larger and larger dinosaurs, birds with teeth, and insect-eating marsupials. In 15 more miles we reach the Monroe County line and find the giant dinosaurs ruling the earth, but the toothed birds have been replaced by modern-type birds. The dominance of the dinosaurs is brief, however, and by the time we cross into New Jersey they have disappeared.

As we pull into Great Meadows, New Jersey, we find some animals that begin to look familiar—carnivores, hoofed animals, and such prosimians as lemurs and tarsiers. A short 18 mile drive takes us to the Passaic River where more and more modern-type mammals appear. Monkeys and apes are becoming numerous and diversified. As we enter Newark, New Jersey, we see an abundance of elephants, camels, and horses, and glimpse ape-like creatures that are not quite apes nor quite like Man as we know him. But as we leave Newark and cross the Hudson River this ape-like creature begins to walk erect and we see him crouched before a campfire in front of a rock shelter. When we enter Manhattan and reach Broadway and 42nd Street we find a succession of glaciers descending over the northern parts of Europe, Asia, and North America, and we see little bands of men and women, clad in the furry skins of animals, huddled before fires in caves, or, in the periods between glaciations, camped in the open around fires roasting meat or chipping pebbles to form knife blades or projectile points. As we proceed across 42nd Street toward Grand Central Station we observe numbers of these people making drawings on the walls of caves. Some 40 or 50 feet from the Station we see men planting or harvesting such crops as millet, rice, and corn. At five feet and one inch from the entrance to the Station we witness the birth of Christ and only six inches from the entrance we see a group of men signing the Declaration of Independence. At slightly more than two inches from the entrance we witness the birth of a man who, at this very moment, is 70 years old.

Compared with the age of the earth our own lifetime is as two inches of the distance from San Francisco to New York City! Man himself, as a producer of culture, is merely the final half mile of this journey. Truly the lifetime of each of us is but the duration of a snap of the fingers when viewed against the vast expanse of time during which life itself has existed on earth.

The Primates, as an order, arose some 75 million years ago and hence it is this period of time in which we are most interested. Therefore, it is necessary that we become acquainted with the nomenclature of the chronological periods into which this span of time is conventionally divided. The last 75 million years of the earth's history is called the Cenozoic (from the Greek, meaning "recent life") era. It, in turn, is divided into two periods, the Tertiary, representing 74 million years, and the Quaternary, embracing but the last one million years. The Tertiary period is subdivided into five "epochs"—Paleocene, Eocene, Oligocene, Miocene, and Pliocene, each of varying durations. The Quaternary period begins with the Pleistocene ("most recent") epoch which was a time of extensive glaciations and lasted about one million years, and ends with a Recent epoch. The Recent is generally calculated to have begun some 25,000 years ago and is the epoch in which we now find ourselves. It might be convenient for the purpose of reference to chart these divisions as follows:

Duration in millions of years	Era	Period	Epoch
.025 1.0	Cenozoic	Quaternary	Recent Pleistocene
11.0 16.0 11.0 19.0 17.0		Tertiary	Pliocene Miocene Oligocene Eocene Paleocene

Temporal and Spatial Distribution of the Prosimians

Primate fossils have been found in widely scattered areas of the world. There are huge gaps in time separating fossils of the same or closely related phylogenetic lines. Representatives of the Lemuroidea known by the family name of Plesiadapidae have been unearthed in both the United States and France, and a number of tarsiiforms such as *Palenochtha, Paromomys, Plesiolestes,* and *Navajovius* have been discovered in the United States. These are among the few Primate fossils that have survived from Paleocene times. In the subsequent Eocene epoch both lemur and tarsier fossils were recovered from Europe and North America, and in addition two possible Pongidae known as *Amphipithecus* and *Pondaungia,* both found in Burma.

From Eocene times until the beginning of the Pleistocene, there are no further fossils that can be assigned to the Lemuriformes. In the Pleistocene and in the Recent all fossil Lemuriformes have been recovered in Madagascar where the existing families are found. It is difficult to try to reconstruct the evolutionary fate and migrations of the lemurs on the basis of the present evidence. It is perhaps unwise to assume that further excavations in Europe and Africa will not uncover lemuroid fossils of Oligocene, Miocene, and Pliocene times. Nevertheless it seems likely that, wherever the origin of the lemurs—in North America or in Europe—they were forced to migrate south. On the one hand the North American varieties may have moved south into Central and South America where they either became extinct or contributed to the evolution of the New World monkeys. The European lemurs evidently migrated out of Europe and into Africa, whence they were driven, by conditions that we are unacquainted with, to Madagascar. In Madagascar the lemurs apparently flourished and some 20 different genera evolved. The best known fossil lemur is that of *Notharctus*, found in Wyoming and described in a monograph by William King Gregory, "On the Structure and Relations of *Notharctus*, an American Eocene Primate."[1] Gregory felt that the American lemur was more primitive than the European varieties and hence some primatologists would ascribe the origin of the Lemuroidea to North America. The accompanying outline map (Fig.7) shows the most likely history of the Lemuriformes, based upon available evidence.

The infraorder Lorisiformes consists of the so-called Lorisiform lemurs. The genera *Loris* and *Nycticebus* are found in India, southeast Asia, Indonesia, and the Philippines. The genera *Arctocebus, Perodicticus, Galago,* and *Euoticus* occupy equatorial Africa. Early Miocene deposits in East Africa have produced fossil fragments of Lorisiformes resembling the modern *Galago*. The only fossil Lorisiform recovered elsewhere consists of a single molar tooth found in the Pliocene of India. It has been given the name *Indraloris*. Until more fossil material is

[1] Gregory, W. 1920. On the Structure and Relations of *Notharctus*, an American Eocene Primate. *Memoirs of the American Museum of Natural History*, new series III, Part II, pp. 49–243.

FIGURE 7. *Postulated Migrations of the Lemuriformes*

forthcoming it is difficult even to speculate about the origin and migrations of these prosimians.

It is the tarsier, however, who is the most important prosimian from our point of view, since it was from his ancestral line that the Old World monkeys and Hominoidea originally branched out, according to most students of the subject. Whether or not the tarsioid line also gave rise to the New World monkeys is a moot point. Gregory (*Evolution Emerging*) states: ". . . it seems that the South American *Homunculus* may . . . have been derived either from such a very primitive Paleocene North American tarsioid as *Paromomys*, or from a relatively advanced Eocene lemuroid such as *Pronycticebus*" (p. 470).[2] Today only one species of tarsier exists, the Spectral Tarsier, found from the Philippines to the East Indies. In early Tertiary times, however, there were perhaps 25 different types or "genera" living in

[2] Gregory, W. 1951. *Evolution Emerging*. New York: The Macmillan Company.

North America and Europe. The earliest fossils of Paleocene age
are found in the United States. Perhaps both Lemuriformes and
Tarsiiformes evolved from primitive tree shrews in North
America. The early Tarsiiformes of Paleocene, Eocene, and
Oligocene times are placed by Simpson into the family Anapto-
morphidae, consisting of several subfamilies.[3] Their age and
provenience are listed below:

SUBFAMILY	EPOCH	DISTRIBUTION
Paromomyinae	Paleocene	United States
Omomyinae	Eocene	United States and Belgium
Anaptomorphinae	Eocene	United States
Necrolemurinae	Eocene	Europe and England
Pseudolorisinae	Eocene	France

Two of the North American Omomyinae are not of Eocene
age. One, *Navajovius*, is from the late Paleocene; the other,
Macrotarsius, belongs to the early Oligocene and is the most
"recent" tarsioid fossil to be found. Because the North American tarsioids are older and more primitive in some respects than
their later European cousins, it might be argued that the latter,
like the European lemuroids, originally migrated from North
America. On the other hand, it is perhaps equally plausible to
contend that the European tarsioids evolved independently from
primitive Old World tree shrews. At any rate the North American tarsioids seem to have vanished in early Oligocene times
(Fig. 8), while across the Atlantic their relatives left Europe and
migrated eastward, eventually occupying their present habitat
off the Asiatic Coast. It may be helpful to glance at the accompanying map (Fig. 9) in order to compare the tarsioid history
with that of the lemuroids shown in Figure 7.

Temporal and Spatial Distribution of the Cercopithecoids

Unlike the tarsioids, there are many living genera and species of
Cercopithecoidea, but relatively few fossil forms. What is more,
there is practically no temporal overlap between the fossil

[3] Simpson, G. 1945. The Principles of Classification and a Classification of Mammals. *Bulletin of the American Museum of Natural History*, vol. 85.

	North America	Europe	East Indies
RECENT			Spectral Tarsier
PLEISTOCENE			
PLIOCENE			
MIOCENE			
OLIGOCENE	Macrotarsius		
UPPER EOCENE	Chumashius Dyseolemur Yumanius	Necrolemur Microchoerus Pseudoloris	
MIDDLE EOCENE	Uintanius Omomys Hemiacodon Washakius Anaptomorphus Euryacodon	? Periconodon Necrolemur Nannopithex	
LOWER EOCENE	Absarokius Loveina Shoshonius Tetonius Paratetonius	Teilhardina	
UPPER PALEOCENE	Navajovius Paromomys		
MIDDLE PALEOCENE	Palaechthon Palenochtha Plesiolestes Paromomys		

FIGURE 8. *Temporal and Spatial Distribution of the Tarsioids*

lemuroids and tarsioids, on the one hand, and the fossil Old World monkeys on the other. The former pertain to the Paleocene and Eocene (with a single exception) while the latter come from the Lower Oligocene and subsequent epochs. Fossil

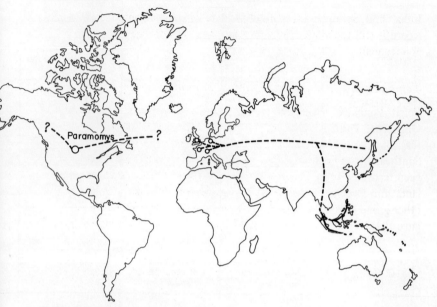

FIGURE 9. *Postulated Migrations of
the Tarsioids*

Cercopithecoidea have been found, for the most part, in more
southerly latitudes—in South and East Africa, Egypt, Italy,
Greece, Czechoslovakia, South Russia, Iran, and India (see Fig.
10). It will be noted that *Oreopithecus* has sometimes been included among the Cercopithecoidea. Recently many additional
remains attributed to this form have been found in Italy and
there is currently much dispute among paleontologists about its
proper taxonomic position. We shall discuss the *Oreopithecus*
in a later Problem.

The distribution, chronology, and morphology of the Cercopithecoid fossils lend a measure of support to the hypothesis
that the European tarsioids not only migrated eastward to their
present location but that some groups moved southward, perhaps evolving on the way into the primitive monkey forms whose
fossils are scattered from South Europe to India. The latter, in
turn, continued to migrate to their present homes in Africa,

India, and Southeast Asia. Unfortunately, the paleontological record is still too scanty to allow us to make any categorical pronouncement.

Temporal and Spatial Distribution of Hominoids

Fossil Pongidae have been found dating as early as Lower Oligocene. Perhaps the best documented phylogenetic line is that of the Hylobatinae or gibbons, who now are found in Southeast Asia. Fossils ascribed to the gibbon ancestral line have been recovered from Europe (Germany, Austria, France, Switzerland, and Czechoslovakia) and Africa (Egypt and Kenya). Another group of apes, generally referred to as the Dryopithecinae, have left remains in Europe, Africa, and India datable to

	S. and E. Africa	Egypt	Europe	S. Russia and Persia	India
RECENT					
PLEISTOCENE	Parapapio Dinopithecus				Presbytis Papio
UPPER PLIOCENE	Simopithecus				
MIDDLE PLIOCENE		Libyithecus	Dolichopithecus		Cercopithec. Macaca
LOWER PLIOCENE			Oreopithecus? Mesopithecus	Mesopithecus	
LOWER OLIGOCENE		Apidium? Moeripithecus?			

FIGURE 10. Fossil Cercopithecoidea

Miocene and Pliocene times. More recent fossil material, pertaining to the Pleistocene epoch, is extremely difficult to assign taxonomic rank, and has been the subject of great controversy. Such forms include *Gigantopithecus* from China, and *Australopithecus* from South Africa. Three much earlier fossils have been provisionally treated as Pongidae of uncertain affinities. They are *Pondaungia* and *Amphipithecus*, found in the Upper Eocene of Burma, and *Xenopithecus*, found in the Lower Miocene of Kenya. The chart in Figure 11 presents the names and temporal and spatial positions of the fossil Pongidae.

The New World Monkeys

Although the New World monkeys have pursued their own evolutionary pathway and are unrelated to the Hominoidea and Cercopithecoidea except through a common primitive tarsioid ancestry, it would not be amiss in this discussion of the distribution of the Primates in time and space to mention the paleontological record of the Ceboidea. It is, unfortunately, extremely scanty. The first fossil form, a poorly preserved skull found in the Lower Miocene of Patagonia, was given the name *Homunculus* by its discoverer, Ameghino, who thought it was a direct ancestor of Man. Later studies showed its close affinities with the family Cebidae. *Dolichocebus*, ancestral to the family Callithricidae, was recovered from the Upper Oligocene of Patagonia. From the Upper Miocene of Colombia come two fossil forms, *Cebupithecia* (assigned to the subfamily Pitheciinae of the family Cebidae) and *Neosaimiri* (apparently ancestral to the genus *Saimiri* of the subfamily Cebinae). Pleistocene fossils include *Xantothrix* from Jamaica, and various representatives of the living *Callicebus*, *Alouatta*, and *Cebus* from Central and South America (Remane, 1956).[4]

Thus far no fossils of hominid rank have been found that can be dated earlier than the beginning of the Pleistocene epoch. In general, two kinds of hominid fossils may be distinguished: one is considered to be morphologically quite different from modern Man and has been termed Archaeanthropic by Weidenreich and

[4] Remane, A. 1956. Paläontologie und Evolution der Primaten. *Primatologia*, 1:267–378.

	Europe	India	Egypt	Kenya	Burma
PLEISTOCENE					
UPPER PLIOCENE		*Ramapithecus*			
MIDDLE PLIOCENE					
LOWER PLIOCENE	*Pliopithecus* *Paidopithex* *Dryopithecus*	*Bramapithecus* *Hylopithecus* *Sivapithecus* *Palaeosimia* *Sugrivapithecus*			
UPPER MIOCENE	*Pliopithecus* *Dryopithecus*				
MIDDLE MIOCENE	*Pliopithecus* *Dryopithecus*				
LOWER MIOCENE			*Pliopithecus*	*Zenopithecus* *Limnopithecus* *Proconsul* *Sivapithecus*	
LOWER OLIGOCENE			*Propliopithecus* *Parapithecus?*		
UPPER EOCENE					*Pondaungia?* *Amphipithecus?*

FIGURE 11. *Temporal and Spatial Distribution of the Fossil Pongidae*

Paleanthropic by Keith, or *Homo erectus* by Coon; the other is morphologically practically identical to modern Man and was termed Neanthropic by Keith and *Homo sapiens* by Coon. The primitive hominid fossils have all been recovered from Pleistocene sites, whereas the modern types stem from Late Pleistocene and Recent times.

A complete up-to-date listing of the many hominid fossils has been provided by Coon in his *The Origin of Races;*[5] however, many of these consist of a few teeth or fragments of skull or limb bones, and actually have contributed very little of a positive nature to our knowledge about human evolution. They are more tantalizing than informative. The fossils of primitive hominids listed in Table 1 are the main sources for our present interpretation of hominid evolution in the Pleistocene, and they will be discussed in a later problem. In the table the common name, date of discovery, temporal position, and location of the remains is indicated.

Geochronometers: the Measurement of Geologic Time

One of the most fascinating aspects of the story of human evolution is the development of methods and techniques for determining the age of fossil remains. Until a few years ago only *relative* chronology could be obtained by interpreting the sequence of geological strata containing evidences of past life. This kind of "dating" enabled paleontologists to record the succession of life forms in a particular area but it posed numerous difficulties in matching sequences in different parts of the world. For example, in two geographical areas I and II the paleontological records might be fairly accurately worked out, from bottom to top, as follows:

AREA I	AREA II
E	V
D	W
C	X
B	Y
A	Z

In Area I animals represented by fossils found in stratum B followed in time those found in stratum A but immediately preceded those occurring in stratum C. The same applies to Area II. When an attempt is made to equate in time the strata of Area I

[5] Coon, C. 1962. *The Origin of Races.* New York: Alfred A. Knopf, Inc.

with those in Area II, so that one could say that A was contemporary with Z, B with Y, etc., many problems arise. For one thing, the relative thickness of a geological layer is not indicative of its temporal duration. Under some conditions 80 feet of deposition might take place in a few hundred years, while under others only 6 feet might be deposited over several thousand years. Although as a general rule the deepest stratum may be considered the oldest and the one immediately overlying it the next oldest, and so on until we come to the top layer which is the youngest, there are many exceptions that make the application of this rule extremely hazardous. The natural succession of geological strata in the earth may be disturbed by such phenomena as erosion, submerging and upthrust, and overthrust. In such cases only experts in historical geology can interpret the stratigraphic record.

In addition to stratigraphy there have been worked out many other methods whereby relative chronology can be established more or less reliably under particular circumstances. The succession of European glaciations and interglaciations has been established partly on the basis of fluvio-glacial terraces. Alternation of cold glacial and warm interglacial conditions produces alternate deposition and erosion along rivers, each erosion cutting down the bed of a river and leaving the previous deposit in the form of a terrace on each bank. In time, a series of such terraces reflects the succession of glaciations and interglaciations.

The series of beach levels around the seacoasts give testimony, likewise, to the alternate lowering and raising of the land in response to the weight of the glacial mass and the relief from this weight due to the melting of the ice. In addition, the alternate freezing and melting of the ice affected the level of the sea, causing more rapid changes in the land-sea relationship. The interpretation of the geological story behind these series of raised and "drowned" sea beaches affords supplemental evidence of relative chronology and permits us to calculate when land bridges existed, such as those between the Chuckchi Peninsula and Alaska and between Southeast Asia and Indonesia.

Many of us are familiar with the lateral and terminal moraines left by successive glaciations in northern America. These, plus the wide sheets of bottom-moraine and the plateaus formed by

TABLE 1. *The Spatial and Temporal Distribution*

Common Name	Date of Discovery
JAVA	
Pithecanthropus I	1891–Dubois
Mandible A	1891–Dubois
Mandible B	1936–von Koenigswald
Pithecanthropus II	1937–von Koenigswald
Pithecanthropus III	1938–von Koenigswald
Pithecanthropus IV (Pithecanthropus robustus)	1939–von Koenigswald
Homo modjokertensis	1936–Geol. Survey
Mandible C (Pithecanthropus dubius)	1939–von Koenigswald
Meganthropus palaeojavanicus (Mandible D)	1941–von Koenigswald
Solo Man	1931–33–Oppenoorth
Wadjak Man	1889–Dubois
AUSTRALIA	
Keilor	1940–workmen
Talgai	1884–workmen
Cohuna	1925–workmen
CHINA	
Sinanthropus I-XIV	1927–37–Pei, Black, Teilhard de Chardin, Weidenreich
Tze-Yang Woman	1951–workmen
Liu-Kiang Man	1958–workmen
EUROPE	
Fontechavade	1947–Henri-Martin
Montmaurin	1949–
La Chapelle aux Saints	1908–Bardon and Bouyssonie
La Ferrassie	1909–Peyrony
La Quina	1911–Martin
Le Moustier	1908–Hauser
Swanscombe	1935–36–Marston
Heidelberg	1907–workmen

Location	Age
Trinil	Middle Pleistocene
Kedung Brubas	Middle Pleistocene
Sangiran	Middle Pleistocene
Sangiran	Middle Pleistocene
Sangiran	Middle Pleistocene
Sangiran	Early Pleistocene
Modjokerto	Early Pleistocene
Sangiran	Early Pleistocene
Sangiran	Early Pleistocene
Ngandong	Upper Pleistocene
Wadjak	Upper Pleistocene?
Near Melbourne	Recent?
80 miles from Brisbane	Upper Pleistocene?
Murray R., S. Wales	Recent?
Choukoutien, near Peking	Middle Pleistocene
Szechuan province	Upper Pleistocene
Kwangsi province	Upper Pleistocene
France	Riss-Würm Interglacial
France	Riss-Würm Interglacial
France	Würm Glaciation
France	Würm Glaciation
France	Würm Glaciation
France	Würm Glaciation
England	Mindel-Riss Interglacial
Germany	Mindel-Riss Interglacial

TABLE 1. *The Spatial and Temporal Distribution*

Common Name	Date of Discovery
EUROPE (cont.)	
Steinheim	1933–Berckhemer
Neanderthal	1856–
Ehringsdorf	1914–25–workmen, and 1935
Saccopastore	1929–Sergi
Circeo	1939–Sergi
Spy	1886–De Puydt and Lohest
Gibraltar	1848?
Teshik-Tash	1938–Okladnikov
Krapina	1899–Gorjanovic-Kramberger
ASIA	
Shanidar	1953–60–Solecki
Mugharet al-Tabūn	1931–32–Garrod
Mugharet al-Skhūl	1931–32–Garrod
Galilee	1925–Turville-Petre
Jebel Qafza	1933–
Shukba	1928–
Amud Cave	1961–Suzuki
Kaar 'Akil	1938–Doherty and Ewing
AFRICA	
Australopithecus africanus	1924–Dart
Plesianthropus	1936–Broom
Paranthropus robustus	1938–Broom
Australopithecus	1947–Dart
Paranthropus crassidens	1948–Dart
Telanthropus capensis	1949–Robinson
Rhodesian Man	1921–miner
Zinjanthropus	1959–Leakey
Olduvai Child	1960–Leakey
Chellian-3	1960–Leakey
Tchad	1961–Coppen
Kanjera 1–4	1932–Leakey
Ternefine	1954–Arambourg
Saldanha	1953–Singer and Jolly

Location	Age
Germany	Mindel-Riss Interglacial
Germany	Würm Glaciation
Germany	Riss-Würm Interglacial
Italy	Riss-Würm Interglacial
Italy	Würm Glaciation
Belgium	Würm Glaciation
Spain	Würm Glaciation
Uzbekistan, USSR	Würm Glaciation
Yugoslavia	Würm Glaciation
Iraq	Würm Glaciation
Israel	Würm Glaciation
Israel	Würm Glaciation
Israel	Würm Glaciation
Israel	Würm Glaciation
Israel	Würm Glaciation
Israel	Würm Glaciation
Lebanon	Würm Glaciation
Taung	Lower Pleistocene
Sterkfontein	Lower Pleistocene
Kromdraii	Lower Pleistocene
Makapansgat	Lower Pleistocene
Swartkrans	Lower Pleistocene
Swartkrans	Lower Pleistocene
Broken Hill	?
Olduvai	Early Pleistocene
Olduvai	Early Pleistocene
Olduvai	Middle Pleistocene
Fr. Equat. Africa Tchad	Lower Pleistocene?
Lake Victoria	Upper Pleistocene
Algeria	Middle Pleistocene
South Africa	Upper Pleistocene

the outwash of glacial gravels, permit geologists to reconstruct the sequence and extent of the various glaciers. Further details are obtained from trails of drift and bottom river gravels left by solifluxion, a term denoting the movement of surface deposits over deeply frozen subsoil in a glaciated area. These movements occur during seasonal thawing of the surface of a glacier and consist of sludging of the surface deposits over the glacier, leaving mixed materials on ridges and summits and depositions of gravels in river bottoms.

Depositions of fine yellowish-brown loam, called loess, borne by the wind in cold dry steppe areas at times of maximum glaciation, can often be given relative ages. They also provide information regarding climatic conditions. The types of fossil flora and fauna found in these and other deposits have proven of great aid in reconstructing climatic changes.

Those parts of the world which underwent glaciation were thus undergoing, at the same time, rapid and marked changes in topography and geological structure. Relative chronology is therefore somewhat easier to obtain in such areas than it is in regions where there were no glaciations in Pleistocene times and the rates of deposition and erosion were consequently slower and less dramatic. For this reason, many of the fossil sites in the southern hemisphere and in the equatorial zone are not easily dated with reference to those in northern Europe and Asia. The problems of relative dating during the Pleistocene in areas not subjected to successive glaciations are generally quite specific and require detailed knowledge of the local river systems, terraces, fauna and flora, climate, and stratigraphy. However, in the tropics, pluvial periods were roughly equivalent to the Pleistocene glaciations of Europe and North America. Thus, a series of pluvial (or wet) phases alternated with a series of interpluvial (or dry) periods. Unfortunately, it has become apparent that in Africa, for example, there were regional variations on this theme, making correlations even between various African sites extremely tenuous.

It can be readily imagined from the above that the subject of Pleistocene chronology is a most difficult and controversial one. The literature is very extensive and quite formidable for one who has little basic knowledge of geology. Nevertheless, a most enlightening introduction to the subject can be obtained from F. Zeuner, *Dating the Past*.[6]

It is now generally recognized that at the beginning of the Pleistocene three modern mammals had begun to be widely distributed: *Equus*, the true horse; *Elephas*; and *Bos*, oxen. They were part of the Villafranchian fauna which preceded the first, or Günz, glaciation. In Java, however, the horse never made an appearance. The typically Villafranchian fauna of the Djetis beds in Java might suggest an Early Pleistocene age for this stratum, but the occurrence of some typically Middle Pleistocene forms plus the probability of a lag in time before the Asiatic Villafranchian fauna arrived in Java, make it more likely that these beds, and, hence, the fossil hominids found in them, belong to the beginning of the Middle Pleistocene. Problems such as these abound in most areas of the world and present obviously serious obstacles to putting fossil men in a reliable temporal juxtaposition.

So far we have been discussing methods of obtaining *relative* chronology. In the past twenty years, however, new techniques have been discovered whereby *absolute* chronology, that is, actual age in years, can be determined. These chronometers include: Carbon-14, Potassium-argon, Uranium-lead, Fluorine, and Rubidium. There is every indication that not only will these chronometers be improved but that new ones will be added.

The carbon-14 or radiocarbon method is restricted to dating under 30,000 years (Oakley, 1958, claims 70,000 years), hence it is primarily useful for sites in the late Middle and Upper Pleistocene and Recent epochs. Carbon-14 is heavy carbon with an atomic weight of 14 instead of the usual 12. The atoms of carbon-14 take on radioactivity as a result of the bombardment of nitrogen atoms by cosmic rays in the upper atmosphere of the earth. The radioactivity, however, is gradually lost by a process of disintegration, even while new carbon-14 atoms are being formed. The two processes, disintegration of carbon-14 atoms and formation of new ones out of carbon-12, result in a constant proportion of radioactive carbon to carbon-12 in the carbon

[6] Zeuner, F. 1958. *Dating the Past*, 4th Ed. London: Methuen and Co., Ltd.

dioxide of the atmosphere. Since both animals and plants take in carbon dioxide, the process of disintegration or loss of radio-activity of the carbon-14 atoms takes place at the same rate as in the atmosphere, that is, the proportion of carbon-14 to carbon-12 remains the same as in the atmosphere. When the plant or animal dies, no new carbon-14 atoms are taken in, but the rate of disintegration of the remaining carbon-14 atoms continues until no more radiocarbon remains. As the amount of radio-carbon in the dead animal or plant tissue diminishes, the rate of disintegration correspondingly diminishes until the radiocarbon is entirely used up. During the life of the animal or plant the rate of disintegration is 15.6 per minute per gram of carbon in their tissues. After death the rate of disintegration decreases until after 5760 years it has been reduced to 7.8 disintegrations per minute per gram of carbon. For this reason carbon-14 is said to have a "half-life" of 5760 years. This places an outside limit on such dating to about 70,000 years.

The pioneering work on radiocarbon dating was done by W. F. Libby at the University of Chicago, as one of the by-products of the research undertaken to develop the first nuclear fission. Since then, several new methods for measuring the rate of carbon-14 disintegration have been worked out, each adding to the sensitivity of recording, hence to the precision and ac-curacy of the date and the reduction of range of error. These new methods include: liquid scintillation, carbon dioxide Geiger counter, acetylene proportional counter, carbon dioxide propor-tional counter, and methane proportional counter. The gas counters have been steadily replacing the solid carbon counters since the latter were recording the increased radioactivity of the atmosphere as a result of atomic and nuclear bomb explosions.

Thus far, in all radiocarbon methods used, the absolute size of the error is in direct proportion to the estimated age of the specimen. An age estimate of, say, 35,000 years may be accom-panied by a standard deviation of $\pm$ 3500 years, but in the case of samples given an age of 50 years, the standard deviation may be as great as $\pm$ 100 years! The weakness of the radiocarbon method lies not in the technological aspect but in the manner of collection of the carbon specimens themselves. The possibility always exists that the specimen may be contaminated during removal from the soil and during handling. In addition, much depends upon the collector's judgment about whether the carbon material is actually associated with the artifacts, fossils, and geological strata which he is interested in dating. The latest dates obtained through the radiocarbon techniques are usually published in *Science* and the reader is advised to consult the index of this weekly journal for further reading on this subject.

The uranium method is one used for assessing the absolute age of geological formations that are of great antiquity. It is by uranium dating that we now estimate the age of the earth as almost five billion years. Radioactive disintegration of uranium leads to the formation of lead, but the process of disintegration is far slower than is the rate of radiocarbon disintegration. The half-life of uranium is 4,560,000,000 years, a rate determined quite accurately by measuring the rate of ejection of electrons in the reaction whereby uranium is reduced to lead, helium, and electrons. Similarly, it has been found that the element rubidium breaks down to form strontium and discharge electrons, and the dating results from the use of this nuclear reaction correspond quite closely to those obtained from the uranium method.

A newer method gives great promise for untangling many of the knotty chronological problems associated with hominid evolution and culture history of the past million years. The potassium-argon method relies upon the fact that potassium contains a radioactive isotope, potassium 40, which disintegrates into calcium 40 and argon 40. The half-life of potassium 40 is 1,300,000,000 years, which means that it is more applicable to younger strata, such as those of the Tertiary period, than is the uranium or rubidium method. It is reported by Oakley that the potassium-argon method has now reliably dated the beginning of the Miocene at 26 million years.[7] Similarly, volcanic ash of Upper Pliocene age has been given a date of 2,600,000 years, with a possible date of 12 to 13 million years for the beginning of the Pliocene. The youngest date yet obtained by the potassium-argon method is 230,000 years for the latter portion of the Mindel-Riss interglacial period.

[7] Oakley, K. 1958. Dating the Stages of Hominoid Evolution. *The Leech*, 28:112–115.

We have, then, three types of chronometers with which to obtain absolute age. One, the uranium method, enables us to date geological events that occurred as early as the origin of the earth itself, some five billion years ago; another, the potassium-argon method, is of particular value in assigning dates to Tertiary phenomena; and the third, the carbon-14 method, is limited to the last 70,000 years of the earth's history.

We have thus far neglected to mention a fourth and earlier method of absolute dating, dendrochronology, because its application is limited in time to perhaps the last 2000 years and in space to certain areas where conditions are optimal. Dendrochronology is the technique of ascertaining the cutting date of wood found in association with archaeological materials. It is based upon the counting of annual tree rings, whose varying thicknesses reflect seasonal weather conditions and which, in sequence, form a pattern that is distinctive for any given region. Once a master pattern is established in any area, the ring pattern of a particular specimen can be matched against it, thus providing a fairly exact indication of the year in which the specimen was cut and presumably used. However, a master pattern must be worked out for the region to which the wood specimens belong and this demands that trees be available which are not only long-lived but reflect seasonal variations in the width of their annual rings. Tying in the earliest ring pattern of living trees with that of prehistoric trees enables the dendrochronologist to construct a master pattern. Tree-ring dating has proven most advantageous to archaeologists in the southwestern part of the United States where the method was first worked out by A. E. Douglass almost 40 years ago. At present the master tree ring chart in the Southwest goes back to the beginning of the Christian era. Other areas in which dendrochronology is being applied are: Finland, Sweden, Norway, Germany, England, Alaska, and certain portions of the Mississippi Valley.

Of all the newer methods of establishing relative or absolute chronology, perhaps none was introduced in so dramatic a way as the fluorine test, first developed in 1893 by Carnot. This method, now called the F-U-N system of relative dating, is based on the fact that in permeable soils, usually in the temperate zone, bone takes on fluorine and uranium at a slow rate and simultaneously gradually loses its nitrogen. The rates at which these processes go on differ greatly according to the environments in which the bones are found, but an aggregation of contemporaneous bones found in the same locale and under identical conditions will contain the same amounts of fluorine, uranium, and nitrogen. The system, therefore, is applicable only to the relative chronology of a given site. For example, if a bone of recent age happened to be intruded into a deposit containing bones of much older age, it would easily be recognized as younger since it would contain more nitrogen and less fluorine and uranium than the truly old bones. Ideally, the relative amounts of the three elements will agree but it is regarded as sufficient to establish contemporaneity if only two give similar readings. Currently the following methods are employed to make the determinations: for nitrogen, a micro-Kjeldahl technique; for uranium, the method of radiometric assay; and for fluorine, the X-ray powder diffraction technique.

In 1950 the fluorine test by itself was applied to the various fragments of the famous Piltdown fossil by Oakley and his associates. The circumstances leading to this decision were most unusual, and we can outline them only briefly here. In 1912 a number of fossil specimens were collected from the gravels of an ancient river deposit in Sussex, England by an amateur archaeologist and geologist named Charles Dawson. They consisted of thick fragments of a human skull, an ape-like jaw bone with two teeth in place, hippopotamus and elephant teeth, some flint tools, and a bone implement. Presumably all these specimens were in association in the gravels which were considered to be of early Pleistocene age. In the succeeding years almost every anatomist, anthropologist, and paleontologist of note from all over the world examined these bones at the British Museum and expressed opinions about how the skull should be reconstructed from the fragments and whether or not the jaw bone (mandible) belonged to this particular skull. If the skull and mandible were truly part of the same individual, then a most remarkable enigma was posed because while the skull by most criteria was not unlike that of modern Man, the jaw was clearly ape-like in its morphology. This combination ran counter to what most students

of human evolution had been lead to believe was the true anatomical course of events in the evolutionary progression of the
human skull towards its modern status. Certainly, a skull cap
of this modern type in early Pleistocene times was most dis-
concerting to established concepts, based upon all other existing
fossils from the Pleistocene. Indeed, one anthropologist believed
that Piltdown Man (or *Eoanthropus*, as he was called by some)
was an example of "disharmonic evolution." A famous anatomist
felt that the skull and jaw "are in harmony and formed parts of
the same head." G. Miller, however, in 1915 had judged the
Piltdown mandible to be that of a chimpanzee,[8] and Franz
Weidenreich, in 1932, insisted, on the basis of his vast knowledge of anatomy and primatology, that the skull was that of
modern Man while the jaw was that of a modern anthropoid
ape. He concluded, in a 1943 assessment of the Piltdown problem, with these prophetic words: "The sooner the chimaera
'Eoanthropus' is erased from the list of human fossils, the better
for science."[9]

In applying the fluorine test to the various specimens of the
Piltdown assemblage Oakley found only slight traces of fluorine
in the skull fragments and mandible but large amounts in the
elephant and hippopotamus teeth. Spurred on by this incon-
trovertible evidence that the skull and jaw were recent while
the other fossils were probably truly early Pleistocene, the investigators proceeded with other tests. They found that the jaw
was that of a modern orang-utan or chimpanzee, as predicted by
Weidenreich many years previously, but considerably altered to
make it appear ancient and prevent any attempt at direct articulation with the base of the skull. The fragments of the latter had
also been treated by chemicals to give the impression of great
age whereas in reality they were parts of a relatively modern
skull. Recently radiocarbon tests were applied to the Piltdown
fragments giving dates of 500 ± 100 years for the mandible and
620 ± 100 years to the skull. Thus a 50-year-old fraud was finally

[8] Miller, G. 1915. The Jaw of Piltdown Man. *Smithsonian Miscellaneous Collections*, 65:1–31.
[9] Weidenreich, F. 1943. The Skull of Sinanthropus Pekinensis.
Palaeontologia Sinica, new series D, No. 10. Chungking: Geological
Survey of China.

exposed and, in the words of Weidenreich, the "chimaera Eoanthropus" was "erased from the list of human fossils."[10]

We see, then, that in the very important areas of time and space there are many sizeable gaps in our knowledge. There is some comfort to be derived, however, from the assurance that these gaps will be narrowed as more fossil discoveries inevitably come to light and that newer and more precise methods of dating will be developed. It must be kept in mind that spatial distributions and absolute and relative chronology alone will not solve the problems still confronting us as we attempt to unravel the story of human evolution, any more than a knowledge of the comparative anatomy and physiology of modern animals will by itself permit the reconstruction of phylogenetic lines. It is true that had such chronometers as carbon-14 and fluorine been available in 1912 there would not have been such acrimonious and long-drawn-out disputation among comparative anatomists as was carried on over the Piltdown fragments. Nevertheless there are many cases, as with the Mount Carmel skeletal material, where the interpretation rests not so much upon dates or location but upon the application of our knowledge of genetics and biological principles of evolution.

Having surveyed the important sites of Primate fossils as they exist in space and in time, we can now list a few of the problems that still await more satisfactory data for solution.

1. The fate of the North American lemurs and tarsiers after the end of the Eocene epoch
2. Ancestral forms of the gorilla, chimpanzee, and orang-utan
3. Pre-Pleistocene hominid fossils
4. Absolute chronology for the various fossil-rich sites in Africa so that temporal correlation is possible
5. Correlation of the geological sequences in China, Java, India, and Africa with the glacial phenomena of the Pleistocene of Europe

Perhaps this is as good a place as any to make a direct plea to all people who might, by chance, come across evidence of a fossil-bearing deposit in some quarry, river bed, terrace, or cliff. Do not disturb it! Call the nearest university or museum and

[10] Oakley, K. P. and J. S. Weiner. 1955. Piltdown Man. *American Scientist*, 43:573–583.

report your find. The job of dating, recording, and interpreting the material is infinitely more difficult if it is removed from its geological context. The removal of such important fossils as Rhodesian Man, Talgai, Keilor, Cohuna, and Heidelberg, accidental though it may have been in each case, made it impossible to assess their full significance and precluded the possibility of reliable dating.

FOUNDATIONS OF THE THEORY OF EVOLUTION

Man's intellectual, social, and spiritual natures are altogether exceptional among animals in degree, but they arose by organic evolution . . . It has also been shown that purpose and plan are not characteristic of organic evolution and are not a key to any of its operations. But purpose and plan are characteristic in the new evolution, because Man has purposes and he makes plans. Here purpose and plan do definitely enter into evolution, as a result and not as a cause of the processes seen in the long history of life. The purposes and plans are ours, not those of the universe, which displays convincing evidence of their absence.

G. C. SIMPSON, *The Meaning of Evolution,* 1949

Thus, the Teaching of the Church leaves the doctrine of Evolution an open question, as long as it confines its speculations to the development, from other living matter already in existence, of the human body. (That souls are immediately created by God is a view which the Catholic faith imposes on us) . . . Christians cannot lend their support to a theory which involves the existence, after Adam's time, of some earthly race of men, truly so called, who were not descended ultimately from him, or else supposes that Adam was the name given to some group of our primordial ancestors.

"False Trends in Modern Teaching," *Encyclical Letter of Pope Pius XII,* "Humani Generis," 1950

Introduction

Almost as early as we have written records, thoughtful men were speculating about how the earth and its many forms of organic life originated. We can assume, from observations of the origin-myths of modern primitive peoples, that long before Man could transmit his language to the permanency of stone and papyrus, he devised systems for accounting for the presence of himself and the animal world about him. In most mythologies Man is regarded as the ultimate product of creation. Nevertheless, in most primitive societies Man regards himself as akin to animals and in his myths constantly refers to animals that were once men, and men who are metamorphosed animals.

As early as the sixth century, B.C., the Greek philosophers Anaximander and Archelaus postulated the evolution of man from lower animals, thus anticipating the remarkable discoveries of the nineteenth century. The father of medicine, Hippocrates (460–357 B.C.), was also a comparative anatomist and taxonomist since he devised the first classification of animals, dividing them into 50 types. His contemporary, Democritus, pointed out that parts of an organism might be specially selected and adapted. Aristotle (384–322 B.C.) placed Man specifically among those animals now called mammals, noting that Man's brain made him unique in the Animal Kingdom. Little by little as history ran its course, accretions to Man's knowledge about himself and his relationship to other animals were made by the early anatomists, physicians, historians, and philosophers. The story of the beginnings of evolutionary thought is a fascinating one but must be omitted from this text out of considerations of space. The reader, however, is urged to become familiar with this aspect of our cultural heritage by reading Henry Fairfield Osborn's *From the Greeks to Darwin.*

Lamarckism

From the historical point of view we shall concern ourselves only with the two men who had such a tremendous impact not only upon evolutionary thought but upon the entire future course of cultural and social development: Jean Baptiste Lamarck (1744–1829) and Charles Darwin (1809–1882). Although Lamarckism, the name given to the particular system of evolution that Lamarck promulgated, has now been convincingly discredited as a valid explanation of biological phenomena, it had a profound effect upon Darwin and still lingers on, consciously or unconsciously, in the minds of some biologists and laymen alike. The pregnant woman who begins to attend concerts in the hope that her future offspring will *ipso facto* acquire musical talent evinces a form of Lamarckism, though she be totally unaware of the name or source. For a period in its recent history the U.S.S.R. officially adopted Lamarckism as its biological and social credo, but abandoned it when it became clear that further advances in the biological sciences were seriously impeded.

The phrases "transmission of acquired characters" and "response to pleasure or pain" are probably familiar to most of us. In brief, Lamarck felt that any animal was stimulated by a particular environmental situation to feel either pleasure or pain. In response to this reaction the animal would consciously strive to seek further pleasure or to avoid the pain. In so doing he would either acquire greater development of a bodily structure or tend to diminish its size. Thus, by "use or disuse" of an organ or structure, he would, in his own lifetime, attain greater or lesser development of the affected organ or structure. The change that was effected in him he would pass on to his offspring. Under similar and continuing environmental stress, the offspring in turn would favor or disfavor the member concerned, developing or attenuating it still further. This process would continue until in future generations a new organ or structure would be present or the old one would have disappeared.

Let us take an example that Lamarck himself used. Imagine a herd of animals that habitually browse upon the leaves of shrubs and the lowest branches of trees. A blight suddenly affects the flora in such a way that the shrubs are wiped out and the low-lying branches of the trees are denuded of foliage. The animals, if they are to continue to eat (which is a pleasurable function), must stretch their necks to the utmost to reach the higher leafy branches. In so doing their necks gradually get longer, perhaps an inch or two. They have in their own lifetimes acquired a longer neck through strenuous use. Their offspring are born and reach adulthood with necks already an inch or two longer than their parents'. If the blight continues, they in turn are obliged to reach even higher for food, and in so doing acquire an additional two inches. And so the process continues, each generation passing on the longer neck it had acquired in its

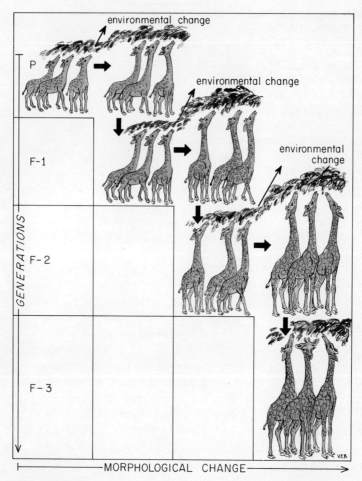

FIGURE 12.
Lamarckism

own lifetime. Eventually the descendants of our browsing animals become giraffes! An illustration of these postulated events is presented in Figure 12.

The influence of this theory upon Darwin can be seen in statements such as the following, taken from his *The Origin of Species*:

With animals the increased use or disuse of parts has had a more marked influence; thus I find in the domestic duck that the bones of the wing weigh less and the bones of the leg more, in proportion to the whole skeleton, than do the same bones in the wild-duck; and this change may be safely attributed to the domestic duck flying much less, and walking more, than its wild parents.

and,

Not one of our domestic animals can be named which has not in some country drooping ears; and the view which has been suggested that the drooping is due to the disuse of the muscles of the ear, from the animals being seldom alarmed, seems probable.[1]

It is only fair to point out that while Lamarckism, in its grosser aspects, is no longer a tenable hypothesis, it has been suggested by Moody (1962, pp. 344–346) that there still is a possibility that antibody induction of mutations may be an example of the transmission of acquired characters.[2] There is some evidence, not yet effectively overthrown, that environmental damage to the lens of the eye will result in the formation of antibodies which, perhaps, enter the germ plasm of the subject (in this case rabbits), inducing a specific gene mutation which then results in defective eyes in the offspring. If the experimental results of Guyer and Smith (Guyer, 1927) and others should be confirmed, it would be the first *bona fide* support of the Lamarckian idea,[3] but at a biochemical level of which Lamarck could never have dreamed.

Darwinism

It remained for Darwin to advance an hypothesis about how evolution worked which, to this day, remains the bulwark of our understanding. Since his day there have been innumerable accretions to our knowledge, but they have been for the most part

[1] Darwin, C. 1928. *The Origin of Species*. Great Britain: The Temple Press, Letchworth.

[2] Moody, P. 1962. *Introduction to Evolution*, 2nd ed. New York: Harper and Row.

[3] Guyer, M. 1927. *Being Well-Born*, 2nd ed. Indianapolis: The Bobbs-Merrill Company.

supplemental and modifying rather than negating. The primary agent of biological evolution is still recognized as "natural selection," the "preservation of favourable individual differences and variations, and the destruction of those which are injurious."[4]

As was the case with Lamarck, Darwin used a number of phrases and terms which have become almost household expressions. Chief among these are: "variation," "survival of the fittest," and "struggle for existence." A proper understanding of the concepts represented by these terms is essential if we are to appreciate the biological principles of evolution and to apply them to man. Let us therefore discuss them one at a time, beginning with the very basic fact of Variation.

Darwin emphasized the fact that the individuals of any population, be it birds, rodents, or Man, differ among themselves with regard to any trait whatsoever. It comes as no surprise to us that this is true of Man, since we are primarily occupied with observing the members of our own species. We look about us and see differences in skin color, hair form, eye color, nose and ear shapes, lip thickness, body build, and stature. Indeed, such differences, particularly in the head and face, play fundamental roles in our social interactions. If we delve deeper into the body, using techniques common to medicine, we would find similar variation in such traits as blood types, blood sugar levels, blood sedimentation rates, and even in the relatively more stable pH values. Most of us do not have the opportunity of examining the human skeleton, but if we had occasion to measure and observe the bones of numerous skeletons from a prehistoric cemetery, as archaeologists often do, we would be struck by the variation in lengths, widths, diameters, and circumferences for each bone. We would soon be convinced that variability in Man, as in other animals, is a fundamental biological theme or *law*. No matter how minute the character, it shows a certain degree of variability, whether it be in shape, chemical constituency, proportions, color, rate of flow, length of life, or metabolism.

Is such variability characteristic also of other forms of organic life? If we can not answer this question, it is because we do not have the familiarity with such forms that we do with Man. The

[4] Darwin, C. *Op. cit.*

zoologist, however, knows, as did Darwin, that every species of animal reflects the same basic theme of individual variability. Members of the so-called White race, for example, are often heard to exclaim: "I just can't tell one from the other" in speaking of members of another race. This simply reflects the preoccupation of each segment of the human race with itself.

While for every trait there is individual variability within any one species or population, the amount of variation is not without limit. Generally the range of variation for each trait is in itself a characteristic of the population, and can be expressed in terms of the normal curve since for any species of animal not under domestication and not including Man himself, the distribution of any biological trait roughly approximates that of the normal curve. Let us therefore examine the properties of such a family of curves and see how they apply to the principles of biologic variation.

The normal curve is really a family of curves that is described by the equation:

$$Y = \frac{1}{\sigma\sqrt{2\pi}} e^{-\frac{1}{2}\left(\frac{X-\mu}{\sigma}\right)^2}$$

The properties of the normal curve include the fact that it is bell-shaped, is bilaterally symmetrical, and its two slopes approach but never reach the horizontal axis (Fig. 13). A line drawn from the peak of the curve to the horizontal axis (or x

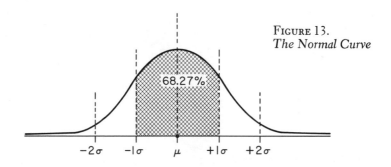

FIGURE 13.
The Normal Curve

68.27%

-2σ -1σ μ $+1\sigma$ $+2\sigma$

axis) divides the curve into two symmetrical halves such that the area included in one half is equal to the area included in the other. This line is called the mean, or μ. Each slope, as it descends from the mean, changes from a convex to a concave shape. The precise point at which this change occurs is called the point of inflection. If a perpendicular is dropped from this point to the x axis, the distance on the x axis from μ to the point of intersection of this perpendicular is called a *standard deviation* and is denoted by the Greek letter σ. The area under the curve enclosed by the x axis and the perpendiculars from the points of inflection and the peak represents 68.27 percent of the total area under the curve. If we double the distance along the x axis from the mean to one standard deviation on either side of the mean, in other words mark off two standard deviations, and erect perpendiculars, we then have included 95.46 percent of the total area. Three standard deviations on either side of the mean includes 99.74 percent, etc. The areas included within various fractions of standard deviations are worked out in tables called "Areas of the Normal Curve," which are available in any book on statistics.

With the exception of the properties stated above, there is an infinity of normal curves, some of which are drawn in Figure 14. It will be noted that two normal distributions may differ in their means, their standard deviations, or both. They may be identical in means and standard deviations and yet differ in shape (see Fig. 15). These characteristics will be very important when we discuss variability in the hominid line.

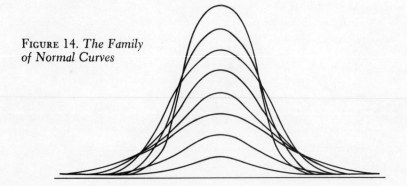

FIGURE 14. *The Family of Normal Curves*

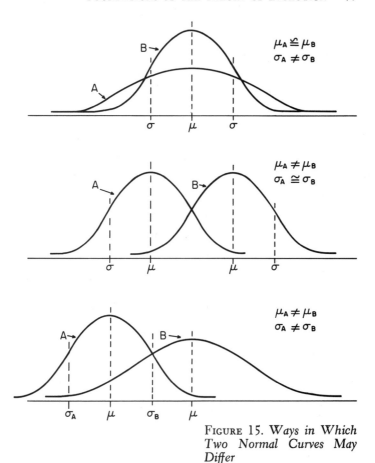

FIGURE 15. *Ways in Which Two Normal Curves May Differ*

Now let us return to the equation of the normal curve. The symbols used in this equation have the following meanings:

Y = the height of any one point on the curve measured from the x axis

X = any specific point on the x axis

π = a constant (3.1416)

e = a constant (2.7183)

σ = one standard deviation of the distribution

μ = the mean of the distribution

Actually, then, there are only two unknowns, σ and μ. Once the standard deviation and mean are known, the specific curve of the family of normal curves is identified. It is obvious from the equation and from the drawings in Figures 13 and 14 that with other conditions remaining constant, as the standard deviation increases the curve becomes flatter and the farther one must go from the mean to include 68.27 percent of the area.

How does all this apply to the variability of a trait within a population of animals? Suppose you had the unenviable task of measuring the lengths of the upper canine teeth of 1000 adult Bengal tigers. A simple statistical analysis of the results might show that the mean length of the canines was 50 millimeters with a standard deviation of 10 mm. You had found, of course, that there was a minimum and a maximum size limit, namely 25 mm. and 73 mm. In this respect, then, there are finite limits to the range of variability in biological populations. Nevertheless, the characteristics of the normal curve will apply reasonably well in describing the distribution of our tiger teeth. We can be confident that about 68 percent of the 1000 tigers will have canines ranging in size from 40–60 mm., and that 95 percent will have canines falling between 30 and 70 mm. Obviously the farther one goes from the mean the smaller will be the number of tigers having canines of these extreme dimensions. Thus, we would expect to find only rarely tigers with teeth as short as 25 mm. or as long as 75 mm. Plotting the distribution of canine dimensions we might get a histogram such as shown in Figure 16. Although the actual curve represented is not a true normal one, it is close enough to the fitted normal curve so that our statistics are applicable.

It is clear, then, that any population will, with respect to any given trait, present to the environment a range of variability that in its distribution will approximate a normal curve. What is more, the succeeding generation will be characterized by much the same distributions of its traits. While Darwin was unaware of the reasons why this is so, he nonetheless had observed that "like tends to produce like." "No one can say," he asserted, ". . . why the child often reverts in certain characters to its grandfather or grandmother or more remote ancestor." By the same token he could not explain why in many instances parents

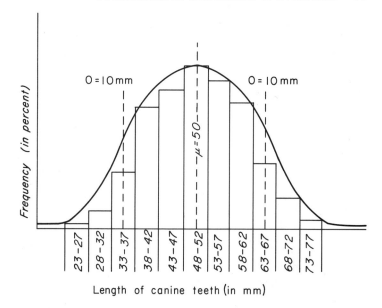

FIGURE 16. *The Hypothetical Distribution of Canine Dimensions of
Tigers*

have offspring which differ from them in many traits. If we were
to plot the distribution curves of a series of generations with regard to the variability of a single trait, we might find the situation shown in Figure 17.

This indicates that from generation to generation the mean
may vary or "oscillate" slightly without revealing any definite
trend in one direction or the other. The standard deviation,
however, which is a measure of the degree of homogeneity of a
population, ordinarily remains fairly stable.

It is pertinent at this point to consider the subject of variability in terms of modern breeding procedures. The poultry-
man may wish to improve his flock of turkeys by developing
birds with larger breasts and hence more white meat. Observing
that a few of his turkeys already have fairly well developed
breasts (being on the extreme end of the range of variation),
he isolates and interbreeds them. The offspring, tending to re-

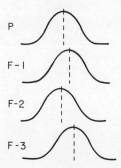

FIGURE 17. *Distribution Curves of a Series of Generations with Regard to the Variability of a Single Trait*

semble their parents, have a mean breast thickness similar to their parents, but they too exhibit a range of variation in this trait. The breeder then cuts out these second generation turkeys representing the upper half of the range and interbreeds them. By this process of selective breeding, he upgrades his flock in the direction he desires. In many ways this is the system whereby evolution proceeds, except that in the wild state it is the natural environment and not Man that does the selecting.

Every animal species inhabits a particular niche in the environment to which it is peculiarly adapted by virtue of its anatomical and physiological characteristics. But the natural environment is constantly changing, sometimes dramatically and with great speed and at other times almost imperceptibly. Volcanoes, earthquakes, floods, and drought can wreak great changes in a geographical area in a very short time. Changes in ocean temperatures may require hundreds of years. In any event, environmental change places stresses upon the animal life already adapted to a particular complex of conditions, necessitating readaptation to the new situation or resulting in extinction. The real question is: how does a population adapt to a changing environment? Darwin's terms to describe what happens—*struggle for existence* and *survival of the fittest*—were not too well chosen, since they are easily susceptible to misinterpretation. There is no conscious or unconscious struggle on the part of the members of a species for existence, and one must be wary of defining what "fittest" means. The process whereby this is accomplished Darwin has called *natural selection*, but selection bears the connotation of someone or some "power" doing the selecting whereas Darwin merely meant selection as the end result of "the aggregate action and product of many natural laws."

As we have seen, a population constantly displays a range of variation for each of its multitude of characteristics. The mean and standard deviation of each trait distribution probably have, besides their strictly arithmetic nature, a biological significance in that they mark those values of the trait which best adapt the animal to its environment. If the environment changes in such a way that these same central values no longer best adapt the animal to the new conditions, then it may well be that some of the individuals whose values for this trait are above two standard deviations from the mean may, by chance, be better adapted to the new environment. Their chances of surviving and hence producing offspring (who, it will be remembered, will tend to resemble their parents) will be slightly better than will those of the individuals having values less than two standard deviations above the mean. Those animals occupying positions at the opposite end of the range of variation will be placed in an extremely hazardous situation and might even fail to reach the age of reproduction, thus leaving no offspring. If the environment continues to change in the same direction generation after generation, favoring these values in the higher end of the successive curves of distribution, there will be a gradual shift in the means toward the higher values.

This process is illustrated, in oversimplified terms, by the diagram in Figure 18, using the same animals and scheme as presented in the case of Lamarckism in Figure 12. It will be observed that in each generation a normal curve of distribution is maintained, but the mean is shifting toward the greater dimensions of neck length. This is because the continued environmental pressure, in the form of higher and higher placement of the leaves above the ground, favors the animals who, in each generation, have inherited the longer necks of their parents, hence occupy the right half of the distribution curve. The animals represented on the left half of the curve are simply unfor-

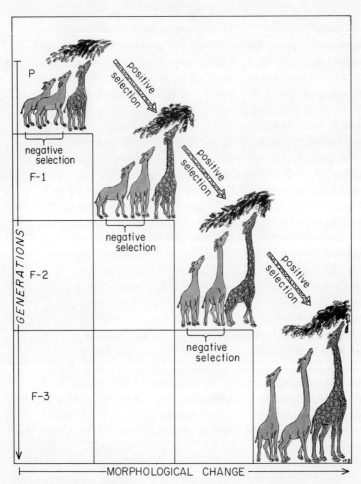

FIGURE 18. *Darwinism*

tunate. They were not endowed with the means to reach the leaves as successfully as their relatives with the longer necks. Therefore, the former tend to be undernourished, to have fewer offspring, and to die before the age of reproduction.

It is important to realize that a sudden marked change in the environment may be catastrophic for the species, since it presents a situation to the population wherein no members have the requisite adaptive qualifications. In other words, the new environment may call for a degree of development of the trait which is beyond the range of variation presented by the species. None of the individuals of the species can, therefore, survive and the species becomes extinct. There are numerous examples of extinction of species and whole genera in the fossil record. We will recall that in Problem II we mentioned the dominance of dinosaurs and reptiles in general during the Mesozoic era. They were widespread on land, in the air, and in the sea. Suddenly, in the geological sense, the dinosaurs and many of the marine reptiles completely disappeared. This occurred at the end of the Cretaceous period, some 70 million years ago. We do not know the reason for the dramatic extinction of this ruling group but one plausible explanation is that by the end of the Mesozoic there was a climatic change resulting in somewhat higher temperatures. Now it is known that the testis is sensitive to heat and that living reptiles are sterilized by temperatures only slightly above those optimal for their maximum activity. The huge body size of the dinosaurs would mean that these reptiles would cool off very slowly compared to the smaller reptiles and in hotter temperatures would seldom reach body temperatures that would permit spermatogenesis.

Many lines of large mammals, as *Equus* (modern horse), *Archidiskodon imperator* (mammoth), *Smilodon* (saber-toothed cats), and *Megatherium* (giant ground sloths) were once widespread throughout North America but became extinct at the end of the Pleistocene. The reasons for their extinction are not known, but perhaps it was related to the change to warmer climates attendant upon the retreat of the last glaciation.

Although the diagram in Figure 18 gives the impression that perceptible changes in response to environmental change can be observed in each successive generation, this is far from the true situation. A definite shift in the distribution curve for any trait could only be measured in terms of thousands of generations. This is precisely the time scale afforded by the fossil record. Enough time lapse is represented by each fossil in a phylogenetic line so that changes in the form and proportions of the skeletal and dental elements can be readily observed. You will recall that in a generation-by-generation record there will also be shifts in the mean of each distributional curve but they would be in the nature of oscillations with no discernible trend. These generational shifts are due, not to environmental change, but to chance sampling error, as will be explained later when we talk of genetic drift. Evolution by generations is called *microevolution*, as opposed to evolution by eras, or *macroevolution*.

The main ingredients of Darwin's theory of evolution can now be summed up as follows. Every species of animals presents, for each trait, a range of variation that approximates a normal distribution. The species is more or less well adapted to the ecological niche it occupies in the world. Those members of the species whose traits lie in the central portion of the distribution curve are presumably best adapted to the environment. The environment then begins to change very slowly, thus changing the adaptive values of certain characteristics so that those on one or the other end of the range better equip the animal to meet the environment than do the values in the middle of the range which once were favored. The result is a slow shift in the mean values so that over many generations the curve of distribution will not even overlap the ancestral curve and a noticeable and measurable difference will be effected. In every case those animals at the unfavorable end of the range of variation will tend to die off or have fewer offspring than those at the favorable end of the range. In the former instance we say that *negative selection* was operating, while in the latter the process is called *positive selection*. Positive selection occurs in the case of traits with *adaptive value*. The whole process is so slow that it cannot be observed generation by generation, even by means of statistical analysis. That is why we have used the word "tend" with reference to the elimination of animals on the unfavorable end of the distribution curve.

We have continually used the word "environment" as if we all had mutual understanding of the meaning of this term. Actually environment has different meanings, depending on the context in which it is used. The natural environment of a herd of deer includes, of course, the temperature, winds, rainfall, topography, flora, rivers, soil composition, etc. It also involves other types of animals present, including predators and even the proximity of other herds of deer. When we speak of the environment of the embryo and fetus, however, we are referring primarily to the condition of the mother, her food supply and nutritional status, the uterus and fetal membranes, and the placental barrier between mother and fetus. The environment of a gene, on the other hand, consists of the other genes, the nuclear karyolymph and membrane, nucleoli, mitochrondria, centrioles, the Golgi substance, the cell membrane, and other elements of the cell, plus other cells and intercellular substance. In the cases of the herd of deer, the fetus, or the gene, the respective environments are constantly undergoing change. The natural environment of the deer generally changes slowly over the course of hundreds of years; that of the fetus and the gene is much more rapid, to be measured in terms of seconds, minutes, and hours.

Mendel and the Beginning of the Science of Genetics

Darwin[5] himself was aware of certain shortcomings in his theory of natural selection. He ascribed to heredity the phenomenon of transmission of characters from parent to offspring, but knew nothing of the mechanism of heredity. He was cognizant of the common occurrence of offspring that did not resemble either parent but could not explain how this came about. By a most ironical turn of events, Darwin was unaware that at the time he was working on his *The Origin of Species* an Augustinian monk by the name of Gregor Johann Mendel was developing the basic principles of inheritance in a monastery garden at Brünn, Moravia.

Mendel worked with a large variety of plants, such as garden peas, snapdragons, pumpkins, beans, maize, columbines, and violets, but his experiments with some 34 types of garden peas are best remembered, since they form the basis for the modern science of genetics. Unfortunately, Mendel published his paper "Experiments in Plant Hybridization" in a rather obscure Moravian journal in 1866 and it escaped the notice of biologists throughout the world until 1900. It is interesting to speculate if Darwin, had he the opportunity to acquaint himself with Mendel's results, would have considerably modified certain por-

[5] Darwin, C. *Op. cit.*

tions of his evolution theory. Nevertheless, it is a tribute to the genius of Darwin that the subsequent development of genetics has not overthrown but rather has substantiated the major tenets of his theory and carried it still further.

In 1900 three European botanists, working independently, reached conclusions identical to those of Mendel. Each "rediscovered" Mendel's work, and, in the highest tradition of scientific integrity, gave full credit to Mendel for being the discoverer of what are now known as Mendel's Laws. The three scholars, De Vries, Correns, and von Tschermak, subsequently made important contributions of their own to the field of genetics. The science of genetics, by this strange series of circumstances, had its birth in 1900, and is therefore one of the youngest sciences in the totality of human knowledge.

Genetics provides us with the mechanism or process by which evolution occurs and helps fill in the gaps in the theory of evolution that Darwin himself was the first to point out. This is not the place, however, to enter into an exposition of the history of genetic thought over the past six decades. To become acquainted with this subject the reader is advised to begin with Mendel's "Experiments in Plant Hybridization." An excellent biography of Mendel is provided by H. Iltis, *The Life of Mendel*. A concise but interesting review of the history of genetics, with additional references, is given in E. O. Dodson, *Genetics* (Chapter 22).

There are other aspects of Darwinism that we have not as yet considered. Darwin never claimed that natural selection was the only force operating to produce evolution. Other evolutionary agents include: sexual selection, hybridization, migration, and isolation. These and other principles and mechanisms in evolution are best discussed after we have become acquainted with the facts of heredity, for it is the application of genetic principles to Darwin's concepts that has resulted in modern evolutionary theory, or Neo-Darwinism as it is called.

THE MECHANISM OF EVOLUTION

Thy body, true, may crumble into dust,
But in unnumber'd shapes 'twill be revived.
Nor wilt thou need to start thy life anew.
Thy son shall suffer for thy deadly sins—
Thy maladies thou wilt to him transmit.
All thou hast master'd, all thou hast learnt and felt,
Shall be thy very own throughout the ages!

LUCIFER in *The Tragedy of Man*,
Imre Madach

Introduction

In the relatively brief period of its existence as a science, genetics, the science of heredity, has expanded so rapidly and in so many different directions, that today it encompasses too vast a field of knowledge to cover even superficially in a single volume, let alone a single chapter. Nevertheless, there are facts from each area of genetics that are pertinent to our story of human evolution, so our task is to select what is deemed important and to delegate the rest to the reader's interest in further study. In so doing we must borrow information from the fields of population genetics and physiological genetics.

Darwin had come as close as the knowledge of his day permitted to the explanation of how a trait is inherited. He stated in *The Descent of Man*:

. . . every unit or cell of the body throws off gemules, or undeveloped atoms, which are transmitted to the offspring of both

83

sexes, and are multiplied by self-division. They may remain undeveloped during the early years of life or during successive generations; their development into units or cells, like those from which they were derived, depending on their affinity for, and union with, other units or cells previously developed in the due order of growth.[1]

The Genotype and the Phenotype

In the modern explanation of inheritance two aspects of the organism must be taken into account, the *genotype* and the *phenotype*. The phenotype may refer to a single trait or the sum total of all traits of the organism. It may be defined as: any characteristic of the organism as it is observed at any moment in the life span of that organism. A *phenotypic* trait is the product of the continuous interaction of the genetic constitution and the environment up to the point where that trait is observed. Such a trait may be eye color, morphology of a molar tooth, or basic metabolic rate. It may be an anatomic or physiologic character, or a biochemical or psychological entity. The *genotype* may refer to a discrete genetic element or the total aggregation of genes. It is the basic unit (or units) of inheritance, received from both parents, that reacts with its environment to produce a particular phenotypic trait. With regard to the blood group system the phenotype of an individual may be A and his genotype might be determined to consist of an A and an O allele. Ordinarily we use the terms *genotype* and *phenotype* with reference to a single trait, since we are a long way from knowing either the total phenotype or total genotype of any kind of organism. When we examine and describe the bones and teeth of a fossil we are dealing with phenotypic traits, the genotypes for which are completely unknown to us.

Within the nucleus of each cell of the body there are 46 threadlike structures called *chromosomes*. The genetic material is located on these structures. There are cells in the gonads, however, which undergo changes resulting in the production of daughter cells or *gametes* which contain in their nuclei only 23 chromosomes, or the *haploid* number, instead of the usual

[1] Darwin, C. 1871. *The Descent of Man.* New York: D. Appleton and Company.

46, or *diploid* number. In the male these gametes are produced in the testis and are called *sperms;* in the female they are produced in the ovaries and are termed *ova.* The rates of production of sperms and ova are vastly different. The female generally produces one mature ovum per month, or roughly 400 during her entire reproductive period of about 33 years. The male, on the other hand, is continually manufacturing sperm in a most prolific manner. A single ejaculation will contain more than 200,000,000 sperm suspended in the semen, only one of which normally will succeed in impregnating the single ovum that may be present in the oviduct. The fusion of sperm and ovum into a single cell called the *zygote* restores the diploid number of 46 chromosomes and signals the initial stage in the development of a new individual.

The new individual does not remain a single-celled animal for much longer than 24 hours, when cleavage occurs. The *zygote* undergoes a process whereby it divides into two cells, each containing the diploid number of chromosomes. This process, which begins with the zygote and does not cease until the organism dies, is called *mitosis.* It is of particular importance that we understand the role that mitosis plays in the development of the organism. One of its functions is to provide for increase in size of the individual by increasing the number of cells through successive cleavages. At the same time it ensures that each cell's nucleus will contain not only the same number of chromosomes, or diploid number, but that the chromosomes, and hence the genes, in each cell will be identical to those in every other cell of the body. Furthermore, mitosis not only continues throughout the life of the individual but it takes place in almost all parts of the body.

The Meiotic Process

The process whereby sex cells are transformed into mature sperm and ova is known as *meiosis.* Unlike the mitotic process, meiosis does not commence until the end of the pubertal period and ceases sometime between the ages of 48 and 55, although its duration is extremely variable. It has a reductive rather than a duplicative function, since it reduces the chromosome number of the specialized sex cells from the diploid to the haploid number in the gametes. Whereas mitosis guarantees the exact duplication of genes in each new somatic cell, meiosis guarantees that no two gametes will be identical genetically. It is this function of meiosis that is the basis of variability in any sexually reproducing species. A further fundamental role of the meiotic process is to shuffle the genes so thoroughly that any mutation will be thrown into a great variety of gene combinations a sort of testing process. Meiosis, then, while not absolutely indispensable to evolution (it plays no role in asexual reproduction), is a mechanism whereby the evolutionary rate is greatly speeded up. It becomes quite clear that the real purpose of sex is not alone reproduction (since asexual creatures reproduce) but the assurance of continuing variability within the species. Variation, as we have seen in the previous Problem, allows a species to "face the future with confidence," that is, at least some of its members will be equipped to survive in a slowly changing environment. The higher invertebrates and all the vertebrates employ the sexual method of reproduction. In each phylum of the Animal Kingdom the usual method of reproduction is sexual, although there are some forms of life, such as amoeba, coelenterates, and bryozoans, that reproduce asexually. There are several methods of reproducing sexually, the most common being the biparental one. Others include *paedogenesis, metagenesis, parthenogenesis,* and *hermaphroditism.* Some protozoans, like *Volvox,* a colonial flagellate, retain both sexual and asexual methods of reproduction, and may very well afford some clues as to the evolution of sex itself.

In sexually reproducing species variability is thus assured by both meiosis and by mutations. In asexually reproducing species variability must depend upon mutations alone. However, it must be remembered that the forms which still retain this method of reproduction are very simple and inhabit a type of environment (marine) where the rate of change is exceedingly slow. Forms of life which, in the course of evolution, left the sea for the land and the air, were subjecting themselves to ecological situations that were more apt to undergo relatively rapid change, hence for them the constant maintenance of a range of variation in each generation was a *sine qua non* for survival.

Because the meiotic process that is the core of sexuality is so important for an understanding of evolution, we shall now outline some of its essential features, again using Man as our example.

The Nature of the Gene

In 1944, Avery, MacLeod and McCarthy demonstrated that the hereditary agent had the properties of a highly polymerized deoxypentose nucleic acid (DNA).[2] This laid the foundation for subsequent studies of the biochemical nature of the genetic material. An excellent summary of the discoveries leading up to our present understanding of this subject is provided by Zamenhof (1959).[3] We now know that the chromosome is composed of nucleoprotein, about two-thirds of which consists of nucleic acids. The nucleic acids have been shown to be the carriers of genetic information in small viruses, bacteriophages, and bacteria and presumably play the same role in higher organisms. The specific kind of nucleic acid found in the chromosomes is of the *deoxyribose* type (DNA). A DNA molecule consists of a pair of long spiraled strands, each containing about 10,000 smaller molecules called *nucleotides*. Each nucleotide is in turn made up of three smaller molecules. One is a *nitrogenous base*, a second is a pentose type *sugar*, and a third is *orthophosphoric acid*. The nucleotide molecule is about 1/30,000 of an inch long and less than 1/12,000,000 of an inch in diameter. Since the DNA molecule consists of a double strand of nucleotides, the latter are arranged in pairs with the nitrogenous components in juxtaposition and united by weak hydrogen type bonds. The nitrogenous bases are of two kinds: *purines* and *pyrimidines*. There are primarily two kinds of purines, *adenine* and *quanine*, and two kinds of pyrimidines, *cytosine* and *thymine*. Other types of pyrimidines and purines need not concern us here.

The structure of a small segment of a DNA molecule can be

[2] Avery, O., MacLeod, C. and McCarthy, M. 1944. Studies of the Chemical Nature of the Substance Inducing Transformation of Pneumococcal Types. *Journal of Experimental Medicine*, 79:137ff.

[3] Zamenhof, S. 1959. *The Chemistry of Heredity*. Springfield, Illinois: C. C. Thomas.

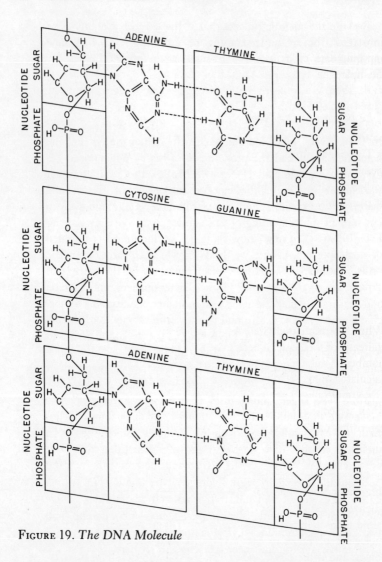

FIGURE 19. *The DNA Molecule*

represented according to the famous Watson-Crick model as
shown in Figure 19. Apparently the three components of a
nucleotide are always linked together by covalent bonds in the
same way, while nucleotides of the same strand are similarly
joined by the phosphorus atom of the orthophosphoric acid and

an oxygen atom of the sugar molecule. Each pair of nucleotides, opposing each other on the two strands, are joined by bonds of the hydrogen type. Although the latter are individually rather weak, there are so many of them in the 10,000 or so series of paired nucleotides in each DNA molecule that their cumulative strength gives the molecule enormous stability compared to other proteins.

The paired nitrogenous bases are not identical but are complementary such that a specific purine will always be matched with a specific pyrimidine and *vice versa*. A possible sequence of paired nitrogenous bases would be as follows:

$$
\begin{array}{l}
\text{Adenine} \longrightarrow \text{Thymine} \\
\text{Thymine} \longrightarrow \text{Adenine} \\
\text{Cytosine} \longrightarrow \text{Guanine} \\
\text{Adenine} \longrightarrow \text{Thymine} \\
\text{Guanine} \longrightarrow \text{Cytosine} \\
\text{Adenine} \longrightarrow \text{Thymine}
\end{array}
$$

When we recall that there are some 10,000 rungs in the spiral staircase of a DNA molecule it is obvious that an enormous number of different patterns or sequences is possible. It has been calculated that $10^{10,000}$ such sequences are possible in a single DNA molecule. The significance of this figure can be grasped when we consider that the distinctive information-bearing characteristics of DNA are thought to reside in the particular sequence of the purine-pyrimidine pairs. Recent research has suggested that the unit of recombination (*recon*) may be defined as "the smallest element in the one-dimensional array that is interchangeable (but not divisible) by genetic recombination" (Benzer, 1957).[4] It is estimated that the size of a recon would be no more than two nucleotide pairs. If there are about 150,000 molecules of DNA in the human haploid number of chromosomes, and if there are, on an average, 10,000 nucleotide pairs in each such molecule, then there could be as many as 750 million recons in the human cell. The classic concept of a gene as the unit of recombination, of mutation, and of function, is no longer

---

[4] Benzer, S. 1957. The Elementary Units of Heredity. In *A Symposium on the Chemical Basis of Heredity*, edited by W. McElroy and B. Glass. Baltimore: The Johns Hopkins Press.

adequate, according to Benzer, and must be abandoned in favor of three separate concepts: the *recon* (unit of recombination), the *muton* (unit of mutation), and the *cistron* (unit of function).

The cells that are destined to become gametes are known as *spermatogonia* and *oögonia*. They contain the diploid number of chromosomes. In our example (Fig. 20) let us suppose, to facilitate clarity and understanding, that the human species has a diploid number of 4, instead of 46. One pair of chromosomes represents the 22 pairs of autosomal chromosomes, the other is the sex pair, designated XX in the female and XY in the male. Since each pair of chromosomes in the primordial sex cell consists of one chromosome from the father and one from the mother, this distinction is maintained in the diagram by solid black for the maternal and cross-hatching for the paternal contribution. The meiotic process can now be depicted in a number of stages, as illustrated in Figure 20.

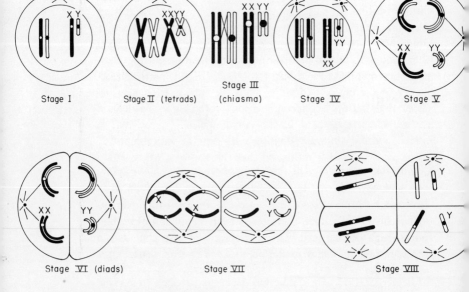

Stage I   Stage II (tetrads)   Stage III (chiasma)   Stage IV   Stage V

Stage VI (diads)   Stage VII   Stage VIII

FIGURE 20. *The Meiotic Process*

Stage I.   *Synapsis.* The paternal and maternal chromo-
                somes of each pair come into close contact,
                point for point.
Stage II.   *Synapsis.* Each chromosome synthesizes an ex-
                act duplicate of itself, the "daughter" chromo-
                some lying by its side. Instead of a pair of
                chromosomes there is now a *tetrad.*
Stage III.   *Chiasma* and "crossing-over." The strands of
                the tetrad become twisted with each other and
                exchange various homologous segments.
Stage IV.   The "aster" becomes duplicated, the tetrads be-
                gin to contract, and the nuclear membrane be-
                gins to dissolve.
Stage V.   *Anaphase.* The tetrads line up in an equatorial
                plane with the asters located at opposite poles
                (*metaphase*). The centromere of each diad grav-
                itates toward the nearest pole, drawing its diad
                along with it (*anaphase*).
Stage VI.   The two pairs (diads) in each tetrad are sepa-
                rated, one set of diads going to one pole, the
                other to the opposite pole, whereupon a mem-
                brane forms along the former equatorial plane,
                separating the original sex cell into two cells,
                each containing the diploid number of chromo-
                somes.
Stage VII.   In each "daughter" cell the diads are arranged
                along an equatorial plane, the single aster having
                again duplicated itself. The two members of
                each diad then gravitate toward opposite poles.
Stage VIII.   The two cells then divide, each forming two
                daughter cells. Each daughter cell now has but
                one member of each of the original tetrads, or
                the haploid number of chromosomes.

The four daughter cells of the spermatogonia become sperm,
but generally only one of the four daughter cells of the oögonia
becomes a mature ovum. Since an ovum must contain sufficient
cytoplasm to nourish the developing embryo, there is probably
not enough of this substance to provide for more than one of
the four daughter cells. At any rate the other three polar bodies
disintegrate.

Crossing-over is the very heart of the meiotic process since it
is the mechanism which can shuffle the genes in so many ways

that it is extremely doubtful if any two gametes could ever be identical in all their genes. This would mean that, outside of *monozygotic* or "identical twins," no two people living or dead could be genetically identical except by an almost miraculous twist of fate. Since crossing-over has such significant implications not only for evolution but for the interpretation of biological variation in the context of modern society, let us examine this phenomenon more closely.

We may now define a gene as a particular sequence of nucleotides on a pair of homologous chromosomes which acts, under the influence of a specific substrate, to effect a specific biochemical reaction.

Mendelism

A specific gene occupies a specific place—*locus*—on a specific pair of homologous chromosomes. The term *homologous* refers to the fact that the two members of a pair of chromosomes, one a paternal and one a maternal chromosome, are alike in that at equivalent loci there are genes having the same functions. Although at one specific locus called "I" the function of the gene is to determine the type of antigenic substance that will be attached to the red blood cells, on the paternal member of the pair this gene may contain information that will result in the production of antigen A, while on the maternal chromosome the corresponding gene may be a potential producer of antigen B. In such a case, although both genes carry out the same function of antigen determination, they do it somewhat differently. The existing variations of a specific gene are called *alleles*. If the two alleles on a pair of chromosomes are identical the chromosomes are said to be *homozygous* for this gene. If they are different, the chromosomes are called *heterozygous* for this gene.

Let us consider a trait which is inherited on the basis of a two-allelic system—the so-called "taster, non-taster" trait. In 1932 it was discovered that some people taste the synthetic chemical phenylthiocarbamide (PTC) as a very bitter substance while others are unable to taste it at all. Subsequent investigations showed that about 70 percent of the American White population are tasters, while 91–96 percent of various Negro populations tested are tasters. Apparently the ability to taste PTC is determined by the presence of a dominant allele (D) while a non-taster is homozygous for the recessive allele (d). There are thus the following three genotypes in the human population with the corresponding phenotypes:

Genotypes	Phenotypes
DD	Taster
Dd	Taster
dd	Non-taster

The possible kinds of marriage in a population with respect to this trait are therefore:

1. DD × DD (homozygous dominant × homozygous dominant), or Taster × Taster
2. DD × Dd (homozygous dominant × heterozygote), or Taster × Taster
3. DD × dd (homozygous dominant × homozygous recessive), or Taster × Non-taster
4. Dd × Dd (heterozygote × heterozygote), or Taster × Taster
5. Dd × dd (heterozygote × homozygous recessive), or Taster × Non-taster
6. dd × dd (homozygous recessive × homozygous recessive), or Non-taster × Non-taster

An individual heterozygous at this locus will produce an equal number of D and d eggs or sperms as a result of "segregation" during the process of meiosis. Since the mating of a D sperm with a d ovum, or a d sperm with a D ovum, etc. is strictly a matter of chance in the case of a marriage of two heterozygotes, the laws of probability can be applied in many ways to the problems of inheritance. Let us see how this works. In marriage (1) above, since both mates will produce nothing but D gametes, all the offspring of this marriage will possess the genotype DD and will be tasters. In marriage (3) one of the mates will produce nothing but D gametes while the other will produce only d gametes. Each of the offspring will therefore receive a D from one parent and a d from the other. Hence all offspring will be heterozygotes (tasters) although one parent is a taster while the other is a non-taster. The "Mendelian ratios" of offspring to the various kinds of marriages are as follows:

Parents	Offspring	
	Genotypic Ratio	*Phenotypic Ratio*
1. DD × DD	all DD	all tasters
2. DD × Dd	1 DD : 1 Dd	all tasters
3. DD × dd	all Dd	all tasters
4. Dd × Dd	1 DD : 2 Dd : 1 dd	3 tasters : 1 non-taster
5. Dd × dd	1 Dd : 1 dd	1 taster : 1 non-taster
6. dd × dd	all dd	all non-tasters

The application of the binomial expression $(p + q = 1)$ will give us the expected frequencies of the various genotypes in the population provided there is random mating with respect to the taster, non-taster trait. Let us let r represent the frequency of the recessive allele d, and $1 - r$ the frequency of the dominant allele D. Therefore, $r + (1 - r) = 1$; that is, the sum of the two frequencies must equal 100 percent. By expanding this expression to the second power we get $r^2 + 2r(1 - r) + (1 - r)^2 = 1$, where r^2 is the frequency of the genotype dd, $2r(1 - r)$ is the frequency of the genotype Dd, and $(1 - r)^2$ is the frequency of the genotype DD. Since this distribution is equally applicable to males and females, it is obvious that the frequency of offspring of marriages of dd parents will be $r^2 \times r^2 = r^4$; that is, the frequency of offspring of two particular genotypes will be the product of the frequencies of each. In this way, by expanding the trinomial expression to the second power we get:

$$r^4 + 4r^3(1 - r) + 6r^2(1 - r)^2 + 4r(1 - r)^3 + (1 - r)^4 = 1$$

A simple and useful way of presenting this expression is as follows:

	r^2	$2r(1 - r)$	$(1 - r)^2$
r^2	r^4	$2r^3(1 - r)$	$r^2(1 - r)^2$
$2r(1 - r)$	$2r^3(1 - r)$	$4r^2(1 - r)^2$	$2r(1 - r)^3$
$(1 - r)^2$	$r^2(1 - r)^2$	$2r(1 - r)^3$	$(1 - r)^4$

We can now consider the following propositions:

1. The frequency of offspring from matings of non-tasters with tasters (dd × DD; dd × Dd) is:

$$4r^3(1 - r) + 2r^2(1 - r)^2 = 2r^2(1 + r)(1 - r)$$

2. Of these two kinds of marriages, non-taster offspring will be produced only by the dd × Dd type and of all the offspring of this mating only one-half will be non-tasters. The frequency of non-taster offspring of dd × Dd marriages will therefore be:

$$\frac{4r^3 (1-r)}{2} = 2r^3(1-r)$$

3. The proportion of non-taster offspring to the total number of offspring of marriages between non-tasters and tasters will thus be:

$$\frac{2r^3 (1-r)}{2r^2(1+r)(1-r)} = \frac{r}{(1+r)}$$

4. The frequency of offspring from matings between tasters (DD × DD, DD × Dd, and Dd × Dd) will be:

$$(1-r)^4 + 4r(1-r)^3 + 4r^2 (1-r)^2 = (1-r)^2 (1+r)^2$$

5. Non-taster offspring will be produced only by the marriage Dd × Dd, and will represent only one-fourth of all the offspring of this type of marriage, or:

$$\frac{4r^2(1-r)^2}{4} = r^2(1-r)^2$$

6. The proportion of non-taster offspring to the total number of offspring of marriages between tasters will therefore be:

$$\frac{r^2 (1-r)^2}{(1-r)^2 (1+r)^2} = \frac{r^2}{(1+r)^2}$$

These proportions, derived from the expression $p^2 + 2pq + q^2 = 1$, give us the expected proportions of the genotypes in a population that is mating at random. The expression itself is known as the Hardy-Weinberg Law, discovered independently by Hardy and by Weinberg in 1908. It is of profound importance in population genetics because it tells us that there is no change in genotypic proportions in a population from one generation to the next, provided the population is mating at random.

In 1932 Snyder applied the ratios derived from the Hardy-Weinberg Law to a large sample of parents and offspring divided into tasters and non-tasters in order to determine whether the various proportions of taster and non-taster offspring observed in the sample agreed with the expected proportions. He found that the observed and expected ratios agreed almost perfectly, hence could assume that the taster trait was inherited according to the rules of simple Mendelian dominance.[5]

It should be noted, however, that a population may not remain in *equilibrium;* that is, its genotypes may not stay in the proportions given by the Hardy-Weinberg Law. This is the result of any one of a number of conditions such as: non-random mating within the population, natural selection of one or two of the three genotypes, and intermixture with another population with different gene frequencies.

Of equal importance for evolution is the application of the binomial expression to a recessive pathological trait to show the frequency of "carriers" (non-affected individuals who are heterozygotes) to affected individuals.[6] For example, it is estimated that there is, in general, one albino to every 20,000 normally pigmented people in the world's population. Since albinism is inherited as a simple recessive trait, there are three genotypes possible: AA, Aa, and aa. Letting q represent the frequency of a, and p the frequency of A, then the frequency of the genotype *aa* (albinos) in the population will be q^2. Therefore:

$$q^2 = 1/20,000$$

and,

$$q = 1/141 \text{ and } p = 140/141 \text{ (since } p + q = 1)$$

Substituting these values of p and q in the equation $p^2 + 2pq + q^2 = 1$, we find that the frequency of carriers ($2pq$) is approximately 1/70. Thus a mutant allele that acts as a recessive may attain a relatively high frequency in the population with only rare expression in homozygous form. A mutant may thus be "stored" in a population in heterozygous form, possibly as insurance against the day when it might confer an advantage upon the population as a result of a changing environment. The mathematically oriented reader is advised to consult Li (1955) for a

[5] Snyder, L. 1932. Studies in Human Inheritance. IX. The inheritance of Taste Deficiency in Man. *Ohio Journal of Science*, 32:436–440.

[6] Snyder, L. 1934. Studies in Human Inheritance. X. A Table to Determine the Proportion of Recessives to be Expected in Various Matings Involving a Unit Character. *Genetics*, 19:1–17.

more sophisticated and detailed presentation of this aspect of population genetics.[7]

It is probable that the human species is multi-allelic at each of its many genic loci. At the I locus, for example, there are four alleles—O, B, A_1, and A_2. They may occur on the paired chromosomes in any of ten possible combinations: A_1A_1, A_1A_2, A_2A_2, A_1O, A_2O, OO, A_2B, A_1B, BO, and BB. These allelic combinations comprise the possible *genotypes* of man at the I locus. They produce a total of six *phenotypes*, distinguishable by the application of various serum antibodies to the blood: O, A_1, B, A_1B, A_2B, and A_2.

Let us imagine that a pair of homologous chromosomes contains eight heterozygous loci and two homozygous loci, as indicated in Figure 21A. The homozygous loci are A and G. When synapsis occurs, each chromosome produces an *exact* duplicate of itself, so that there are now two paternal and two maternal chromosomes (Fig. 21B). Crossing-over may occur between the adjacent paternal and maternal chromosomes at the loci indicated, and between the outer paternal and maternal chromosomes at the E and F loci. The result is that each tetrad, after crossing-over, is now distinctive (Fig. 21C). None is identical to the original paternal or maternal chromosome, or to any others of the tetrad.

Now, crossing-over may take place at many different sites along the chromosome length, involving very short sequences of nucleotides as well as very long ones. Apparently this is a random process. Since there may be 1.5 billion nucleotide pairs in the 23 haploid number of chromosomes in Man, it becomes quite clear that the number of germ cells or gametes produced that are distinctive from all others in at least one locus is truly fantastic. Reflect that a woman produces around 400 mature ova in her reproductive lifetime and a man produces many billions of sperms. Of these only three or four ova and sperm will, on the average, join to produce new individuals. What are the chances, then, of any two people, living or dead, having identical genotypes? Obviously they are so small as to be beyond the need for consideration.

[7] Li, C. 1955. *Population Genetics*. Chicago: University of Chicago Press.

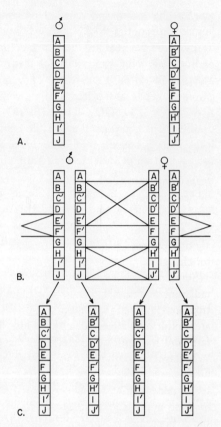

FIGURE 21. *Chromosomal Individuality Resulting from Crossing-over*

By this means, then, has Nature provided absolute insurance of variability among the individual members of a species. But if the only mechanism for producing variability were meiosis, would this be sufficient to permit the adaptation of a species to a constantly changing environment? Obviously the answer must be no. Meiosis can only shuffle and reshuffle the existing genes in a population. Eventually most combinations would have been tried over the course of thousands of years and the adaptive potentialities of all traits would have been realized. In other words, the full range of variability of each trait would finally be reached, but there would be no possibility of extending the range beyond the capabilities of the fixed gene pool of the species. As new environmental situations called for adaptive responses that the population was inherently unable to make, extinction would be the inevitable result.

Fortunately for species survival, a source of new kinds of genes exists in the form of *mutations*.

Mutations

Mutations are changes in the genetic material. Precisely what is involved when a gene mutates is another question that remains unanswered. Some have suggested that the sequence of nucleotides is changed or interrupted. We have seen that one property of the gene is its great stability, since it remains unchanged through countless mitotic divisions. On the other hand, another property of the gene, strangely enough, is its propensity for change.

Some mutagenic agents are known to us. They include such radiation sources as: X-rays, ultraviolet light, gamma rays, neutron bombardment, and cosmic rays. Chemical mutagenic agents are: sulfur and nitrogen mustards, methyl iodide, dimethyl sulfate, and the self-oxidizing agents ferrous ion and ascorbic acid.

Mutagenic agents that produce the so-called spontaneous mutations are not known to us but it is well established that different genes mutate at different rates. In corn, for example, the *Sh* gene mutates at a rate of 1.2 per one million gametes while the *R* gene mutates at the rate of 492 per million. Muller has estimated that the average gene in the fruit fly, *Drosophila*, will remain stable for about 100,000 years, for a rate of one mutation per one million gametes.[8] The mutation rates of many genes in Man have been computed. They have been expressed by Penrose (*Recent Advances in Human Genetics*) in terms of number of mutations per million gametes per generation, as shown in Table 2.[9] It is apparent from these facts that mutation rates vary widely with different genes, and that the average mutation rates in one species may be quite different from that in another.

[8] Muller, H. 1950. Our Load of Mutations. *American Journal of Human Genetics*, 2:111–176.

[9] Penrose, L. 1961. *Recent Advances in Human Genetics*. Boston: Little, Brown, and Company.

TABLE 2. *Estimates of Mutation Rates in Man*

Gene for	Number of mutations per 1 million loci per generation
DOMINANT DISEASE	
Epiloia	8
Chondrodystrophy	45–70
Aniridia	5
Microphthalmos (without mental defect)	5
Retinoblastoma	4–23
Partial albinism and deafness	4
Multiple polyposis of colon	13
Neurofibromatosis	100
Arachnodactyly	6
Huntington's chorea	5
Acrocephalosyndactyly	3
RECESSIVE DISEASE	
Sickle-cell anaemia	10,000
Juvenile amaurotic idiocy	38
Albinism	28
Ichthyosis congenita	11
Total color blindness	28
Infantile amaurotic idiocy	11
Amyotonia congenita	20
Epidermolysis bullosa	50
Microcephaly	49
Phenylketonuria	25
Thalassemia	400
Schizophrenia	500
Cystic fibrosis of pancreas	700
Spastic diplegia	2,000
SEX-LINKED DISEASE	
Hemophilia	20–32
Pseudohypertrophic muscular dystrophy	43–95

SOURCE: L. S. Penrose, *Recent Advances in Human Genetics.* Boston: Little, Brown and Company, 1961.

The average *rate* of mutation in Man is probably five to ten times that of *Drosophila,* but since a human generation is reckoned in terms of 25 years and a *Drosophila* generation slightly over one month, the *absolute time* lapse between mutations is considerably less in *Drosophila* than in Man. For example, if a gene in *Drosophila* and one in Man had the same generational mutation rate of 10^{-6} (purple color eye and epiloia, respectively), it would take 100,000 years before a mutation would occur in the descendants of that particular *Drosophila* gene, and about 25 million years before a mutation would occur in the descendants of the human gene.

It has been known for the past 25 years that mutation rates may vary within the same species and that populations of the same species may have different mutation rates. In addition it is known that mutation rates themselves are influenced by other genes called "mutator" genes. The implications of these findings for evolutionary theory are of great potential significance. It would appear that mutation rates themselves may be subject to environmental selective forces, thus speeding up or slowing down the rates of mutation of specific genes and, in effect, indirectly influencing the rates of evolution both within and between phylogenetic lines.

In 1927, H. J. Muller determined that irradiation of *Drosophila* resulted in a great increase in the mutation rate. Since that time many biologists have experimented with various mutagenic agents to induce mutations in such forms as fruit flies, mice, paramecia, bacteria, and plants. In 1945 a human population was tragically subjected to the destructive force of the first atomic bombs. Since that explosion over Hiroshima, and the subsequent one over Nagasaki, the living victims of these disasters and their progeny have been the subject of intensive study by Japanese and American scientists in an effort to determine the effects, both somatic and genetic, of these massive doses of radiation. The results of these studies will be discussed in a later Problem. Much of our knowledge of the genetic damage caused by irradiation comes from the recent experiments conducted on mice at the Oak Ridge National Laboratory by the Russells (1954).[10] In spite of the fact that we now can induce mutations in plants and certain experimental animals, no one has yet successfully *directed* a mutation, that is, obtained purposefully a particular desired mutation. The outcome of induced mutations

[10] Russell, L. and Russell, W. 1954. Pathways of Radiation Effects in the Mother and the Embryo. *Cold Spring Harbor Symposia on Quantitative Biology*, 19:50–58.

is still unpredictable. The scientist must use the wasteful method of producing great numbers of mutations and selecting the desired ones for study.

It must be realized that mutations are "accidental" changes in the structure of a gene. It is almost certain that, as such, the vast majority of mutations are detrimental, in some degree, to the individual organism. Indeed, most mutations that have been observed have been of distinct *disadvantage* to the organism in which they have occurred. This is not to be wondered at, however, since a mutation that might confer an advantage upon an individual would no doubt have long been incorporated into the species by positive selection processes. Dobzhansky's views (1949) on this subject are well worth quoting:

The extreme rarity or even absence of mutations that improve the viability in normal strains and under normal conditions is not surprising. The structure of each gene and of the genotype as a whole is a product of a long historical process controlled by natural selection . . . since the mutations which we can observe have taken place innumerable times in the history of the species, any mutation which constitutes an improvement over the "normal" condition has had a chance to become established. The genetic structure of the wild type with which laboratory experiments are started is presumably always fairly close to the highest level of adaptation attainable by the species in its present environment. To enhance the probability of detecting mutations favorable to the viability one must either lower the adaptive level of the initial genotype, or conduct the experiments in an environment different from that in which the species normally lives.[11]

This statement contains the key to understanding why most if not all mutants are harmful to the individual organism. Consider a modern high speed electronic computer—the giant electronic "brain," which in a few minutes can do calculations that would take a team of mathematicians years to perform. The vast network of intricate transistors, wiring, and dials is the culmination of hundreds of years of accumulated human knowledge in many fields. Now suppose that we hand a chimpanzee a sledge hammer and allow him to strike the computor just once anywhere at will. What are the chances that this random blow will

[11] Dobzhansky, T. 1949. *Genetics and the Origin of Species*, rev. ed. New York: Columbia University Press.

improve the efficiency of the computer? A gene mutation is somewhat analagous in that it is a haphazard change in a gene that over thousands and perhaps millions of years has been meshed into the gene pool of a population by the trials and tribulations of an exacting selective process on the part of a changing natural environment. The chance that it will confer a selective advantage upon the *individual* is extremely remote.

The Meaning of Mutations for the Individual and for the Species

I have purposely italicized the word "individual" in the previous sentence in order to emphasize the very important fact that while mutations are generally detrimental to the individual organism, they are absolutely essential for the ultimate survival of the species. This seeming paradox necessitates that we assume two quite different points of view when we regard the world about us. The common viewpoint that we all share by virtue of the fact that we *are* individuals contemplates and evaluates all social, physical, and biological phenomena in terms of their relation to our own individual well-being and interests. In this sense, all mutations are bad since they adversely affect us, our children, and our circle of friends and acquaintances. On the other hand, we are also members of a phylogenetic line which has endured and evolved for millions of years and which, we like to think, will persist indefinitely in time. The same mutations which harm us as individuals will offer some insurance to the species that it will be able to meet and adapt to changing conditions in future millennia. Can we, occasionally, step out of our role as individuals, and look at Man as a continuing stream of life, much as the biologist looks at generation after generation of *Drosophila?* It is only in this way that we can hope to arrive at relatively unbiased opinions about the present and future course of human evolution.

In Problem I we had gained a certain perspective in time and space which reduced us as individuals to ultramicroscopic specks on the broad canvas of organic evolution. Such an experience should shake our egocentrism to the core, and impress us with the insignificance of the individual when viewed against the vast numbers of generations of individuals that have come and gone as the species slowly evolved. The great events we witness that seem so earthshaking fade into nothingness when placed in such a perspective. As Nietzche wrote in *Also Sprach Zarathustra*:

"Little has ever occurred once thy noise and smoke has passed away. What difference if a city becomes a mummy, and a statue lies in the mud."

But now we can read new meaning into our existence as droplets in the onrushing flow of evolution. Within each of us are the tiny particles of inheritance that have lived in the cells of hundreds and thousands of generations of our ancestors. This unbroken stream of germ plasm was bestowed upon us by our parents and we in turn shall pass it, with perhaps a few changes (mutations) to our own offspring. This is the heritage of our species, entrusted temporarily to us so that we in turn may confer it upon the next generation. In terms of evolution our function as individuals is to safeguard and to transmit a segment of the gene pool of human phylogeny—a segment to which has been added a mutation or two to enhance, perhaps, the potentialities for survival of our species at some far distant point in the future.

The Rate of Mutations

Now we see ourselves as we truly are—minute in size, momentary in time, but momentous in the scheme of evolution.

If one of our functions is to contribute mutations to the genetic package we receive and will pass on to our children, it is pertinent to estimate just how many mutations are involved. Muller ("Our Load of Mutations") has conservatively calculated that "each individual, on the average, carries 8 slightly dominant, detrimental mutant genes in heterozygous condition."[12] Morton (1960) estimated that:

. . . the average person carries heterozygously the equivalent of 3–5 recessive lethals acting between late fetal and early adult stages, due to a mutation rate to such genes of .03–.05 per gamete per generation.[13]

[12] Muller, H. *Op. cit.*
[13] Morton, 1960. The Mutational Load Due to Detrimental Genes in Man. *American Journal of Human Genetics*, 12:348–364.

Muller concluded that the minimum mutation rate in Man is .1 per gamete with a maximum of .4 per gamete. If we take a mean figure for both Muller's and Morton's estimates, we arrive at a mean mutation rate of .3 per gamete per generation for both dominant detrimental and recessive lethal genes. In the total mature ova produced by the human female (about 400) we would then expect to find about 120 such mutants. Muller extended his argument, with the aid of certain assumptions, to claim that in 40 generations (about 1000 years) the number of mutant genes per individual will rise from 8 to 12. All students of the subject of mutation rates in Man agree, however, that such estimates are extremely tenuous and that much more knowledge about the genetic basis of human disease as well as the mutation phenomenon itself is needed before we can arrive at reliable results.

Mutations and Their Effects

In stressing the fact that mutations probably never confer an advantage upon the individual, we must not convey the impression that all mutations have an obviously harmful effect. True, there are many mutations so *lethal* that they destroy the organism very early in embryonic life. Some lethals are known in plants which destroy the gamete before fertilization. Other mutations will cause the death of the individual in late fetal life or in infancy, while still others do not take effect until late in life. The latter are usually called *sublethal* genes. In Man we have not yet recognized lethal genes which cause death in the embryo or early fetus, although such genes undoubtedly exist. In *ichthyosis congenita* death occurs at any time between the late fetal period and early infancy. Another hereditary disease that results in early death of the infant is *multiple telangiectasis*. In *amaurotic idiocy* and *retinoblastoma* death occurs within the first few years of life. *Hemophilia* causes death in males often before the age of reproduction, while *diabetes mellitus* (unless treated) leads to death any time between adolescence and middle age.

Lethal and sublethal genes are characterized by their behavior as *dominants* or *recessives*. A lethal allele that manifests some effects even in the heterozygous state is a true dominant lethal gene. An example is *thalassemia* (Mediterranean or Cooley's anemia) which, in the homozygous state (thalassemia major), often leads to death before adulthood, and in the heterozygous condition results in mild abnormalities (thalassemia minor). Lethal or sublethal recessive alleles may be divided into two types: those whose presence can be detected in the heterozygous state but whose lethality is expressed only in the homozygous condition, and those whose presence in the heterozygote can not be detected. *Xeroderma pigmentosum* is an example of the former in which multiple cancerous growths occur in the homozygote leading usually to adult death but in the heterozygote is expressed only as heavy freckling. In *amaurotic idiocy* the homozygote suffers complete degeneration of the central nervous system and dies in childhood, but the heterozygote enjoys normal health.

Some lethal and sublethal genes occur in the sex pair of chromosomes and, depending upon their location, are termed *X-linked* or *Y-linked* genes. These *sex-linked* genes may be either dominant or recessive. To understand this type of inheritance we must consider briefly the nature of the sex (XY) chromosomes. The female produces only ova that contain an X chromosome, while the male produces sperm half of which contain an X and half a Y chromosome. The Y chromosome is considerably shorter than its X homologue since it lacks many of the loci that normally occur on the X chromosome. On the other hand, a small segment of the Y chromosome contains loci which do not occur in the X chromosome. Those segments in either the X or Y chromosome which lack homologues in the other are called *differential* segments. The genetic condition found in the differential segment of the Y chromosome is termed *hemizygous* since it is essentially a single-allelic state and hence no allele in this segment could properly be called either dominant or recessive. The inheritance is called *holandric*. Human examples of X-linked recessive traits are hemophilia, the anhydrotic type of ectodermal dysplasia, one form of gargoylism, male pseudohermaphroditism, one form of hydrocephalus, and pseudohypertrophic muscular dystrophy (Penrose, 1961;[14] Fraser, 1961[15]). Two traits that are apparently due to sex-linked dominant alleles are hypophosphatemic rickets (Graham *et al.*, 1959[16]) and dark brown teeth (Haldane, 1937[17]). The Y-linkage of some 17 abnormalities was seriously challenged by Stern (1957[18]), but recent investigations by Slatis and Apelbaum (1963[19]) renew the possibility that one of these, hairy pinna of the ear (hypertrichosis), is indeed inherited in this manner.

Evidently heredity plays an important role in certain infectious diseases, in which the likelihood of infection and the degree of virulence is affected by the genetically determined susceptibility of the host. In such cases, however, the genetic mechanism is by no means as simple as in the hereditary diseases mentioned above. For example, in children with *hypogammaglobulinemia* there is defective synthesis of gamma globulin leading to defective immune mechanism and resulting in high susceptibility to bacterial infections and viral hepatitis. Dissemination of *coccidioidymycosis* is many times more frequent in the darkskinned populations than in Whites. The genetic disease *sickle-cell anemia* predisposes the subject to *salmonellosis*. Predisposition to *diabetes mellitus* is known to be inherited, although the genetic mechanism is apparently complicated, but the diabetic, in turn, is predisposed to skin infections, pyelonephritis, and tuberculosis. Even more involved is the inheritance of such constitutional and developmental factors as body build and maturation. Nevertheless many investigators have pointed out correlations between anthropological charac-

[14] Penrose, L. 1961. Mutation. In L. Penrose (editor), *Recent Advances in Human Genetics*. Boston: Little, Brown and Company.

[15] Fraser, F. 1961. Genetics and Congenital Malformations. In A. Steinberg (editor), *Progress in Medical Genetics*. New York: Grune and Stratton.

[16] Graham, J., McFalls, V., and Winters, R. 1959. Familial Hypophosphatemia with Vitamin D-resistant Rickets. *American Journal of Human Genetics*, 11:311–332.

[17] Haldane, J. 1937. A Probable New Sex-linked Dominant in Man. *Journal of Heredity*, 28:58–60.

[18] Stern, C. 1957. The Problem of Complete Y-Linkage in Man. *American Journal of Human Genetics*, 9:147–166.

[19] Slatis, H. and Apelbaum, A. 1963. Hairy Pinna of the Ear in Israeli Populations. *American Journal of Human Genetics*, 15:74–85.

teristics and such diseases as poliomyelitis, tuberculosis, duo-
denal ulcer, gastric ulcer, rheumatic fever, diabetes, gall bladder
disease, migraine, etc.

Hereditary Syndromes

One of the most significant aspects of inheritance from the
standpoint of evolution is the occurrence of *hereditary syndromes*. A hereditary syndrome may be defined as manifold
phenotypic abnormalities that result from a single mutant allele.
The existence of hereditary syndromes is dramatic evidence of
the function of genes as enzymes or enzyme-synthesizers in long
series of biochemical sequences leading to the final phenotypic
traits. From such syndromes we learn that a normal allele is
not only essential for the ultimate attainment of a single normal
characteristic but is involved in the normal development of
other, *apparently unrelated*, phenotypic traits. In other words, a
gene plays many roles in the development of the organism. The
multiple effects of a single gene are referred to as *pleiotropic*.
In medical genetics, where these effects are seen only as abnormalities, they comprise the hereditary syndrome.

There are many hereditary syndromes known in Man and the
genetic mechanism of some of them have been worked out. Let
us take for example the well-known Apert's syndrome (*acro-
cephalosyndactyly*). This disease is characterized by an irregular
egg-shaped head, a small nose, syndactyly or polydactyly, a
broad steep forehead, atypical ears, cleft lip and cleft palate,
low intelligence, pseudohermaphroditism, spina bifida, and abnormal bone morphology. A single dominant mutant is responsible. The fact that such widely separated and apparently unrelated phenotypic traits as ear shape, number of fingers, shape of
the long bones, and intelligence are traceable to a common gene
raises some interesting questions that cannot be evaded if we are
truly to seek understanding of the nature of Man. At this point
let us examine Table 3 in which are listed some of the hereditary
syndromes in which "mental behavior" appears to be developmentally subject to the same genes as are other so-called "physical traits." These syndromes have been grouped by G. A. Jervis
according to the physiological system affected or to the em-

TABLE 3. *Hereditary Syndromes Involving Mental Behavior (after G. A. Jervis)*

I. Dermodysplastic mental deficiencies (syndromes characterized by cutaneous lesions).
   A. Tubero-sclerosis—mental retardation, tumors of skin, organs, and sometimes in peripheral nerves.
   B. Neurofibromatosis (Recklinghausen's disease)—multiple skin pigmentation, subcutaneous nodules, often mental defect.
   C. "Naevoid" mental defect (Sturge-Weber's disease)—local dilatations of blood vessels of the face, calcification of cortex of brain, epilepsy, and mental deficiency.
   D. Follicular dyskeratosis (Darrier's disease)—skin disease with mental defect.
   E. Albright's disease—skin pigmentation, bone lesions, sometimes mental deficiency.
   F. Xerodermic idiocy—ulcers of skin and mental defect.

II. Dysostotic mental deficiencies (syndromes characterized by lesions of the osseous system).
   A. Cranio-facial dysostoses.
      1. Crouzon syndrome—acrocephaly, bulging eyes, small orbits, sometimes increased intracranial pressure.
      2. Apert syndrome—acrocephaly, bulging eyes, eyes widely separated, small nose, fused fingers, and lowered intelligence. Sometimes cleft lip and palate, atypical ears, pseudohermaphroditism, and skeletal abnormalities.
      3. Greig syndrome—eyes widely separated (hypertelorism), retarded growth, abnormalities of extremities, and mental deficiency.
   B. Dysostoses of extremities.
      1. Marfan's syndrome (arachnodactyly)—long limbs, spidery hands and feet, skeletal, ocular, and cardiac defects, and mental deficiency.

III. Metabolic mental deficiencies.
   A. Disorders of lipid metabolism (cerebral lipidoses).
      1. Gargoylism—dwarfism, short neck, large asymmetrical head, grotesque face, bushy eyebrows, thick lips, wide teeth, large tongue, protruding abdomen, and mental retardation.
      2. Nieman-Pick's disease—protruding abdomen, anemia, loss of weight, yellow-brown skin pigmentation, and severe mental retardation.
      3. Gaucher's disease—protruding abdomen, rigidity of neck and extremities, and marked mental retardation.

TABLE 3 (cont.)

B. Disorders of amino acid metabolism.
   1. Phenylketonuria (Folling's disease)—small head, broad teeth, back and head bent, extremities flexed, severe mental defect.
   2. Wilson's disease—cirrhosis of liver and mental defect.
C. Disorders of carbohydrates metabolism.
   1. Galactosuria—abnormal metabolism of galactose, enlarged liver, intolerance to food, cataracts, and mental retardation.
   2. Glycogenosis—failure to metabolize glycogen, excessive amounts of glycogen in liver, heart, skeletal muscle, or central nervous system, and mental defect.
D. Disorders of pigment metabolism within central nervous system.
   1. Hallervorden-Spatz disease—progressive muscular rigidity, mental deterioration.

---

bryonic tissue derivatives involved.[20] For example, *gargoylism*, *Gaucher's disease*, and *Nieman-Pick's* disease all involve disorders of lipid metabolism, in which the liver and spleen become greatly enlarged, and profound impairment of the central nervous system resulting in behavior ranging from imbecility to idiocy.

If we accept the principle that abnormalities and pathologies which result from a mutant allele are indicative of the fact that the allele in its normal state is necessary for the normal morphology and functioning of the traits in question, then it is difficult to avoid the inevitable corollary: genes which, in their mutant form, cause defects in the central nervous system resulting in behavior classified as aberrant, imbecilic, moronic, or idiotic, are responsible in their normal state for behavior that is considered within the range of "normal" or "acceptable." The dichotomy of mind and body is no longer a tenable concept, since both are inextricably linked by the biological processes of development. This is not to say, of course, that heredity is the sole determinant of the phenotypic characteristics of any trait, since we have already observed that the phenotype is the product of the interaction of both genes and environment.

The implications of this principle are profound, since it re-

[20] Jervis, G. 1952. Genetic Factors in Mental Deficiency. *American Journal of Human Genetics*, 4:260–271.

quires that a proper understanding of human behavior must be based upon knowledge of the basic anatomy, physiology, and biochemistry of the central nervous system. It also makes it clear that behavioral traits are subject to the same biological laws of evolution and inheritance as are physical traits. This view is succinctly presented by H. J. Muller in his paper on "Our Load of Mutations" as follows:

> It should be obvious that the same general principles apply to the inheritance of intellectual capacities and emotional proclivities as to the so-called physical traits . . . so far as the genetic basis of mental traits is concerned, the processes of mutation and selection and the laws concerning the rise and fall of gene frequencies, equilibria, etc., apply in the same manner.[21]

Inasmuch as the very core of human evolution is the unusual development of the mental abilities of Man rather than the slight quantitative changes in his anatomy, it is misleading to emphasize the latter to the exclusion of the former as is the case in most textbooks on the subject. We shall return to this subject in a later Problem.

Types of Mutations

There are still a number of aspects of heredity that are pertinent to our study and which we must at least touch upon before closing this Problem. One is with regard to mutations. The types of mutations we have been discussing are referred to as *point* mutations, that is, changes in the genetic material at a single locus. There are also mutations in which whole sequences of genes are rearranged or even reversed, and sometimes whole chromosomes may be involved. The former are called *position effects*, the latter involve such changes as *trisomy, monosomy,* and *polyploidy*.

Position effects include such segmental rearrangements as *inversion, deletion, duplication,* and *translocation. Inversion* is the reversal of a segment in a chromosome so that in synapsis in order for homologues to pair a loop is formed in the area where the inversion has occurred. The reversal is due to two separate breaks in the chromosome, permitting the segment thus

[21] Muller, H. *Op. cit.*

cut off to be inverted. Inversions have been noted in *Drosophila* but have not yet been demonstrated in Man. *Deletion* is a situation where such a segment, instead of being reversed, is lost, resulting in a chromosome which lacks certain consecutive loci. During synapsis the corresponding segment present in the normal chromosome forms a sort of loop, since it can not lie alongside a homologous segment, and this can be observed under the microscope. Recently a case was reported of a woman with primary amenorrhoea in whose blood, marrow, and skin cells there was present only one normal X chromosome plus a small additional chromosome interpreted to be the remnants of the second X chromosome after deletion of a segment. To my knowledge this is the only case of deletion in Man reported in the literature.

Translocation is a phenomenon in which two *non-homologous* chromosomes exchange segments. During synapsis the two sets of tetrads are bound together since homologous points adhere, even though on different tetrads. As a result of such reciprocal translocation, three types of gametes are produced: one contains a normal chromosome from each of the two tetrads, a second contains one normal chromosome plus one translocated chromosome, and a third contains two translocated chromosomes, one from each of the two tetrads. As can be seen in the diagrammatic representation of translocation in Figure 22, the second type results in gametes which contain a duplication of part of one chromosome and a deficiency of part of the other. Four different kinds of autosomal reciprocal translocations are known in Man (Ferguson-Smith, 1961).[22] Two involve clinical types of *mongolism*; the others are *polydysspondylism* (a syndrome involving subnormal intelligence, absence of a rib and half a vertebra, fusion of vertebrae, and retarded maturation) and a case of *Klinefelter's syndrome* (small testes, absence of spermatogenesis, increased excretion of gonadotrophin, and occasionally eunuchoidism, gynecomastia, and feeble-mindedness).

A not uncommon phenomenon is the occurrence of numerous duplicated segments in chromosomes, as seen in the salivary glands of *Drosophila*. Such duplications may be the result of

[22] Ferguson-Smith, M. 1961. Chromosomes and Human Disease. In A. Steinberg, *Progress in Medical Genetics, pp.* 292–334.

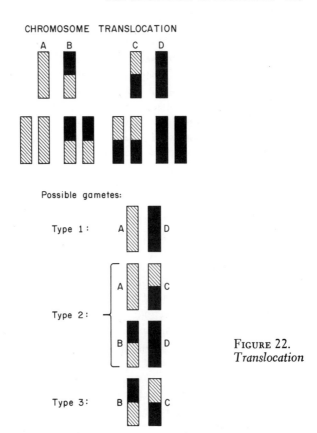

FIGURE 22.
Translocation

unequal crossing over during synapsis. Chromosomes with duplicated segments loop upon themselves or upon other chromosomes so that homologous segments lie side by side. Duplication
may be of great significance in evolution since it is one way in
which additional chromosomal material may be accumulated
within a species (Snyder and David, 1957). Although duplication has been demonstrated in *Drosophila* and *Sciara*, there does
not yet appear to be any confirmation of this phenomenon in
Man.

Changes in the diploid number of chromosomes constitute
mutations that have been the subject of recent intensive investigation in Man. This followed the discovery by Tjio and Levan

in 1956 that the normal diploid number in Man was 46 and not 48.[23] In 1959 Hungerford and associates devised a simple method of separating and fixing chromosomes in the metaphase stage of mitosis in blood cells, permitting easy observation and measurement.[24] This in turn led to the study of chromosome morphology and identification and its application to clinical medicine. Although a detailed discussion of chromosome morphology is beyond the scope of this book, a few salient features of this new field of genetics may be pointed out.

The Karyotype

One result of these investigations has been the study of the *karyotype* or normal morphological pattern of the human chromosomes. The criteria for identifying the individual pairs of chromosomes are: (1) the relative length of each chromosome, and (2) the ratio of the long arm over the short arm. Other features are aids, such as the presence of satellites. Each chromosome is characterized by the presence, somewhere along its length, of a *centromere*. It divides the chromosome into two parts, called the long arm and the short arm. The arm ratio is one if the centromere is so located that both arms are of equal length. The centromere varies in its location on different pairs so that in some cases it is almost terminal. On this basis, then, the chromosomes can generally be readily identified, as seen in the drawing in Figure 23, and are conventionally given by number.

Although autosomal point mutations can not be assigned to individual chromosomal pairs, mutations involving an extra chromosome (trisomy) or a deficiency in a chromosome (monosomy) can be located in the karyotype. For many years it had been postulated that an abnormal karyotype could be responsible for certain human pathologies, but it was not until 1959 that this was first confirmed by the discovery of an extra X chromosome in a male affected with Klinefelter's syndrome. The

[23] Tjio, J. and Levan, A. 1956. The Chromosome Number of Man. *Hereditas*, 42:1.
[24] Hungerford, D., Donnelly, A., Nowell, P. and Beck, S. 1959. The Chromosome Constitution of a Human Phenotypic Intersex. *American Journal of Human Genetics*, 11:215–236.

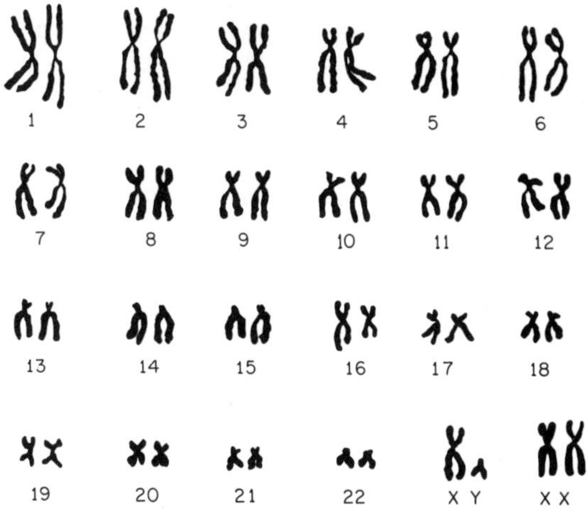

FIGURE 23. *The Human Karyotype*

XXY karyotype of this disease has been reaffirmed many times since. Another abnormal karyotype centering upon the sex chromosomes is associated with *Turner's syndrome,* a disease in which the affected individual is phenotypically a female with short stature, webbing of the neck, infantile genitalia, primary amenorrhoea, and occasionally other anomalies. In Turner's syndrome the karyotype has been established as XO, that is, the absence of the second sex chromosome. It is thus an example of monosomy (diploid number of 45) while Klinefelter's syndrome is an example of trisomy (diploid number of 47).

Most individuals with abnormal karyotypes are severely affected with multiple abnormalities and are usually sterile. The search for the presence of aberrant karyotypes in the many inherited malformations and syndromes in Man has not thus far been very rewarding. Most such entities show normal karyotypes. Some cases of Mongolism and two other syndromes appear to be examples of autosomal trisomy. In the former the trisomic pair may be either 21 or 22, since the two cannot yet be distinguished (Ferguson-Smith 1961).[25] The affected chromosome pairs of the latter are not absolutely identified but are thought

[25] Ferguson-Smith, M. 1961. *Ibid.*

to be either 13, 14, or 15 in the one type, and 17 or 18 in the other.

Penetrance and Expressivity

Two characteristics of genes often combine to render the task of the human geneticist even more difficult. They are *penetrance* and *expressivity*. Penetrance refers to the ratio between affected phenotypes and affected genotypes. If ten persons are known to be homozygous for a recessive mutant allele and only two of them show any phenotypic effect, the penetrance of the mutant is said to be 20 percent. This, of course, complicates the analysis of the mechanism of inheritance. Penetrance ranges in human alleles from almost zero to 100 percent. In the ABO blood group locus every genotype is phenotypically expressed, hence the penetrance is 100 percent. When the penetrance falls below 30 percent the mode of inheritance is extremely difficult if not impossible to ascertain. Sometimes the level of penetrance is dependent on the criteria upon which diagnosis of a condition is based. A condition known as *congenital hip dislocation* is inherited very likely as a dominant. An investigation of numerous pedigrees of this affliction among the Apache Indians of Arizona[26] revealed several in which the affliction "skipped" a generation or was present less often than expected in siblings. However, this was on the basis of an "all or none" manifestation of frank dislocation, indicating a penetrance far less than 100 percent. When x-rays showed that many of the apparently normal individuals had hip dysplasias and subluxations, the penetrance was adjusted upwards considerably.

Expressivity refers to the degree to which a mutant allele manifests itself in the afflicted individual. The *Adair-Dighton syndrome* (blue sclerotics), caused by a dominant mutant allele, is characterized by brittle bones, blue sclera, and deafness. In some individuals, however, deafness may not occur and fragility of bone may be confined only to one portion of the extremities. In

[26] Kraus, B. and Schwartzmann, J. 1957. Congenital Dislocation of the Hip Among the Fort Apache Indians. *Journal of Bone and Joint Surgery*, 39A:448–449.

addition, the age of onset of deafness may vary considerably. In mutants of reduced penetrance and variable expressivity it is very likely that environmental factors act to suppress the effects. It is also possible that the influence of particular constellations of genes in which the mutant occurs may help curb its deleterious potentialities.

The Interactions of Genes with Environment

We have indicated earlier that genes either act as enzymes or mediate the synthesis of enzymes which then catalyze particular biochemical reactions. Long series of successive biochemical reactions lead ultimately to the final structures and processes which we observe as the phenotype. The specific and immediate intervention of a gene in a biochemical milieu is known as the *primary* action of a gene, as contrasted with the phenotypic effect of the gene which is the final result of a series of reactions initiated by the primary action. Undoubtedly many other genes interpose their coded information along the biochemical steps leading to the final effects. If any one of these genes happens to be a mutant, it interrupts or "blocks" the normal sequence of reactions and causes abnormal expressions of those final effects dependent on the subsequent steps in the chain of reactions.

Fortunately we have an example of such a biochemical chain of events in Man. Thanks to the original work of Garrod in 1909[27] and the subsequent research of Haldane,[28] Beadle,[29] and Harris,[30] the sequence of biochemical events in the metabolism of the amino acids *phenylalanine* and *tyrosine* is now well worked out. Phenylalanine cannot be synthesized by Man, hence must be ingested. In the series of steps involved in the degradation of phenylalanine once it enters the body, numerous enzymes are required. It is well established that these enzymes are directly re-

[27] Garrod, A. 1909. *Inborn Errors of Metabolism*. London: Henry Frowde.

[28] Haldane, J. 1954. *The Biochemistry of Genetics*. London: George Allan and Unwin, Ltd.

[29] Beadle, G. 1945. Biochemical Genetics. *Chemical Review*, 37:15ff.

[30] Harris, H. 1959. *Human Biochemical Genetics*. Cambridge: Cambridge University Press.

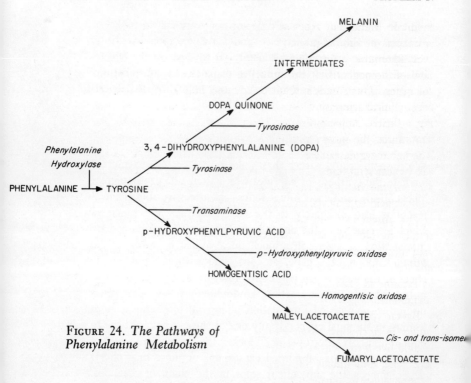

FIGURE 24. *The Pathways of Phenylalanine Metabolism*

lated to individual genes. In the presence of a mutant there is a deficiency of the enzyme and the appropriate reaction is blocked. In the diagram in Figure 24, the metabolic pathway is considerably simplified, but the effects of four types of blocks are shown. They lead to the well-known metabolic defects of phenylketonuria, tyrosinosis, alkaptonuria, and albinism.

Let us begin with the enzyme *tyrosinase* which is involved in two steps: the conversion by oxidation of tyrosine to dopa, and of dopa to dopa quinone. The absence of this enzyme results in total *albinism* which is characterized by complete absence of the pigment melanin in the skin, eyes, and hair. Although the pigment cells, melanocytes, are present, they lack tyrosinase. In addition to the absence of pigmentation, many albinos have lowered intelligence and lack physical vigor. Albinism is inherited as a simple Mendelian recessive. Heterozygotes show no clinical symptoms of the condition.

Alkaptonuria is an inherited condition marked by the excretion of homogentisic acid into the urine, resulting in black coloration. Until middle age the affected individual shows no other clinical symptoms, then develops the symptoms of deforming arthritis. Apparently two types of inheritance lead to alkaptonuria, the most prevailing of which is by a recessive gene. The heterozygote cannot be detected but the homozygote shows the typical symptoms. The condition is caused by deficiency of the enzyme *homogentisic oxidase* which breaks down homogentisic acid to maleylacetoacetate.

The absence of the enzyme p-hydroxyphenylpyruvic oxidase results in blocking the conversion of p-hydroxyphenylpyruvic acid to homogentisic acid, causing excretion in the urine of large quantities of p-hydroxyphenylpyruvate. This condition is known as *tyrosinosis*. The mode of inheritance of this inborn error of metabolism is unknown.

By far the most serious of the four inherited metabolic disorders is *phenylketonuria*, a defect that occurs once in every 40,000 live births in the United States. It is inherited as a recessive gene, and unlike the other conditions can be detected in heterozygotes by means of phenylalanine tolerance tests. As can be seen in Figure 25, a deficiency of the enzyme *phenylalanine hydroxylase* results in an accumulation of excess phenylalanine which is converted to phenylpyruvic acid. This in turn is collected in the blood and spinal fluid, causing severe damage to the central nervous system. It also interferes with tyrosine metabolism, so little melanin is produced. There is also excessive excretion of phenylalanine products in the urine. Phenylketonurics are characterized by idiocy or by imbecility (I.Q. of 30 or less), light skin, blond hair, blue eyes, and presence of phenylpyruvic acid in the urine. If treatment, consisting of a diet free of phenylalanine, is initiated soon after birth, the prognosis is good.

From this and other metabolic systems that have been investigated both in Man and in lower animals, a picture emerges of the nature of the hereditary syndrome. Obviously the earlier in

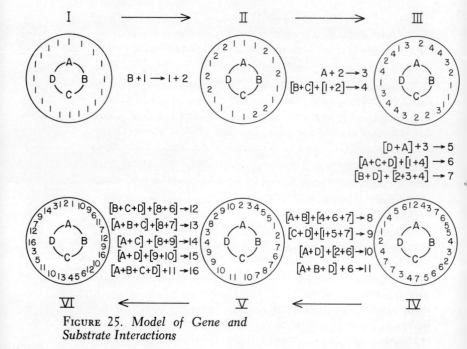

FIGURE 25. *Model of Gene and Substrate Interactions*

a biochemical sequence a genetic block occurs, the more numerous and varied will be the abnormal expressions in the phenotype. If, on the other hand, a mutant gene acts toward the end of the metabolic chain of reactions, the more restricted will be the effect on the organism. Mutation of genes concerned with such basic processes as cellular differentiation and histogenesis would undoubtedly result in death of the zygote or early embryo. The complexity of the subject has been stressed by G. W. Beadle, whose work on the genetic control of biochemical reactions in Neurospora won for him a Nobel Prize. He stated:

. . . The organism is not merely a bag of chemical reactions, but a complex and highly integrated system in which reactions are systematically related in both time and space. If one gene in the system is altered, one reaction will be modified. But, although this relation may be a relatively simple one, the subsequent consequences will usually be multitudinous. In fact, if all representatives of almost any gene in an organism are removed or replaced by a completely inactive form of the gene the chances are very great that the organism can no longer survive.

—Genes and the Chemistry of the Organism[31]

No representation in plane or solid geometry can properly convey the immense biochemical panorama wrought by the continuous interaction of genes with genes, genes with substrate, and substrate with substrate—a sort of phantasmagoria that unerringly leads not only to a viable functioning organism but to one that is recognizably a member of a particular species. The diagram offered in Figure 25 will merely serve as a guide to some of the basic steps involved, but only the exercise of considerable imagination on the part of the reader, plus the application of those genetic facts and principles already discussed in this Problem, will achieve a proper appreciation of the awesome complexity that is ontogenesis. In this diagram we must imagine that the letters A, B, C, and D represent four genes that constitute the total genotype of an organism. The line connecting them indicates the continual interaction and interdependence of the genetic constitution. The genes are always surrounded by the cellular environment consisting of highly specific organic compounds (substrate), indicated by the figures 1, 2, 3, etc. The circle surrounding each group of letters and figures and numbered in Roman numerals represents the organism in successive moments of development. Between each such stage there are one or more formulae indicating that interaction of specific genes and specific substrates has resulted in the formation of new substrates, which in turn trigger new sets of interactions. When we recall that there are not four but thousands of genes, that there are undoubtedly hundreds of new chemical compounds constantly being formed, and that as the cells increase in number and differentiate these compounds vary according to the type of cell, then we can begin to appreciate what is involved in development. And what is more important, we can begin to put the mutant gene in its proper perspective.

The genetic mechanism that we have attempted to describe in very brief terms must never be lost sight of when we survey the fossil evidence for human evolution and try to interpret its

[31] Beadle, G. 1946. Genes and the Chemistry of the Organism. *American Scientist*, 34:31–53.

meaning and significance. Since Man is an animal, and since he has evolved, the biological principles of evolution must be applied to him as to other species of animals. Whenever and wherever they do not seem to apply, then we may look for other explanations and other principles. Scientific method will hardly tolerate the reverse procedure. It is therefore to a review of the biological principles of evolution that we now turn.

Principles of Evolution

If a single cell, under appropriate conditions, becomes a man in the space of a few years, there can surely be no difficulty in understanding how, under appropriate conditions, a cell may, in the course of untold millions of years, give origin to the human race.

HERBERT SPENCER, *Principles of Biology*

The Effect of Natural Selection on the Genotype

In the first four Problems we were concerned with certain facts, principles, and theories in comparative zoology, geochronology, geography, genetics, and basic Darwinian evolution. Now we must integrate this material in such a way as to produce some modern guideposts to the comprehension of biological evolution. Such an integration is often given the name *Neo-Darwinism*. In a subsequent Problem we shall see how these principles might be applied to human evolution.

To make our task as simple as possible, let us first imagine a hypothetical population of felines called A. This population, at the time we first look at it, exists some two or three million years ago on a tropical island in the Pacific Ocean. It consists of 100 members, 30 of whom are adult females, 30 adult males, and 40 offspring ranging in age from infancy to puberty. Phenotypically this population presents a range of variation in every trait which is approximately represented by a normal curve. Genotypically there is a characteristic kind and number of alleles at each locus. For example, at locus Q there are three alleles, *a*, *b*, and *c*. Since each individual possesses two of the the three alleles at this particular locus, there are 200 Q alleles

123

in the population. Of these, 100 are *a*, 60 are *b*, and 40 are *c*. The allelic frequency, then, at this locus can be stated as follows: $a = 50$ percent, $b = 30$ percent, and $c = 20$ percent. The frequency of alleles at all other genic loci can similarly be stated, only theoretically of course. Since the various alleles at any locus perform their functions in somewhat different ways, the phenotypic range reflects the differential frequencies of these alleles, always subject of course to the modifying influences of the environment. We can state this in another and more familiar way. *The phenotype of an organism is the product of the cumulative effects of continuous interactions between fixed heredity and constantly changing environment up to the moment of observation.*

Environmental influences can change the expression of an allele, but only up to a point—that point being determined by the rigidity of the biochemical pathway in which the allele works its effect. In Man, the genotype AA always results in the blood group phenotype A, regardless, apparently, of environmental influence, but the expression of the mutant allele for blue sclerotics can be considerably modified by various environmental as well as genetic factors.

Now let us further suppose that the function of the genic locus Q is to determine the length of the canine tooth. Allele *a* endows the animal with an average length of 35 mm., *b* with 25 mm., and *c* with 45 mm. The distribution of canine lengths in population A will roughly correspond to the relative frequency of these alleles. If the frequencies of the alleles change, there will be a corresponding change in the phenotypic range for the trait. If they remain constant generation after generation, then the phenotypic range of the population will remain relatively fixed. Since we are, for the purposes of this exposition, omniscient, omnipresent, and omnipotent, we can observe population A over the course of many thousands of years, and we see, in actuality, that the phenotypic range does not remain fixed. In fact, the distributions of other traits change as well as that of canine length. Since significant change in the distribution curves of phenotypic traits is the criterion of evolution, and since any such significant change is dependent upon a shift in the relative allelic frequencies, it would appear that we can now arrive at a definition. Evolution is simply *change in gene frequencies.*

The phenotype is the product of the genotype *in the individual organism*, but in a very significant way the genotype is largely the product of selection of the phenotype *in the population*. This is only an apparent contradiction. We have seen in Problem III that the changing environment "selects" those individuals that are best adapted. In so doing it selects adapted *phenotypes*, not genotypes. By selecting certain phenotypes nature inadvertently and indirectly selects certain genotypes, since the surviving and successful phenotypes will pass their genes on to their offspring.

In our example let us suppose that there is a gradual shift in the environment such that the rodents which form the main element in the diet of our cats begin to acquire thicker skins. Those cats possessing allele c and hence tending to have somewhat longer canines than the rest will be more efficient in catching and disabling the prey. The others, being less successful, are put at a selective disadvantage and gradually become weakened by undernourishment. They tend to have fewer offspring and some even fail to reproduce. The result is that over many generations the frequency of allele c begins to rise while that of a and particularly b drops off. The paleontologist, examining fossil remains of the ancestral forms of this population of two million years ago and comparing them with their modern descendants, would note the great difference in mean canine length. From a mean length of about 35 mm. in the ancestral forms the modern population had evolved to a mean length of 65 mm. If it were in the power of the paleontologist to calculate the respective gene frequencies he might find that the modern population was characterized by the following: $c = 70$ percent, $a = 10$ percent, $b = 0$, and a new mutant allele d present with a frequency of 20 percent.

Change in gene frequencies is the inevitable outcome of the operation of natural selection. There can be little question that the major factor in evolutionary change is natural selection. But, as we have stated earlier, if natural selection could only operate on the *existing* gene pool of a population, there would be no evolution. The allelic composition can, as we have seen, be shuffled and reshuffled so that all possible gene combinations will be realized among the individual members and their descendants, but the limits of phenotypic expression will be sharply circumscribed. It takes new alleles—mutants—to bestow the potentialities of almost unlimited phenotypic plasticity upon the population as it marches through time.

Most mutations occur in a recessive form, hence can be carried in a population without seriously affecting the viability or fertility of the carrier. Since in any generation the population is already well adapted to its environment as a result of genera· tions of previous natural selective processes, such mutations will remain at a relatively low frequency in the population, being constantly thrown into different gene associations through the process of meiosis. As the environment changes, some of them occurring in particular genetic contexts may happen to confer adaptive value upon their carriers, giving them a slight selective advantage over their fellows in the population. In this way the frequencies of the indirectly selected mutations rise. Eventually the aberrant alleles become so common in the population that they can no longer be regarded as "mutants" but rather as "normal" alleles.

The Operation of Genetic Drift

There are other factors besides natural selection which under certain circumstances can change gene frequencies and hence cause evolution. One of these is called *genetic drift*. To illustrate the operation of genetic drift we shall return to our insular feline population. This time, however, let us imagine that there are only five males and five females who make up the *effective breeding population*, that is, only they are of reproductive age and are actually mated and breeding. With respect to the Q locus let us further assume that the genotypes of the five pairs of mates are as follows:

	Male Genotype		Female Genotype
Pair #1	aa	×	aa
Pair #2	aa	×	bb
Pair #3	ab	×	bc
Pair #4	ab	×	ac
Pair #5	ac	×	bc

We note that the frequencies of the three alleles are identical with those in the total population. Pair #1 represents a mating between homozygotes for *a*, pair #2 a mating between a homozygote for *a* and a homozygote for *b*, and pairs #3–#5 matings between heterozygotes. It is obvious that pair #1 will produce only homozygous *a* offspring, since all the sperm of the male and all the ova of the female will contain nothing but *a* alleles. The offspring of pair #2 will all be heterozygotes *ab* since each sperm will contribute an *a* and each ovum a *b* to the zygotes. The kind and relative frequency of offspring of heterozygous mates can be easily computed by the device shown in Figure 26.

Pair #3   Kinds of Male Sperm

		a	b
Kinds of Female Ova	a	ab	bb
	c	ac	bc

Result: Four different genotypes (ab, bb, ac, bc) will be produced, each with a frequency of 25 percent.

Pair #4   Kinds of Male Sperm

		a	b
Kinds of Female Ova	a	aa	ab
	c	ac	bc

Result: Four different genotypes (aa, ab, ac, bc) will be produced, each with a frequency of 25 percent.

Pair #5   Kinds of Male Sperm

		a	c
Kinds of Female Ova	b	ab	bc
	c	ac	cc

Result: Four different genotypes (ab, bc, ac, cc) will be produced, each with a frequency of 25 percent.

FIGURE 26. *Method for Computing Kinds and Frequencies of Offspring of Heterozygous Matings*

When it is indicated that the frequency of the different types of offspring will be 25 percent, we refer to *expected* frequency and not to the frequency that is actually observed in any particular mating. The probability of a female birth is 50 percent and that of a male child is also 50 percent, so that in a family of eight children we would *expect* to find four girls and four boys. But as we are well aware, the *actual* number could be seven girls and one boy. The observed ratio may be far from the expected ratio in such a small sample, but in a sample of 1000 families with eight children each the ratio of boys to girls would be very close to the expected 1 : 1 ratio. Let us assume that mating pairs #3, #4, and #5 each produce a single offspring. In pair #3 the chance that this offspring will *not* be either *ac* or *bc* is 50 percent, or ½. Exactly the same probability exists in pair #4. In pair #5 the chance that the lone offspring will *not* be an *ac*, *bc*, or *cc* is only 25 percent or ¼. Since one of the laws of probability of the joint occurrence of two or more events is the product of their separate probabilities, it can be seen that the probability of *no c* allele occurring among the three offspring of pairs #3–#5 would be: ½ × ½ × ¼ = ¹⁄₁₆ or 6.25 percent. Clearly it would not, therefore, take a miracle for the *c* allele to be entirely wiped out of the population. However, this is an extreme case. Normally we would expect that in a small population chance alone might cause fluctuations in the gene frequency rather than deletion of an allele.

The possible effects of genetic drift in finite groups of various sizes were first calculated by S. Wright, so that such random fluctuations in the frequencies of genes are often referred to as the "Sewall Wright effect." The mathematical basis of these calculations is somewhat complex, but a simple, relatively non-mathematical explanation of the principle of genetic drift is essential since we shall have to consider the possible role of this factor in human evolution.

In our population A there were 40 members of the filial generation. Let us consider a locus W for which there are two alleles, *w* and *w'*. The frequency of each allele is 50 percent. The filial generation will be, in a sense, the product of drawing 2 × 40 of these alleles at random from the parental generation. The question is: how much can the frequency of, say, the *w'* allele be changed in the filial generation from the parental frequency of 50 percent. If we let p = the parental frequency of w, and q = the parental frequency of w', then

$$(p + q)^{2N}$$

will express the chance variation of the gene frequency in N individuals. The possible values of q in the filial generation range

from $\dfrac{2N}{2N} = 100\%$ to $\dfrac{0}{2N} = 0$. The deviation of q in the filial

generation from the value of q in the parental deviation will be $q_p - q_f$, and the variance of this deviation will be (from the variance of any binomial expression):

$$\sigma^2 = \frac{q_p\,(1 - q_p)}{2N} \text{ or, in our example, } \sigma^2 = \frac{.25}{80} = .0031$$

The standard deviation is then $\sigma = \sqrt{.0031} = .056$. Since $q_p = .50$ there is a 34 percent probability that q_f will be between .50 and .556 and a similar probability that q_f will be between .494 and .50. The prospects that q_f will be either less than .332 or more than .668 are about .3 percent.

It can be seen that when the frequency of a parental allele is about 50 percent the deviations from this frequency in the next generation can be relatively large, provided the population is small. If the frequency of the parental allele is quite low (or quite high) the deviation will be correspondingly less. The larger the population size, the smaller will be the deviation. Thus, two variables affect the size of the random fluctuations of gene frequency—gene frequency itself and population size.

In a small population, regardless of what the initial frequency of the allele might be, the effect of genetic drift over many generations might result either in elimination or fixation of the allele, that is, its frequency might ultimately become 0 or 100 percent. In either event there will be no subsequent fluctuation of its value. However, if the initial frequency of the allele is either very high or very low, the chance that genetic drift will cause fixation or elimination respectively is much higher. To put it another way, it will take fewer generations for genetic drift to eliminate an allele of initially low frequency than one of higher frequency.

One of the important consequences of allele elimination or fixation is the loss of heterozygosity at that particular locus. In our example, if genetic drift were to result in the total elimination of allele w' in some future descendant generation of population A, then all genotypes would be ww and there would thus be loss of genetic variability. The only possibility of variation subsequently at this locus would be mutation. We must therefore keep in mind population size and the role of genetic drift when we turn our attention to the evolutionary forces working on Man.

The process we have described will affect not one but all loci in a small population so that eventually all loci will become fixed, that is, will be homozygous. The rate at which loci become fixed (that is, rate of decay of variability) is calculated to be $1/2N$ per generation where N represents the size of the effective breeding population. In other words, in our sample population A with an effective breeding group of 10, about 5 percent of the unfixed genes would be lost in each successive generation. Thus, even though the actual population numbers 100, the effective breeding members are considerably fewer and genetic drift can, in this case, reduce genetic variability to zero in about 20 generations. This points up the fact that a population may be large in total numbers but small with reference to its effective breeding population so that it is subject to significant change as a result of genetic drift.

It is interesting to note that while genetic drift is a purely random process, natural selection is definitely not. In fact, the forces of natural selection are constantly opposing random fluctuation. When the population is small, the effect of natural selection is considerably reduced while that of genetic drift is increased. It is even possible that random fluctuation may eliminate genes which confer greater adaptive value than those that become fixed. There is the possibility, therefore, that genetic drift may actually work against and overcome the selective forces of the environment. In large populations where the effects of genetic drift are practically negligible, an allele need have only slightly greater adaptive value to be positively selected and eventually to achieve high frequency. Because of the reduction in the effectiveness of natural selection in small populations it follows that the effect of mutations is likewise slight. Dobzhansky (1951) illustrates this point by comparing the frequencies of all lethals in various breeding populations of *Drosophila pseudoobscura*.[1] The mutation rates of the strains of this species found in Death Valley, Mexico, and Guatemala are the same, yet the frequency of lethals in the Death Valley strain is half that of the Mexican and Guatemalan strains. This is correlated with the fact that the effective size of the Death Valley population is much lower, since the extremes in temperature during summer and winter drastically reduce the population.

Dobzhansky cites evidence to support the thesis that genetic drift can be a potent evolutionary factor when the populations are small. Strains of *Drosophila* occupying areas only a few miles apart on the same mountain range showed as many differences as those occupying different ranges. What is more, a single population of *Drosophila pseudoobscura* observed at one station in Death Valley at successive weeks over a period of a year and a half showed marked fluctuations in gene frequency. Dobzhansky sums up his views on this subject with the following words:

. . . Restriction of the genetically effective size of natural populations is in all probability an important agent engendering differentiation of species into local groups possessing different genotypes. It must be admitted that . . . we do not have even approximate estimates of the magnitude of population numbers (in Drosophila). And yet, a large and rapidly growing amount of evidence pertaining to different subdivisions of the living world and secured by different methods and by different biological disciplines, attests the existence of phenomena which can most plausibly be accounted for by genetic "drift" in populations of limited sizes. Although it would certainly be premature to conclude that evolution in all groups and at all times is conditioned by the genetic drift, it is reasonable to assume that it is frequently assisted by this factor, the importance of which has only recently become appreciated.[2]

Now let us return to our hypothetical feline population and suppose that by some geological happenstance an impenetrable

[1] Dobzhansky, T. 1941. *Genetics and the Origin of Species*, 2nd ed. New York: Columbia University Press.
[2] *Ibid.*, p. 185.

barrier, perhaps a mountain range, suddenly divided the island in half so that 50 cats occupied each half. Let us further presume that the two new populations were genetically identical. Since the two populations, A and A', are now effectively and completely isolated from each other, they will independently pursue their own evolutionary destinies. Let us assume that henceforth their respective environments will remain identical, although, of course, in actuality this could never happen. Since both populations are extremely small we can discount the effect of either mutations or natural selection. Genetic drift will operate in both A and A' but in different ways since the process is entirely a random one. Within a few generations the gene frequencies of the two populations will diverge, and will continue to diverge with the passage of time. Eventually both A and A' will become genetically fixed, assuming that there is no great increase in population size. This means that each will arrive at a point where there is no more genetic plasticity left in the population so that neither can respond to significant environmental change. An outstanding population geneticist, C. C. Li, states:

Small populations in which every locus has been fixed have no genetic variability left. When environmental conditions change, such populations will be unable to go through genotypic reorganization to meet a new situation. Therefore, no matter how favorable a fixed type may be under present conditions, its ultimate fate in the long process of evolution probably is extinction.[3]

Genetic Drift in Human Populations

The presumed effect of genetic drift in human populations has been studied by Glass and associates (1952)[4] and by Kraus and

[3] Li, C. 1955. *Population Genetics*. Chicago: University of Chicago Press, p. 324.

[4] Glass, B., Sacks, M., Jahn, E., and Hess, C. 1952. Genetic Drift in a Religious Isolate: An Analysis of the Causes of Variation in Blood Group and Other Gene Frequencies in a Small Population. *American Naturalist*, 86:145–160. Glass, B. 1956. On the Evidence of Random Genetic Drift in Human Populations. *American Journal of Physical Anthropology*, 14 n.s.:541–555.

White (1956).[5] The former dealt with a religious "isolate" called the Dunkers in Pennsylvania. This group first migrated from Germany in 1719 and the particular group numbered 350 persons, with an effective breeding population of 100. Seven genetic loci were studied, of which five showed significant differences in gene frequency from both the German population from which the Dunkers originally derived and the United States population in which they now live. Glass and his associates tentatively ascribed these differences to the effect of genetic drift, since it did not seem likely that selective or mutational factors could have been operating.

Kraus and White studied blood groups in three endogamous bands of Apache Indians on the Fort Apache Reservation in Arizona. There were significant differences in gene frequency among the bands, but not within each band in the last three generations. Since the three bands now comprise about 3500 people, it was concluded that the present band differences reflect genetic patterns that originated as a result of genetic drift when the bands were much smaller and before they had arrived in the Southwest. As the bands increased in size, concomitant with their more sedentary type of life in the Southwest, genetic drift had less and less effect so that the earlier differences were maintained.

The effectiveness of genetic drift is dependent not only upon population size but also upon the relative isolation of the group. If our two populations A and A' were not completely cut off from each other and were only in a state of *partial isolation*, there would be a more or less continual exchange of genes as a result of interbreeding between the two groups. Actually, it is unlikely that complete effective separation of two populations originally derived from the same stock was of frequent occurrence in evolutionary history. Partial isolation would act as a brake upon the trend toward genetic divergence, since it would not only tend to "smooth out" differences in gene frequency but would interchange some of the mutations which had arisen independently in each group.

[5] Kraus, B. and White, C. 1956. Micro-evolution in a Human Population: A Study of Social Endogamy and Blood Type Distributions among the Western Apache. *American Anthropologist*, 58:1017–1041.

Isolation, either partial or complete, can be effected in several different ways. It may be due, as we hypothesized in our example, to geological accidents such as the creation of mountain ranges, desert areas, chasms, rivers, lakes, swamps, and the sinking of land bridges. Distance itself may have an isolating effect, so that those groups occupying opposite ends of the geographical range of a population would have less opportunity to interbreed than those spatially less far apart. In the human species there are isolating mechanisms that are peculiar to Man. Such social phenomena as religion, race prejudice, class consciousness, economic stratification, and caste systems often act as barriers to intermixture. Many times these isolating mechanisms are difficult to detect since social subdivisions are not necessarily geographically distinct, nor are their respective members phenotypically differentiated.

Rates of Evolution

If our two populations A and A′ were both of large size and genetic drift was thus eliminated as a major factor in effecting changes in gene frequency, they would nevertheless diverge genetically, hence phenotypically. In such a case divergence would be the result of different and changing environments to which, of course, the adaptive responses of the two populations would be different. The rate of divergence would be a function of the kind and rate of environmental change. Population A might undergo rapid evolutionary change while A′ remained more or less stable genetically in an environment that was relatively constant. Later, the conditions might become reversed so that A′ began to undergo rapid evolution while A reached an adaptive equilibrium with its environment. The particular loci affected are those that are responsible for the phenotypic traits which gain or lose adaptive value as the environment changes.

There is no constant rate of evolution, as G. G. Simpson points out in his *Tempo and Mode in Evolution*.[6] Within a single phylogenetic line there may be alternate rapid and slow rates. When an environment remains relatively constant over

[6] Simpson, G. 1944. *Tempo and Mode in Evolution*. New York: Columbia University Press.

many thousands of years, as in the ocean, a population may reach a high degree of adaptiveness and maintain it with apparently no further evolution. Such apparent stability in phenotype, however, must not be mistaken for evolutionary standstill. It merely means that the rate of change in gene frequencies is extremely slow. Obviously in such a population almost every mutation that arose would be disadvantageous and would be eliminated or kept at a very low frequency by negative selective pressure. There are many examples in the Animal Kingdom of forms that have remained relatively unchanged phenotypically over vast periods of time. Turtles have survived from the Triassic with only minor variations. The same is true of whales, rabbits, bats, and armadillos. Certain living genera of pelecypods (molluscs) have survived some 400,000,000 years with very little change.

Unfortunately, when we speak of fast and slow rates of evolutionary change we do so not in terms of gene frequencies but rather with reference to phenotypic alteration. And with respect to the latter our observations are limited to but a small portion of the phenotype, namely the hard parts—shell, bone, and teeth. It cannot be emphasized enough that our knowledge of the genetic basis of shell, bone, and tooth morphology is extremely limited. The result is that our theoretical model of evolutionary processes is constructed of genes, mutations, and changes in gene frequencies, but empirically we see only a few results of genic action. This means that the greatest caution must be exercised in translating metrical and morphological change in fossil remnants into principles of evolution. Because this point is so important, we shall examine it at greater length.

Just as morphologic change can be observed to occur very slowly over great spans of time, so can we find the opposite to be true in many cases. One example of extremely rapid morphologic alteration in a very short period of time is in the *Sus* (pig) line. In Pleistocene times, less than one million years ago, several groups separated from the main stream of pig evolution, represented today by the wild boar, and began to diverge in different directions. The modern descendants of these divergent forms include a giant forest hog (*Hylochoerus*), the red river hog (*Potamochoerus*), the circular tusked *Babirussa*, and the wart hog (*Phacochoerus*). These pigs, particularly the wart hog, are so different from the generalized *Sus* type from which they originated in Pleistocene times that it is difficult to believe such drastic change in morphology could have been accomplished in so short a time. Nevertheless Colbert sees the wart hogs as "a line that branched from the *Sus* line during Pleistocene times and evolved at a very rapid evolutionary rate to its modern highly specialized expression."[7] Simpson feels that the wart hog and other modern forms should be placed in one genus of the subfamily *Suinae*.[8]

We now face the question: To what extent is morphologic divergence a reflection of genetic divergence? Our answer can only be provisional and precautionary at present. Structural differences in the skeleton between two populations radiating from the same ancestral line do not necessarily mean that there has been significant genetic divergence. The two populations may still be able to interbreed and have viable and fertile offspring.

Our first approach to this problem shall be a consideration of the term *species*. We have used the word frequently in earlier Problems but until now an attempt to define it would have been premature. In general there are two ways in which species is defined, depending on the point of view and interests of the biologist. The paleontologist, whose attention is fixed upon fossilized portions of the body, is apt to place strong emphasis upon structural characteristics as criteria of species status. He defines a species as a population possessing morphological characters which are distinctive enough, in the opinion of a taxonomist, to warrant giving it a specific name or rank. As we can see, such a definition relies heavily upon phenotypic traits and is highly subjective, since the distinctiveness of the characters rests upon the judgment of the observer. It must be remembered, however, that the paleontologist deals not only with populations but with the temporal continuum, that is, the popu-

[7] Colbert, E. 1949. Some Paleontological Principles Significant in Human Evolution. In *Studies in Physical Anthropology*, A Symposium Sponsored by the Viking Fund. Philadelphia: Wistar Institute Press.

[8] Simpson, G. 1945. The Principles of Classification and a Classification of Mammals. *Bulletin of the American Museum of Natural History*, vol. 85.

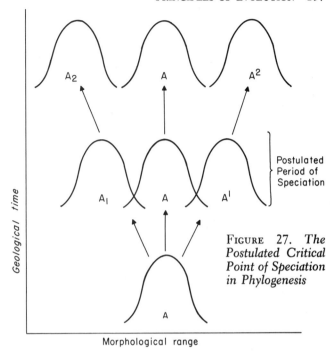

FIGURE 27. *The Postulated Critical Point of Speciation in Phylogenesis*

lation as it persists in time. He is faced with the problem of determining at what point a population changes from one species into another. Simpson has proposed that this be accomplished in the following way. When the range of variation of a critical trait in an ancestral population does not overlap that in a descendant population, the two populations may be regarded as separate species and the point of speciation can be considered as occurring at a point midway (in time) between the two[9] (see Fig. 27). On numerous occasions the fossil remnants of a population are so few that they can hardly be considered an adequate sample from which a valid range of radiation can be constructed. Thus the splitting of a lineage into successive species is rendered even more subjective.

[9] Simpson, G. 1961. *Principles of Animal Taxonomy.* New York: Columbia University Press.

The paleontological definition of species is strictly morphological and, at the present state of our knowledge regarding the genetic determinants of form and structure, is nongenetical. Nevertheless, it remains the only practical method of classifying and arranging populations on the evolutionary scale.

Since, as we have seen, phenotypic traits are expressions of the underlying genetic constitution as it reacts with the internal environment, it follows that a more realistic definition of species would be couched in genetic terms. We might say that two populations which have descended from a common ancestor become two distinct species when their respective "gene pools" have diverged. But how divergent? We realize that when two groups split off from a common line they begin to diverge genetically, so that the change in genetic constitutions and gene frequencies represents a sort of continuum. At what point in this divergent continuum shall we say that speciation has occurred? Obviously if we knew how to calculate the genotypes from the visible phenotypes we would be able to describe the amount of divergence in terms of allelic frequencies. It would then be a simple matter to proscribe statistically the point where speciation could be assigned. This too, however, would be entirely arbitrary. We can conclude, from these simple observations, that genetically divergent evolution is an unmarked continuum and that the division of this continuum into species, genera, and other taxonomic categories would be an arbitrary but useful method of putting evolutionary data into some kind of order. Unfortunately, this method must, for the time being, remain beyond our reach.

Among living members of the Animal Kingdom the species criterion is based upon *reproductive isolation*. If two populations do not, in a natural state, interbreed or hybridize they are regarded as separate species. In some cases when members of two such populations are kept together in captivity they will interbreed but generally their offspring have lowered fertility or are completely sterile. There are many examples in nature of two populations which will not interbreed although morphologically they are difficult to differentiate. Conversely, some populations easily distinguishable phenotypically may interbreed freely when in contact. The mouse genus *Peromyscus* provides illustrations of just such situations. In Vermont, two species of "white-footed mice" show only slight differences in external appearance. The species *maniculatus* has a greyish brown coat, a longer tail, smaller molar teeth, a more pronounced longitudinal black stripe on its back, and a more gracile skull. The species *leocopus* has a reddish brown coat. These differences are distinctive for the members of each species. The two species occupy separate but adjoining territories in Vermont and do not interbreed.[10]

In the Dismal Swamp of Virginia *Peromyscus leocopus* and *Peromyscus gossypinus* have overlapping territories but will not hybridize. In captivity, however, they will interbreed freely and their offspring are vigorous and fertile.

Among fruit flies and mosquitoes there are both species and subspecies which cannot be distinguished from each other except on a statistical basis, yet their hybrid offspring are either partially or entirely sterile (see Huxley, *Evolution, the Modern Synthesis*).[11] On the other hand, easily recognizable populations that are regarded as separate species will interbreed and have full fertile offspring (see Goldschmidt, *Einführung in die Vererbungswissenschaft*, 1928).[12] An example we are all familiar with is hybridization in dogs, in which breeds of vastly different morphological characteristics interbreed and produce viable fertile offspring.

Although reproductive isolation is one step on the road toward evolutionary divergence, it is obvious that morphological differentiation is not a reliable index to its occurrence or presence. Reproductive isolation can be accomplished in several ways. The external characteristics of one population—such as coat coloring, body size and proportions, vocal sounds and calls, body odor, etc.—may not be conducive to mating and may even repel members of another related population. On the other hand

[10] Dice, L. 1933. Fertility Relationships Between Some of the Species and Subspecies of Mice in the Genus Peromyscus. *Journal of Mammalogy*, 14:298–305. Also, Sumner, F. 1932. Genetic Distributional, and Evolutionary Studies of the Subspecies of Deer Mice (*Peromyscus*). *Bibliographia Genetica*, 9:1–106.

[11] Huxley, J. 1942. *Evolution: The Modern Synthesis*. New York: Harper and Row.

[12] Goldschmidt, R. 1928. *Einführung in die verebungswissenschaft*, 5th ed. Berlin.

purely physiological barriers to reproduction may be present even though there is apparent morphological identity. For example, there may be gametic incompatibility, chemical differences in the internal milieu that will interfere with mitotic divisions or cellular differentiation of the early morula or blastocyst, or unfavorable conditions for attachment of the blastocyst to the uterine epithelium. Conditions that could lead to effective sterility range from sexual repellence, incompatibility of ova and sperm, or mutual antagonism between embryo and maternal environment, to constitutional weakness and sterility in the offspring. There are a great many ways, therefore, in which genetic differences arising between two populations from the same lineage may succeed in producing reproductive isolation. Since genes, as we have seen, have multiple effects, the specific genetic differences that bring about reproductive isolation might also be reflected in various phenotypic changes that are easily observed. On the other hand, it is quite possible that effective reproductive isolation could be brought about without apparent corresponding changes in external morphology. In the case of fossil remains the mere similarity of dental and skeletal morphology would hardly be a reliable criterion of genetic divergence affecting the reproductive processes.

By the same token genetic differences might arise between two populations which do not lay down barriers to sexual attraction, interbreeding, or successful reproduction, but do affect various phenotypic traits. In this instance morphological differences between populations, as in dogs, would be readily observed but would offer no clue to the all-important question of interpopulational reproducibility.

J. A. Moore has raised some vexing questions with regard to hybridization between and within various species of the genus *Rana* (frog).[13] He found that in the eastern United States there are 12 species, most of which are relatively stable in the evolutionary sense. In the species *Rana pipiens*, however, there is evidence of a splitting into reproductively isolated subgroups. In experiments with both interspecific and intraspecific (*Rana*

[13] Moore, J. 1949. Patterns of Evolution in the Genus *Rana*. In *Genetics, Paleontology, and Evolution*. Edited by Jepsen, Mayr, and Simpson. Princeton: Princeton University Press.

pipiens) crossings Moore found that *Rana pipiens* crosses with *Rana palustris*, *Rana areolata*, or *Rana capito* produced perfectly normal viable embryos, but when members of this species from the extreme northern and southern ranges were crossed the hybrids were extremely defective. Crossings between varieties of *Rana pipiens* that are not geographically far apart produced normal offspring. Apparently incompatibility increased with distance, so that at the extreme geographical ranges reproductive isolation had developed between groups of what is apparently a single species. Moore's experiments would seem to indicate that there may be considerable inconsistency between the morphological determination of species ranking and the physiologic reality of reproductive isolation.

Another significant result of Moore's work with frogs is the demonstration that hybridization between different species causes inviability in quite different ways. Some interspecific crosses produce hybrids that invariably fail extremely early in development—in fact at the zygote stage. Others result in failure at the gastrulation stage, while some produce hybrids that succeed until the neurula and tailbud stages. Finally, as we have already seen, a few interspecific crosses result in perfectly normal offspring. An additional commentary on the extremely tenuous nature of taxonomic arrangement is the fact that two "species"— *Rana clamitans* and *Rana catesbeiana*—which are very similar morphologically, developmentally, and ecologically, are incapable of successful hybridization. A complicating factor in interpreting this material must not be lost sight of—hybridization was accomplished artificially, not observed in nature.

It would seem, then, that determination of the point of speciation is based upon somewhat different criteria, depending upon whether the vertical (or temporal) continuum or the horizontal (or spatial) continuum is involved. The demarcation of a phylogenetic lineage into species is based upon an arbitrary selection of what morphological traits are "critical" and to what degree of morphological differentiation of such traits speciation may be assigned. Among living animals, however, species rank is dependent primarily upon whether or not a population is reproductively isolated from other populations by one means or another. The important thing we must remember is that neither method is any more than a classificatory device for convenience in producing some order out of a vast array of products of biological evolution.

It must be constantly kept in mind that evolution is genetic divergence. Genetic divergence is the result of relative degrees of isolation so that populations respond differently to different environmental conditions. Dependent upon the sizes of the isolates the rate of genetic divergence varies. If these isolates are quite small genetic drift becomes an important factor in changing the gene frequencies. If the environment is constantly changing, then selective processes operate continuously so that steady pressures are exerted upon the population for changes in phenotype and therefore genotype. The traits that acquire differential adaptive value may be morphological, physiological, or biochemical. If physiological, they may be primarily related to sex characters and reproductive processes, in which case the population may rapidly become isolated from related groups while retaining similar morphological characteristics. If the affected phenotypic traits involve primarily such adaptive characters as hemoglobin counts, melanin deposition, body hair thickness, or length of limbs, then the population may show marked differences in behavior or morphology from its related groups yet be able to interbreed with them and produce viable and fertile offspring.

Perhaps the best method for ascertaining the assumption of specific rank by an animal population would be the determination that statistically significant differences exist in gene frequencies for a certain number of loci. This again would involve some arbitrary judgments. For example, how many loci must show such differences before species rank is granted? Shall each locus be accorded similar weight? And finally, the time when we can determine the specific genetic locus for each phenotypic trait is certainly not in the predictable future.

Problems in Taxonomy

Where, then, do we stand with respect to the problem of speciation? Clearly any attempt to interrupt the steady, unceasing process of genetic divergence and change that is biological evolution and to give labels such as "species," and "family" to its products at any moment of time must be recognized for what it is. It forces nature to fit our preconceptions and may even thwart our attempts to understand its processes.

Perhaps if we were not primarily concerned with Man and his evolution we need not have devoted so much time to a discussion of the meaning of the species concept. After all, the taxonomic system has admirably served many purposes for the paleontologist and the zoologist. It has produced an orderly arrangement of animals and plants, both extinct and living, and has allowed us to reconstruct evolutionary pathways that are logical and in accord with our knowledge of geology, biology, genetics, anatomy, physics, physiology, and chemistry. Can it not also serve the same purposes when applied to Man? Fortunately (or unfortunately) Man has developed an elaborate system of values which color his outlook on the world and his place in it. Words like "species," "subspecies," "race," and "variety" take on value meanings that are foreign to the systematist who deals only in infrahuman animals. Such words carry with them special implications for religious, cultural, social, and other groupings of Man, and have served very often in history as banners leading men into conflict with one another. Therefore it is imperative that we make every effort to understand precisely what these terms mean, not only from the biological point of view but as they might be applied to Man.

When two groups descended from the same ancestral population become reproductively isolated their separate evolutionary destinies are thenceforth ensured. Never again shall their genes be interchanged. We can safely predict that the future holds only continued genetic divergence from each other. However, unless two such groups have become reproductively isolated it is impossible to predict the future course of evolution. Circumstances might favor increased rates of interbreeding, so that the two are brought genetically closer together, perhaps even forming once again a single breeding population. In the course of evolution small groups of a parent population will split off and attain relative degrees of isolation. Intermixture of genes continues, but primarily members of each group tend to breed among themselves. As a result genetic differences arise which bring about differences in the frequencies of certain phenotypic traits. In any one trait, however, there may be considerable overlap in the ranges of variation, so that some members of one group will resemble those of other groups. At this point we might refer to these subpopulations as "subspecies." Should the isolating tendency increase until complete isolation is accomplished then eventually reproductive isolation will result and each group will then attain the status of "species," thus severing its evolutionary ties with all the others. Eventually, too, many of its phenotypic traits will fall into distribution curves which no longer overlap with those of the other groups. It is important to point out that even subspecies may possess certain characteristics which completely differentiate them from each other. In other words, there may be no overlapping of the distribution curves for those characteristics. A case in point is the striking difference in stature between Pygmies and Northern Europeans.

The Principle of Irreversibility

Paleontology has contributed a number of "principles" to the field of evolution as a result of its scrutiny of the radiation of phylogenetic lines. These we must now examine in the light of our present knowledge of genetics. The first is the so-called Dollo's Law, or principle of the *irreversibility of evolution*, first propounded by Louis Dollo in 1890. In brief, Dollo held that in evolution descendants never can return to the ancestral state but that traces of primitive ancestral characters ("étapes intermédiaires") can always be recognized as "secondary characters." These secondary characters remain as mute evidence of an "indestructible past." Once a structure is lost in the course of evolution it can never be regained, but a different structure may arise to subserve the same function should the environmental situation demand it. There are numerous examples from the phylogenetic record of animals which have returned *functionally* but not *structurally* to an ancestral condition. Colbert cites the case of the *Ichthyosaur*, a Mesozoic marine reptile.[14] This animal had evolved from a primitive fish to a terrestrial tetrapod and then left the land for life in the sea. During its sojourn on

[14] Colbert, E. *Op. cit.*

land it had lost the gills of its fish ancestors and acquired lungs. In addition it lost the fins and acquired limbs for terrestrial locomotion. Its vertebral column was typically reptilian and quite unlike the original fish backbone. The large dorsal fin was completely lost. When this reptile deserted the land and re-entered the sea it had to re-adapt to the aquatic environment. It did so by developing a new dorsal fin which was similar *in form* and *in function* to that of a fish but entirely different *in structure*, being completely fleshy in contrast to the bony ray structure of the ancestral dorsal fin. Its four limbs became modified into paddle-like structures that acted like the paired pelvic and pectoral fins of the fish, but unmistakably retained the internal structure of reptilian limbs. The lungs were retained with the consequence that the Ichthyosaur remained an air-breathing animal. The large caudal fin, lost when the animal took to the land, was redeveloped but in a significantly different way. The vertebral column now was deflected into the lower lobe of the tail, whereas in the ancestral forms it was diverted into the upper lobe.

Paleontologists have used the Ichthyosaur as well as the marine mammals (whales, seals, walruses, sea otters, and porpoises) to illustrate the principle that while there may be an evolutionary return in form and in function, there never is a return in structure. These pages from the paleontological record are only illustrations, however, and do not explain why this is so. For such an explanation we must draw upon our knowledge of the genetic and biochemical basis of evolution. This was a privilege denied to the early paleontologists, which makes Dollo's insight all the more remarkable.

The acquisition of a new structure, or the loss of an old one, involves countless mutations and the testing and retesting of these mutations in myriads of genetic relationships. We have seen how complicated and precise are the thousands of biochemical sequences in which the genes mediate their effects. Recalling that mutations are accidental and haphazard changes in gene structure, it is easy to comprehend that the acquisition of such a complex organ as a lung or a segmented limb would require many thousands of generations of evolution directed by highly specific, constant, and unidirectional environmental change. To lose these structures and regain ancestral ones would involve a step-by-step reversal of the precise mutational and environmental changes that had already taken place. Clearly this would take a miracle of major proportions—and as scientists we cannot explain the workings of Nature or hope to advance our understanding of its principles by hiding behind a smokescreen of miracles.

From our discussion of irreversibility, it can be inferred that there are two kinds of structures, those that have derived from a common ancestral base, such as the flippers of seals and the limbs of a bear, and those that are similar in form or function but are derived from different origins, such as the fins of the Ichthyosaur and the shark. The former are called *homologues*; the latter *analogues*. Homologous structures may be quite different in form and/or function but they reveal in their anatomy the unmistakable signs of their common ancestry. Analogous structures exhibit *convergence* in form and/or function but their anatomical composition indicates different evolutionary origins. There is not always a clear-cut distinction between what are homologous and what are analogous organs. The determination of what may be regarded as "similar" either in form or in function is sometimes a very arbitrary matter. These matters strike very close to the heart of taxonomy and have been the basis of many rather acrimonious controversies in the paleontological literature. A detailed consideration of this and other taxonomic problems has been recently provided by G. G. Simpson in his *Principles of Animal Taxonomy*.[15]

Convergence and Divergence in Evolution

Convergence is generally defined as a *similar response of unrelated animals to similar environmental situations*. There are instances in the paleontological record of *allopatric* (geographically separate) groups of only remote common ancestry which have converged in several characteristics. Marsupials had entered Australia before that continent became isolated in late Cretaceous times, but placental mammals had never reached Australia until Man himself arrived there. Marsupial evolution resulted in

[15] Simpson, G. *Op. cit.*

many diverse forms, some of which resembled very closely the mammals of Europe and Asia in certain traits. The Tasmanian "wolf," for example, is a pouched animal very similar in appearance and habits to the true wolf, but of course unrelated. Other descendants of the primitive Australian opposum include the *phalangers*, a squirrel-like animal, the *koala*, which strongly resembles a small bear, the *wombat*, an animal similar in appearance to a woodchuck, and the *kangaroo*, a terrestrial herbivore.

The opposum, ubiquitous in late Cretaceous times, gave rise not only to far-ranging evolutionary descendants in Australia but also in South America, where competition with carnivorous placental mammals was likewise absent. Here, too, flesh-eating marsupial forms developed, similar to placental carnivores in North America, Europe, and Asia. Unlike the situation in Australia, certain placental mammals did enter South America across the Isthmus of Panama before this narrow connection was submerged at the beginning of the Cenozoic Era. These placentals, isolated throughout the Tertiary Period from their relatives on other continents, included some Prosimians and a few small ungulates (herbivorous, hoofed animals). The evolution of these forms in South America resulted in many instances of convergence. Although many of them became extinct their fossil remains indicate that they developed into types similar to the sloths, horses, elephants, and certain other artiodactyls and perissodactyls of other continents.

On the other hand, we find in South America an excellent example of the divergence of closely related forms. A group of small artiodactyls in North America evolved with great rapidity into several specialized kinds of ruminants known collectively as the *Tylopoda*. By the beginning of the Pleistocene some of these groups had migrated to South America while others had moved to Asia. The former became the modern llamas; the latter the modern camels. Although closely related they bear little resemblance to each other in morphology or habits.

Parallelism

The principles of *parallelism* is likewise based upon the assessment of morphological and functional criteria in terms of phylogenetic relationships. It may be defined as the *similar response of related animals to similar* environmental situations. By "similar response" we refer to phenotypic characters and not necessarily to similarity in genotype. Two groups that have diverged from a common ancestry and then, under similar environmental conditions, retain or develop similar characters over a considerable period of time, need not have required identical or even similar genetic constitutions in order to accomplish this. Colbert cites an outstanding example of parallelism, the evolution of the phytosaurs and crocodiles. The phytosaurs were large reptiles who inhabited North America and Eurasia during Triassic times. They resemble crocodiles so closely that it was thought that they were the ancestors of crocodiles. The modern crocodiles can be traced back to the early part of the Jurassic period, while the phytosaurs are known not to have survived past the Triassic. Close scrutiny of the two forms reveals important differences that indicate they were not members of the same lineage but rather of two quite distinct lines which had a common ancestor in early Triassic times in *Ornithosuchus*, the primitive ancestor of the reptiles. The phytosaur line, for reasons unknown to us, became extinct, while the crocodilian line persisted to the present time (see Fig. 28).

Another example of parallel evolution is that of the family Felidae, which is first noted in early Oligocene times. At first there was rapid radiation of these forms but essentially two distinct lines developed. One was that of the "true cats" which persisted to the present in America, Africa, and Asia, and is represented by such forms as the jaguar, tiger, lion, wild cat, cougar, leopard, and house cat. The other line was represented by such forms as *Smilodon*, a Pleistocene cat, and *Hoplophoneus*, an Oligocene cat. The latter had specialized in enormous upper canine teeth with corresponding changes in the cranium and jaws to accommodate them (see Fig. 29). Representatives of both cat lines occupied California in the Pleistocene epoch, but *Smilodon* and allied forms failed to survive, their extinction being associated with the disappearance of the thick-skinned proboscidians upon which they depended for food. Both subfamilies, the Felinae (true cats) and the Machairodontinae (saber-toothed cats), were very similar to each other in size and

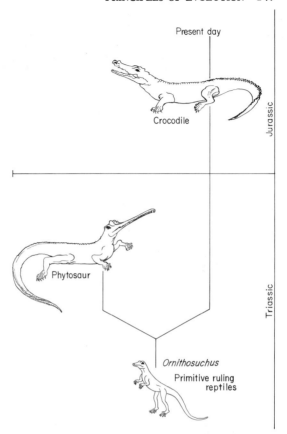

FIGURE 28. *Parallelism in Phytosaur and Crocodile Evolution*

proportions with the exception of the specialized canine development.

Again let us emphasize that parallelism in evolution is deduced from morphological evidence of skeletal and dental elements, and morphological similarity or dissimilarity in itself is not necessarily indicative *per se* of corresponding genetic similarity or dissimilarity. In fact, as we saw in our previous discussion, genetic parallelism would be difficult to imagine over great periods of time even in large populations unless they were inter-

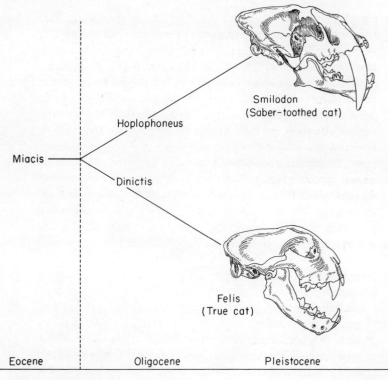

Figure 29. *Evolution of the Saber-toothed and "True" Cats*

breeding to a marked degree. In such a case, however, how could genetic divergence take place to such an extent that certain phenotypic differences as great as those found in true and saber-toothed cats occur?

The Evolutionary Meaning of Extinction

A term that is met with frequently in texts dealing with paleontology is *extinction*. We have used the word quite often thus far without examining its evolutionary meaning and significance. Ordinarily we think of an animal line becoming extinct when, like the dinosaurs toward the end of the Cretaceous period, or the saber-toothed cats at the end of the Pleistocene epoch, it completely disappears, leaving no descendants whatsoever. This is extinction through the cessation of genetic transmission and we might call it *termination*, as suggested by Simpson, or *extinction by catastrophe*. The causes of termination of a phylogenetic line are generally catastrophic, involving changes in the environment which occur so rapidly that no members of the population are equipped to meet them, or which require such critical alteration in the adaptive structure that the existing level and rate of mutations cannot provide the necessary phenotypes. Evolutionary catastrophes include the rapid depletion of animal species which provide the main source of food, a long drought which turns a savannah into a desert, a blight that destroys plant life, or the appearance of carnivorous animals that prey upon the indigenous species. While generally termination is easily recognized by paleontologists, its specific cause is not. We know that the ruling reptiles came to a geochronologically abrupt end but can only make educated guesses as to why it happened.

On the other hand, extinction may occur without interruption of genetic transmission. There are two ways in which this can happen. We are already aware that in the course of evolution as gene frequencies change and new genes become established, replacing older ones, the phenotypes also undergo change as a result. This can be typified for any one trait as a gradual shift in the distribution curve. When certain skeletal and dental characters have been so altered in the course of evolution that their distribution curves no longer overlap with those of the ancestral forms, it is customary to speak of the ancestral form as having become extinct. The descendants are then given new specific or generic ranking. As we can see, this type of *extinction by evolution* is not a biological reality so much as it is a paleontological construct. *Extinction by evolution* and *speciation* are really facets of the same taxonomic device, depending upon which aspect of the evolutionary process one wishes to stress. It is true that in the process of evolution new forms slowly arise out of old ones, but the determination of the point where we may regard the old form as extinct and the new one as a distinct species must remain subjective and without regard to the question of reproductive isolation.

Extinction by evolution is well illustrated in the equid (horse) line. The phylogeny of the modern horse is one of the best documented records in mammalian paleontology. The earliest recognizable ancestor was *Hyracotherium (Eohippus)*, found in North America and Europe in the Eocene epoch. *Hyracotherium* was a forest dwelling, browsing animal with reptile-like brain, short legs with four toes on the front feet and three on the hind, and low-crowned molar teeth with forked roots and well developed cusps. From this ancestral form several forms evolved (or radiated), including the Oligocene horse *Mesohippus* and its descendant *Miohippus*. At this point there was another evolutionary radiation leading to *Hypohippus*, a Miocene horse that became extinct in Pliocene times *by catastrophe*, and to *Parahippus* and *Merychippus*, Miocene horses on the phyletic line leading to the modern horse. A further adaptive radiation led from *Merychippus* to the Pliocene forms *Hipparion* and *Pliohippus*. *Hipparion* suffered extinction by catastrophe, but *Pliohippus* gave rise to the modern *Equus*. Branches of the Pliocene radiation became extinct in North and South America toward the end of the Pleistocene, but the European *Equus* survived as the sole living descendant of ancient *Hyracotherium*.

The horse phylogeny thus illustrates both extinction by catastrophe (*Hypohippus, Hipparion,* and certain groups of *Equus*) and by evolution (*Hyracotherium, Miohippus, Mesohippus, Parahippus, Merychippus,* and *Pliohippus*). *Merychippus*, a three-toed grazing horse continued into the Pliocene with little change as *Hipparion*, but also was represented in the Pliocene by other descendants (*Pliohippus*) which had evolved at so rapid a rate that they possessed but a single toe and are regarded as being a different genus. Thus *Merychippus* achieved extinction in both ways. As *Hipparion* it was blotted out during the Pliocene, but as *Pliohippus* it became extinct by evolving into a form distinctly different in phenotype (see Fig. 30).

Equid phylogeny illustrates a characteristic of evolution that we have referred to earlier, namely the fact that different parts of the body may change at quite different rates, and that a single structure or organ may undergo alternately rapid and slow rates of change. The horse brain remained very small and unconvoluted until the Miocene when it assumed in late *Merychippus*

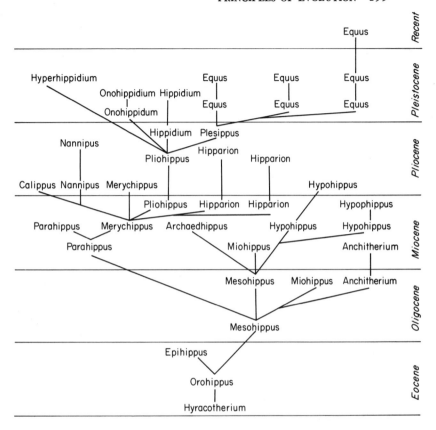

FIGURE 30. *Neo-Darwinian Approach to Equid Phylogeny*

representatives the form characteristic of the modern *Equus*. On the other hand, the limbs and feet underwent extremely rapid evolution in size and architecture. According to Simpson (*Tempo and Mode in Evolution*, p. 12) equid phylogeny illustrates four "basic theorems concerning rates of evolution." They are quoted here since they have important bearing on human evolution.[16]

[16] Simpson, G. 1944. *Tempo and Mode in Evolution*. New York: Columbia University Press.

1. The rate of evolution of one character may be a function of another character and not genetically separable even though the rates are not equal.
2. The rate of evolution of any character or combination of characters may change markedly at any time in phyletic evolution, even though the direction of evolution remains the same.
3. The rates of evolution of two or more characters within a single phylum may change independently.
4. Two phyla of common ancestry may become differentiated by differences in rates of evolution of different characters, without any marked qualitative differences or differences in direction of evolution.

In Simpson's opinion ("Rates of Evolution in Animals"), subspecies require about 10,000 years for their evolution but may take 500,000 years to reach the level of species, while species generally require about 50,000 years to evolve.[17] Some living species, particularly in mammals, are about one million years old. Such opinions, however, obviously rely heavily upon taxonomic decisions that, as we have seen, are tenuous at best.

We return now to the third type of extinction—*extinction by hybridization*. Hybridization cannot be easily verified in the paleontological record but it must have been an important factor in evolution in the past as it is at the present. Whether hybridization ever led to replacement (extinction) of the two parent populations among infrahuman animals has never been proven but in Man there are numerous examples of this in modern times. Some American Indian groups have become extinct not through wars or disease but by absorption into the large populations of Whites and Negroes with whom they interbred. This was particularly true in the case of Indians of the Northeast, Northwest, and Southeast parts of the United States. In the Southwest such tribes as the Papago, Navaho, Apache, Pima, and Hopi raised social, cultural, or religious barriers to hybridization with Whites and other Indian groups, thus retaining to a large degree their original genetic and phenotypic characteristics.

---

[17] Simpson, G. Rates of Evolution in Animals. In *Genetics, Paleontology, and Evolution*. Edited by Jepsen, Mayr, and Simpson. Princeton: Princeton University Press. p. 216.

✓ The Theory of Orthogenesis

One of the most widespread misconceptions of the nature of evolution is that there is an inevitable orderly progression of development from the simple to the complex, from the small to the large, and from the poorly adapted to the well adapted. The term generally given to this sort of thinking is *orthogenesis* ("Creation in a straight line"). Probably it took its inception from the philosophy of the early Greeks, notably Aristotle, who regarded evolution as a progression from inorganic forms through the lower organic forms to the pinnacle of biological creation —Man. Such evolutionary determinism, in which the original purpose of nature was to create the very best, was called "aristogenesis." It persists in various forms to the present day, particularly among those groups who feel that to disregard the orthogenetic principle would be to sweep away the very foundation of religion. After all, predeterminism means a divine purpose and goal in evolution. If evolution is proclaimed to be haphazard and without aim, then, they would argue, the very existence of divine being is denied.

Aristotle first conceived of his aristogenetic plan and then fit the natural phenomena to it. Similarly, once one is wedded to the principle of orthogenesis, it is very easy to find data in the paleontological record to support it. If the opposite procedure is followed, namely of scrutinizing all the available data and then constructing a theory that will accommodate all the facts, a very different concept emerges. It will be seen that there is no orthogenetic principle which "guides" organic evolution. If there were, then it would be possible to predict the course of future evolution. This is a step that no genetically minded biologist would dream of taking.

Orthogenetic evolution can be "supported" only by careful selection of particular phyletic lines out of the complexity of lineages in adaptive radiation. In other words, certain evolutionary lines do show a sort of unidirectional or rectilinear course, if by this we mean an uninterrupted progression from one condition to another. By selecting such lines, however, we ignore related lines which fail to show such progressions. Again, equid phylogeny will provide us with an excellent illustration

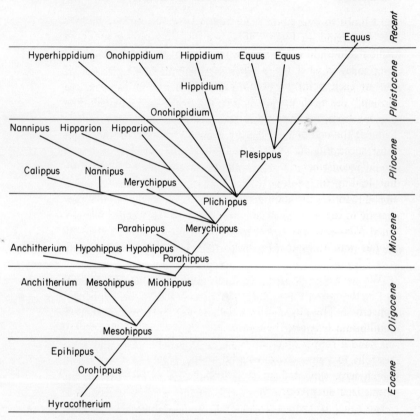

FIGURE 31. *Orthogenetic Approach to Equid Phylogeny*

of how orthogenetic thinking proceeds. In Figures 30 and 31 we have depicted the phylogeny of horses in two different ways. In Figure 31 we draw it with the knowledge of hindsight, aware that the modern horse is the only survivor and firm in the belief that all equine evolution was directed toward its creation. As one can see, there is a direct line leading from *Hyracotherium* to *Equus,* and if one examines the succession of fossils on this line one can observe a rectilinear progression from small size to large size, from low-crowned molars to high-crowned molars, from small unconvoluted brain to large convoluted brain, from short limbs to long limbs, and from several toes to one toe. On the other hand, in Figure 30 we see the same phylogeny drawn without hindsight and without the preconception that what survives today is what the whole evolutionary process was driving for. At each point of adaptive radiation, or "evolutionary explosion," the newly arising lineages are randomly arranged radiating out from the ancestral form. Now, if we happened to be living at the end of the Pliocene and had decided that the horse most successful and most important to us was *Nannipus*, we would reconstruct the equid phylogeny in such a way that the line leading to *Nannipus* was rectilinear (as for *Equus* in Figure 31). In this instance, however, evolution would not be orthogenetic in the sense that there was a steady increase in body size, since *Nannipus* was a dwarf. In other equid branches *Archaeohippus* was a dwarf *Miohippus* and the Shetland pony is a dwarf *Equus*.

We have stressed many times that the changing environment is "in the driver's seat" as far as the direction of evolution is concerned. The phyletic lines that have maintained an adaptive equilibrium between themselves and the environment and have on hand a supply of mutant genes, will be able to readapt successfully to a new environmental shift. Those phyletic branches which have exploited an environment that demanded unusual specialized adaptations may have gone beyond the point of no return, that is, their available store of mutations will no longer allow them to adapt to the exigencies of a new environment. It is impossible to say, at any one point in time, that this or that population, being apparently well-adapted to its present environment, will continue to survive in the future. This is entirely dependent upon how the environment will change and at what rate. Since such matters are beyond our ability to predict, it is clear that orthogenesis is prophecy "after the event." In this sense evolution is truly haphazard.

The Evidence of Embryology

A final principle must now be discussed before we bring this Problem to a close. Like all the others it has stirred up considerable debate as to its meaning, significance, and applicability to the study of evolution. In fact, it has been referred to sometimes as a "theory," sometimes as a "law." The idea of *recapitulation* was first annunciated by von Baer who, in 1828, as a result of his extensive researches into embryological development, came to the following four conclusions (known as the "laws of von Baer"):

1. In development from the egg the general characters appear before the special characters.
2. From the more general characters the less general and finally the special characters are developed.
3. During its development an animal departs more and more from the form of other animals.
4. The young stages in the development of an animal are not like the adult stages of other animals lower down on the scale, but are like the young stages of those animals.

Thus, "ontogeny recapitulates phylogeny." In 1866 the theory was modified by Haeckel to a form known as the "Biogenetic Law." It held that the ontogenetic stages of the embryo recapitulated not the embryonic but the *adult* forms of its ancestors. The arguments for and against each of the two theories have been carefully marshalled by de Beer in his book *Embryos and Ancestors*,[18] and cannot be reviewed here. However, in the light of modern knowledge about embryology and evolution it is obvious that von Baer was essentially correct. Embryos do pass through stages which are reminiscent of the *embryonic* forms of their ancestors. Two important aspects of the recapitulation theory should be kept in mind. First, there is no question that the ontogenetic process contains a great deal of information which *potentially* can throw much light upon the preceding evolutionary history. The problem lies in the interpretation of this evidence in the absence of embryological data in the paleontological record. Second, comparison of the ontogenies of two kinds of animals will provide strong evidence of the degree of affinity between them. That is, the later in ontogenetic development two such animals diverge the more closely related they are in the phylogenetic sense. The earlier in ontogenetic develop-

[18] de Beer, G. 1958. *Embryos and Ancestors*, 3rd ed. London: Oxford University Press.

ment they diverge, the more remotely are they derived from a common ancestor.

Although the recapitulation theory has been much discussed and investigated, it seems to the present writer that its potentialities for contributing to our knowledge of evolution have by no means been exhausted. Its possible application to human evolution will be dealt with in a subsequent Problem.

We now bring to a close our review of the theoretical background of evolution. We have surveyed the Animal Kingdom as it exists today and classified its members in terms of their apparent relationships. The vast reaches of time have been explored and the methods of clocking its passage have been described. We have examined the essential elements of the Darwinian concept of evolution that are the basis of our modern thinking and have reviewed the genetic mechanism that underlies the adaptation of animals to their environment. And in this Problem we have tried to outline some of the important principles of organic evolution that emerge from the integration of Darwinian theory, genetic fact, and paleontological evidence. Even the neophyte will recognize that our treatment has been brief and selective, and that the subject is even more extensive and complicated than we have attempted to indicate. For these reasons the serious and interested student is urged to pursue the various aspects of this multifaceted biological problem with additional reading, perhaps beginning with those texts and articles suggested for each Problem.

For better or for worse, we must now turn our attention to the nature of the evidence itself, the bones and the teeth, from whose structure, shape, and proportions we attempt to reconstruct the evolutionary pathway of Man.

The nature of the evidence: bones and teeth

A bone is a framework of the most curious carpentry: in which occurs not a single straight line nor any known geometrical curve, yet all evidently systematic, and constructed by rules which defy our research.

Sir John Herschel, *On the Study of Natural Philosophy*, 1830

The skeleton begins as a continuum *and a* continuum *it remains all life long. The things that link bone with bone, cartilage, ligaments, membranes, are fashioned out of the same primordial tissue, and come into being* pari passu *with the bones themselves. The entire fabric has its soft parts and its hard, its rigid and its flexible parts; but until we disrupt and dismember its bony, gristly and fibrous parts one from another, it exists simply as a "skeleton," as one integral and individual whole.*

D'Arcy W. Thompson, *On Growth and Form*, 1917

The Primates of the past 70 or 75 million years are known to us only as bits of fossilized bone and teeth, since only these structures of mammalian bodies can survive the erosive effects of soil, weather, and decay. It is from such fragments that paleontologists attempt to reconstruct the entire bony structure and dentition, and then to infer the general appearance and habits of the animal as it once existed. Classes in Physical Anthropology never fail to be astonished when informed that a whole new genus and species of Man with the imposing name of *Meganthropus palaeojavanicus* was erected on the basis of a small fragment of jaw bearing but three teeth. Yet this is a fairly common procedure in paleontology and is not at all as magical as it may sound to the uninitiated. It rests upon a thorough knowledge of skeletal and dental morphology, not only of Man but of most of the other living Primates. Furthermore it requires a detailed familiarity with the existing fossil remains of Primates found throughout the world. If we were to examine the backgrounds of outstanding paleontologists we would find a solid grounding in anatomy and physiology. Without such an appreciation of the structure and function of the entire organism one could easily fall into the trap of regarding the individual bone or tooth as an entity independent from the rest of the body in its genesis, development, and morphology.

There is a common aphorism that "one cannot see the forest for the trees"—meaning that if one becomes overly involved with details the general picture is lost. In the study of human anatomy we might modify this saying to read: "One can better understand the tree if he knows the forest." In other words, we can learn more about the human skeleton if we compare it with others. I have impressed this important principle upon my classes by holding up a human skull and asking the students to write down its peculiarly human characteristics. Since they have no comparative frame of reference, their answers are amazingly naive and parsimonious. They have eyes but they do not see. When, however, I hold up both a human skull and that of a dog or chimpanzee, they immediately begin to "see" traits in the human skull that they could not have observed otherwise. This is a most important lesson in the value of the comparative approach. One cannot truly understand human anatomy by studying only human anatomy.

In this brief Problem we cannot attempt to do more than identify the bony and dental elements of the human skeleton, discuss some of the features that are of significance in the study of human paleontology, and call attention to certain morphological and metrical aspects by comparing them with homologous traits in the chimpanzee, rhesus monkey, and bear. The student is advised to consult, at the very least, an atlas of human anatomy in order to get better acquainted with terminology and sites of origin and insertion of muscles and ligaments. Shakespeare pointed out in *As You Like It* that there are "tongues in trees, books in the running brooks, sermons in stones, and good in everything." Had he been a paleontologist or physical anthropologist he would have added: "history in bones and pedigrees in teeth." For every marking on a bone and every groove and ridge on a tooth contains a story not only of the individual's development but of his evolutionary history. It is but for us to learn how to read and interpret it. Let us begin with the human skeleton.

The Human Skeleton

The skeleton of an adult man (see Fig. 32) is composed of 206 individual bones. They are integrated in such a manner as to comprise the *appendicular* and *axial* components of the skeleton. Their functions are varied. They serve to afford a rigid supporting framework for the body; to protect such organs as brain, heart, lungs, liver, bladder, etc.; to provide leverage to muscles; to serve as a storehouse for marrow where red blood cells are manufactured; and to accumulate supplies of calcium and phosphorus.

Bones may be classified in a number of ways—morphologically, developmentally, and regionally. According to form they may be long, short, rounded, irregular, flat, or shaped like sesame seeds (sesamoid). They may be preformed in cartilage or may develop in membrane or tendon. They occur either in the axial or the appendicular skeleton. The listing of the 206 bones of the human adult skeleton is presented in Table 4 according to the three methods of classification. Each type of bone is given a number corresponding to its location in Figure 32.

Bones show many different kinds of features on their surfaces, such as smooth areas, depressions, and elevations. These are indicative of the attachment, juxtaposition, or penetration of bone by various kinds of soft tissue. A classification of such markings may be arranged as follows:

Smooth areas (where fleshy fibers of muscles attach or over which muscles, tendons, or nerves lie).

Depressions (made by juxtaposition or piercing of bone by vessels).

> Pit
> Groove
> Fossa
> Notch
> Foramen
> Canal

Elevations (caused by attachment of tendons, ligaments, aponeuroses, fascia, and other fibrous tissues).

> Line
> Crest
> Ridge
> Tuberosity
> Tubercle
> Malleolus
> Trochanter
> Spine
> Styloid process

Articular areas (covered with cartilage and articulating with other bones).

> Condyle
> Trochlea
> Head
> Facet
> Face

Some of these markings are shown on the femur drawn in Figure 33A and B. Seen from in front (Fig. 33A) we observe two *trochanters*, a *head*, a *pit*, (or fovea), an intertrochanteric *line*, two *epicondyles*, two *condyles*, and an *articular surface* known as the patellar face. From the back, in addition to the markings already noted, can be seen the trochanteric *fossa*, an intertrochanteric *crest*, a pectineal *line*, the gluteal *tuberosity*, two lines known collectively as the *linea aspera*, a nutrient *foramen*, a popliteal *plane*, an intercondyloid *fossa*, and an intercondyloid *line*.

TABLE 4. *Classification of the Bones of the Adult Human Skeleton (modified after Krogman, 1962)*[1]
(See Figure 32 for location of bone by number)

Region	Number in Figure	Skeletal Unit	Bone	Number of Bones	Developmental Classification	Morphological Classification
	1	Cranium	Frontal	1	Membranous	Flat
			Parietal	2	Membranous	Flat
			Occipital	1	Membr. and Cart.	Flat
			Temporal	2	Membr. and Cart.	Flat and Irreg.
			Sphenoid	1	Membr. and Cart.	Flat and Irreg.
			Ethmoid	1	Cartilaginous	Irregular
	2	Face	Nasal	2	Membranous	Flat
Axial			Vomer	1	Membranous	Flat
			Inf. nasal concha	2	Cartilaginous	Irregular
			Lacrimal	2	Membranous	Irregular
			Zygoma	2	Membranous	Irregular
			Palatine	2	Membranous	Irregular
	3		Maxilla	2	Membranous	Irregular
	4		Mandible	1	Membranous	Irregular
		Ear Bones	Malleus	2	Cartilaginous	Irregular
			Incus	2	Cartilaginous	Irregular
			Stapes	2	Cartilaginous	Irregular

TABLE 4. (Continued)

Region	Number in Figure	Skeletal Unit	Bone	Number of Bones	Developmental Classification	Morphological Classification
	5		Hyoid	1	Cartilaginous	Irregular
		Vertebral Column	Cervical vertebrae	7	Cartilaginous	Irregular
			Thoracic vertebrae	12	Cartilaginous	Irregular
	6		Lumbar vertebrae	5	Cartilaginous	Irregular
	7		Sacrum	1	Cartilaginous	Irregular
	8		Coccyx	1	Cartilaginous	Irregular
	9	Thoracic Cage	Ribs	24	Cartilaginous	Flat
	10		Sternum	1	Cartilaginous	Flat
	11	Pectoral Girdle	Scapula	2	Cartilaginous	Flat
	12		Clavicle	2	Membranous	Short
	13	Arms	Humerus	2	Cartilaginous	Long
	14		Radius	2	Cartilaginous	Long
	15		Ulna	2	Cartilaginous	Long
		Wrists	Navicular	2	Cartilaginous	Short
			Lunate	2	Cartilaginous	Short
			Triquetral	2	Cartilaginous	Short
			Pisiform	2	In tendon	Sesamoid
	16		Multangulum major	2	Cartilaginous	Short
			Multangulum minor	2	Cartilaginous	Short

Appendicular

			Bone	Number	Tissue	Shape
17	Hands		Capitate	2	Cartilaginous	Short
18			Hamate	2	Cartilaginous	Short
			Metacarpals	10	Cartilaginous	Long
			Phalanges	28	Cartilaginous	Long
19	Pelvic Girdle		Pelvis (os coxae) (fusion of ilium, ischium, pubis)	2	Cartilaginous	Irregular
20	Legs		Femur	2	Cartilaginous	Long
21			Patella	2	In tendon	Sesamoid
22			Tibia	2	Cartilaginous	Long
23			Fibula	2	Cartilaginous	Long
	Feet		Talus	2	Cartilaginous	Short
			Calcaneus	2	Cartilaginous	Short
			Cuboid	2	Cartilaginous	Short
			Navicular	2	Cartilaginous	Short
24			Cuneiform I	2	Cartilaginous	Short
			Cuneiform II	2	Cartilaginous	Short
			Cuneiform III	2	Cartilaginous	Short
25			Metatarsals	10	Cartilaginous	Long
26			Phalanges	28	Cartilaginous	Long

[1] Krogman, W. 1962. *The Human Skeleton in Forensic Medicine.* Springfield: C. C. Thomas.

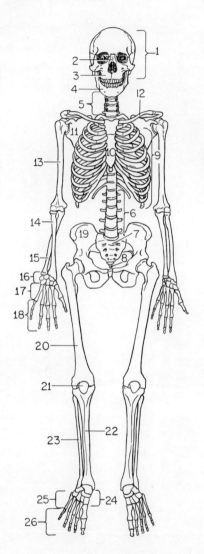

FIGURE 32. *The Human Skeleton*

The Muscle of Erect Posture: Gluteus Maximus

The type, location, and extent of bone elevations provide excellent clues as to the size and shape of the attached muscle, the

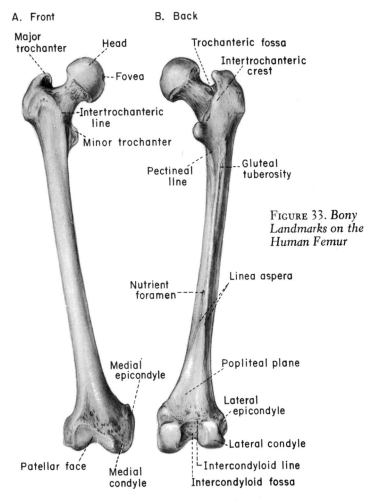

A. Front B. Back

Major trochanter   Head   Trochanteric fossa

Intertrochanteric crest

Fovea

Intertrochanteric line

Minor trochanter

Pectineal line   Gluteal tuberosity

FIGURE 33. *Bony Landmarks on the Human Femur*

Nutrient foramen   Linea aspera

Medial epicondyle   Popliteal plane

Lateral epicondyle

Lateral condyle

Patellar face   Medial condyle   Intercondyloid line

Intercondyloid fossa

amount of force, and the direction and speed of movement that the muscle imparts to the bone. Let us first examine the gluteal tuberosity of the femur and its muscle attachment in Man. This rough ridge of bone is the site of insertion of the thick flat tendon of the Gluteus maximus muscle which arises from the posterior surface of the pelvis, the sacrum, and the coccyx (as shown in Fig. 34A). The muscle acts mainly in two different ways. When the pelvis is fixed, the Gluteus maximus by its contraction

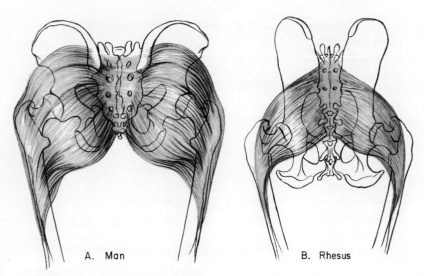

A. Man

B. Rhesus

FIGURE 34. *The Gluteus Maximus Muscle in Man and Monkey*

extends the femur so that it comes to lie in the same vertical axis as the trunk of the body; similarly, when the thigh is fixed, it extends the pelvis or trunk and thus aids greatly in maintaining an erect posture. In other words, this is the muscle primarily responsible for allowing us to rise from a sitting position and to maintain erect posture. It also, because of the location of its origin and insertion, can rotate the entire lower limb outward when the thigh is flexed. One can easily appreciate these two functions of the Gluteus maximus by placing a hand over the buttocks in the sitting position and attempting to rise. The rippling of the muscle as it contracts is readily felt. Similarly, in a standing position with one side against a wall place the right foot against the wall and attempt to turn it outward. Again one can feel the contraction of this muscle.

In the rhesus monkey (Fig. 34B) the arrangement of this muscle-bone complex is significantly different. The muscle itself is relatively smaller than in Man and its site of origin is not as extensive, arising from the transverse processes of the upper two vertebrae of the tail and from the fascia covering the back of the sacrum. It is inserted by a thin aponeurosis into a very slightly raised crest on the posterior part of the femur. Perhaps the most important difference between Man and rhesus in the architecture of this muscle-bone complex lies in the alignment of the Gluteus maximus to the hip joint. As can be seen in Figure 34 the human pelvis is broad and short, with a greater area of attachment to the sacrum. The Gluteus maximus is thus enabled to perform the function of complete extension of the femur upon the trunk. It is therefore relatively simple to determine from the femur and the pelvis the type of movement permitted at the hip joint and the degree to which erect posture and bipedal locomotion can be attained. Man's pelvic proportions are unique in the Animal Kingdom, and, needless to say, so are his completely erect posture and bipedalism.

It must be pointed out quite emphatically that our explanation of erect posture and the role of the Gluteus maximus muscle is greatly oversimplified. No one muscle ever works alone or independently. It may be a prime mover, but it requires the assistance of other muscles to initiate, balance, maintain, decelerate, and restrain movement of the limb. For example, it can be demonstrated that the simple act of picking up a heavy object from the floor while in a standing position involves the movement of practically all the muscles of the body!

The Musculature of the Shoulder and Upper Arm

Let us pick for our next example the relationship between scapula and humerus, which is somewhat analogous to that between pelvis and femur. The head of the humerus articulates with the glenoid fossa of the scapula to form a ball-and-socket type of joint. There is more freedom of movement in the shoulder joint than in the hip joint because of fewer bony restrictions, and because the scapula itself moves and accommodates to the movements of the humerus. The head and upper portion of the shaft of the humerus bears many markings, indicative of the many muscles which are inserted there and regulate its movements. Muscles from the chest, the back, and the scapula insert in the humerus and cause it to abduct and adduct, rotate outwardly and inwardly, flex and extend, and circumduct, depending upon their origin and site of insertion. We shall concentrate primarily on the scapulo-humeral complex.

The humerus, like the femur, possesses a *head*, a *neck*, and two elevations known as *tubercles* (major and minor) rather than trochanters. Seen from in front there are two *crests*, a major and a minor tubercular crest, and an *intertubercular groove*. The posterior aspect of the upper part of the humerus is relatively smooth. The scapula, or shoulder blade, is a triangular-shaped bone. It is flat except for three processes that arise from it; one, the *scapular spine*, arises from the vertebral margin of the back of the scapula and extends lateralward, becoming larger and terminating in a wide flat process known as

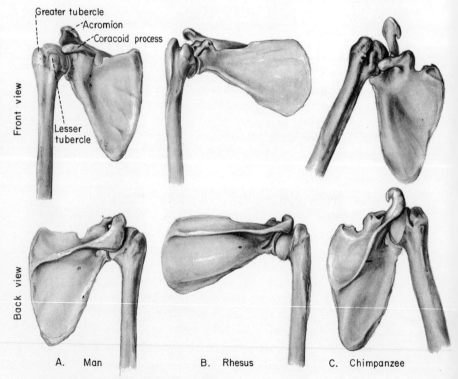

FIGURE 35. *The Humerus and Scapula of Man, Rhesus, and Chimpanzee*

the *acromion*. The spine separates the back surface of the scapula into an upper (*supraspinatus*) and a lower (*infraspinatus*) fossa. The front surface of the scapula, which faces the ribs, is relatively smooth except for a hooked process which arises near the scapular neck and curves forward and then lateralward. It is known as the *coracoid process*. Between the acromion and the coracoid process and forming the upper lateral corner of the triangular scapula is the *glenoid fossa*, which articulates with the head of the humerus. Other bony landmarks of both humerus and scapula are indicated in Figure 35A.

We shall focus upon six muscles which originate from the scapula and are inserted upon the humerus. These are illustrated in the series of drawings in Figure 36. The pertinent data relative to their origins, insertions, and functions are presented in tabular form below:

Muscle	Origin (Scapula)	Insertion (Humerus)	Function
Supraspinatus	Supraspinatus fossa	Upper part of major tubercle	Abduct humerus
Infraspinatus	Infraspinatus fossa	Upper part of major tubercle in back of supraspinatus insertion	Rotates humerus outward
Teres minor	Middle third of axillary border	Lowest and most posterior facet of major tubercle	Abducts and rotates humerus outwards
Teres major	Inferior angle of posterior surface	Minor tubercular crest	Abducts and rotates humerus inwards
Subscapularis	Anterior (rib) surface of scapula	Minor tubercle	Rotates humerus inwards
Deltoideus	Acromion and spine	Deltoid tuberosity	Abducts humerus

Only the chief actions of each muscle are given here, but it should be pointed out that each muscle may act in many different ways, depending upon the position of the humerus and also

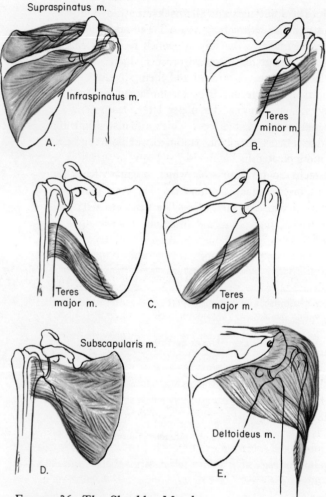

Supraspinatus m.

Infraspinatus m.

A.

Teres
minor m.

B.

Teres
major m.

C.

Teres
major m.

Subscapularis m.

D.

Deltoideus m.

E.

FIGURE 36. *The Shoulder Muscle Complex in Man*

upon which bundles of fibers are contracting. Complete analysis of movement is therefore extremely complicated. We shall confine our analysis to the major movements of these muscles as indicated in the table.

When the arm (humerus) is at the side two of the scapular

muscles will extend it laterally (abduct) from the body—the Supraspinatus and the Deltoid. However, if the scapula is fixed they will only raise the arm about 90 degrees from the side of the body since contact of the greater tubercle and acromion form a mechanical block to further movement. Further elevation of the arm must be accompanied by a rotation of the scapula.

Once the arm is abducted the two Teres muscles, major and minor, will return it to its original position (adduction). These are not the most powerful adductors of the arm, however. This distinction is reserved for *Pectoralis major*, the heavy muscular mass which arises on the chest and is inserted along the major tubercular crest of the humerus, and *Latissimus dorsi*. The principles of mechanics apply to the arrangements of the muscles and bones of the body and this may be illustrated by comparing Teres minor with Pectoralis major. The scapulo-humeral joint is the fulcrum. Both muscles arise from relatively fixed bars (scapula and chest), cross the joint, and are inserted into the movable lever (humerus). Pectoralis major, however, is inserted considerably lower on the movable lever than is the Teres minor. Its origin is, in addition, broader and situated lower with respect to the fulcrum. For these reasons it exerts a more powerful force upon the humerus and at the same time effects speedier movement. Given two muscles of similar size and origin with respect to distance from the fulcrum, the one which is inserted farthest from the fulcrum will provide more powerful movement, but that which is inserted closer to the fulcrum will bring about more rapid movement with less exertion.

When we place our arms at the sides with palms pressed against the thighs it is possible to rotate the arms outwards so that the palms are facing the front, or to rotate the arms inwards so that the palms are facing away from the body. Study of Figure 37 will reveal why the Teres minor and Infraspinatus muscles accomplish outward rotation. They are located in back of the joint and insert on the lateral portion of the humerus. Teres major and Subscapularis perform the opposite function of inward rotation. Teres major is the more powerful rotator of the two because of its relatively lower position on both scapula and humerus. Neither of these muscles, however, can exert a force

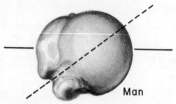

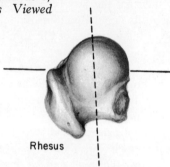

FIGURE 37. *The Humerus of Man and Rhesus Viewed from Above*

comparable to the Latissimus dorsi, a muscle which arises from a broad area on the back and converges toward the joint, passing below it and crossing the front of the humerus to be inserted into the minor tubercular crest. Both Latissimus dorsi and Pectoralis major are powerful abductors and inward rotators of the arm. They oppose each other in one respect, however. The Latissimus dorsi draws the arm backwards (extension), while the Pectoralis major pulls it forward (flexion). It should be obvious that these movements, because of the mechanics involved, are quite limited and relatively weak.

It is apparent that the muscles which are inserted into the upper arm permit a wide variety of movements. If we concern ourselves solely with Man it would seem that there is no function involving the upper arm which he cannot perform. It is only when we compare Man's upper arm with that of certain other animals that we can look at this region with greater understanding of its evolutionary implications and appreciation of Man's lack of specialization. Man's upper limbs do not have the burden of supporting the weight of the body or the responsibility of locomotion. In animls where the limbs have this function the muscles and bones of the shoulder are differently arranged.

Let us first examine the rhesus monkey, an animal that progresses over the ground on all four limbs. In Figure 35A and B we see the scapula and humerus in front and back views. Compare first the shape of the rhesus scapula compared with that of Man. Most striking is the difference in proportions. In Man the longest border is the vertebral and the shortest is the superior; in rhesus the vertebral border is extremely short while the superior and axillary borders are of about equal length. The scapular spine of the rhesus is thin and terminates in a relatively slender acromion process. Its position is such that the supraspinous fossa is narrow and somewhat shallow. The axillary margin shows much less rugosity than does that of Man. When the scapula is in a vertical position with the glenoid fossa facing downwards and laterally, as when the rhesus is walking, the acromion lies directly lateral to the glenoid fossa and prevents the humerus from becoming abducted more than a few degrees. In the vertical position, however, the acromion lies above and behind the fossa with the result that the arm can be abducted with little mechanical interference, an important function for animals that are as at home in trees as on the ground.

There are many points of difference in the humerus, only a few of which shall be pointed out. The intertubercular groove is relatively much wider and somewhat deeper in the rhesus. The tendon of the long head of the Biceps muscle lies in this groove. Since the biceps is the chief flexor of the forearm, and hence plays an important role in both climbing and brachiation, it is no wonder that it is relatively larger in the rhesus. This is clearly hinted at by the size of the groove in which its tendon plays. Similarly the sharp elevation of the greater tubercular crest indicates the large size and thus important role of the Pectoralis major muscle in elevating the arm and adducting it. Latissimus dorsi, an important climbing and brachiating muscle, is somewhat reduced in rhesus in both its origin and insertion. It is much like that of the baboon and other terrestrial quadrupedal animals. Its insertion is by a thin tendon into the intertubercular groove.

The Supraspinatus muscle in rhesus is relatively longer and

thinner than in Man and is a rather weak abductor of the arm. The Infraspinatus is also quite narrow and thus does not permit the variability of movement by contraction of specific fiber bundles that is the property of broader muscles. In the rhesus, Teres major and Infraspinatus are both narrow muscles and run an almost parallel course toward the humerus, a situation duplicated in the baboon. The deltoid muscle arises much as in Man but its insertion in the rhesus humerus is higher on the shaft, indicating greater speed of abduction at the cost of power. Dissection reveals that the deltoid muscle in the rhesus is relatively much thinner than in Man.

A further distinction in the humerus of the rhesus may be observed in a view from above (see Fig. 37). The head faces towards the rear; in Man the head faces medially. This humeral torsion is characteristic of both New World and Old World monkeys. The medial orientation of Man's humeral head is found also in the anthropoid apes.

Let us now examine the shoulder joint and muscle complex of the chimpanzee, an arboreal Primate whose chief mode of locomotion is brachiation. (See Fig. 35.) The scapula is quite unlike that of Man or rhesus. The vertebral and axillary borders are very long but the superior border is quite short. The scapular spine originates from the middle of the vertebral border and pursues an upward course toward the superior lateral angle. It terminates, as in Man, in a heavy broad acromion. The glenoid fossa faces upward and laterally, instead of just laterally as in Man and rhesus. The sites of attachment of Teres major and minor on the axillary border are not as rugged or prominent as in Man. The chimpanzee humerus shows an exceedingly deep intertubercular groove and a particularly rugose minor tubercular crest. The entire major tubercular crest is longer, thicker, and more elevated than in Man.

In general the shoulder-arm musculature of the chimpanzee is more massive than is found in either Man or rhesus. The abductors, Deltoideus and Supraspinatus have larger areas of origin and their tendons of insertion are broader. The rotators, Teres major and minor, show no unusual development, but Latissimus dorsi and Pectoralis major, which are the primary rotators and adductors of the arm, are extremely powerful. Their sites of origin are more extensive than in Man and their tendons of insertion have left heavy markings on the humerus, as we have seen. These muscles are particularly important when the arm is extended over the head and hence fixed. They then pull the trunk toward the arm. The peculiar swinging motion of the chimpanzee as he progresses through the trees, one arm after another, is primarily made possible by the rotating and adducting functions of Latissimus dorsi and Pectoralis major. Subscapularis, an inward rotator of the humerus, is a much thicker muscle in the chimpanzee than in either Man or rhesus. This is reflected in the greater concavity of the front surface of the scapula. Its tendon of insertion into the lesser tubercle apparently exerts enormous pull, since this tubercle is much more pronounced in the chimpanzee than in Man.

In carrying out this brief comparison of muscle-bone relationship in the shoulder region of Man, chimpanzee, and rhesus, our purpose has been threefold: (1) to illustrate how much information is contained in the various markings on bone; (2) to indicate how three different modes of habitual locomotion are each reflected in the mechanical arrangements of muscle and bone; and (3) to emphasize how much more can be learned about human anatomy when a perspective is provided by analysis of the anatomy of other forms.

Differential Bone Lengths

Differences in function are also reflected, but less directly, by differences in proportion and relative size. The depiction of evolution as recorded in progressive changes in form and dimensions has been a special concern of paleontologists and physical anthropologists. The study of such differential changes has come to be known as *allometry* and involves the application of mathematics to changes in form with time. The principal founder of this approach was D'Arcy Thompson, and his book *On Growth and Form*[2] constitutes the basis of a whole new literature on certain principles of growth in both evolution and ontogeny. Space does not permit in this introductory text a

---

[2] Thompson, D. 1945. *On Growth and Form*. Cambridge: The University Press; New York: The Macmillan Company.

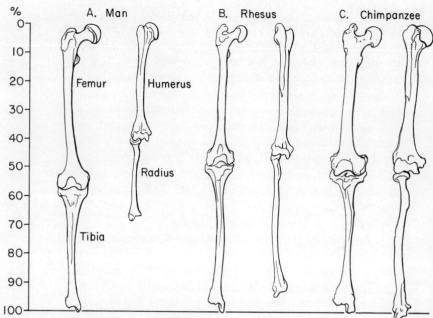

FIGURE 38. *Relative Lengths of the Four Limb Bones in Man, Chimpanzee, and Rhesus Monkey*

proper consideration of allometry, but perhaps some insight into the kind of observations upon which it is based can be gained by a few metrical comparisons of the skeleton.

We might begin by measuring the lengths of four of the limb bones of adult Man: humerus, radius, femur, and tibia. The first two represent the two segments of the upper extremity; the latter two the two segments of the lower extremity. Their lengths, in terms of percentage of length of the femur, are illustrated in Figure 38A. Relationships of the same bone lengths in the chimpanzee and the rhesus are given in Figure 38B and C. Although the percentages expressed in the figure are based upon average lengths, it can be stated that there is no overlapping of the distribution curves of these three Primates. We learn a number of things from this comparison. The long bones of the rhesus, a quadrupedal animal, are of nearly equal lengths. In this animal the upper extremity is about 94 percent of the length of the lower extremity, and the radius is longer than the humerus. The tibia is slightly longer than the femur. In the chimpanzee the femur and humerus are of equal lengths while the tibia is the shortest of the four bones. The relative lengths of Man's limb segments are different from both rhesus and chimpanzee. His femur is by far the longest bone and his radius is much the shortest—a condition just the reverse of the rhesus.

If we compare the relative lengths of the upper (humerus + radius) and the lower (femur + tibia) extremities, we find that in Man the arms are only 69 percent of the length of

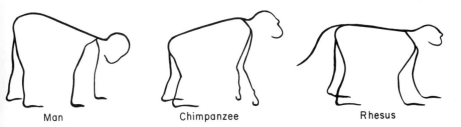

Man   Chimpanzee   Rhesus

FIGURE 39. *The Quadrupedal Postures of Man, Chimpanzee, and Rhesus Monkey*

the legs, while in the rhesus they are 94 percent and in the chimpanzee 103 percent. These differences can be graphically illustrated by drawing all three Primates as quadrupedal creatures with the trunk shown as a straight line resting upon the tops of the four extended limbs (Fig. 39). In Man the trunk tilts precariously forward. In the chimpanzee the trunk is almost horizontal, tilting only slightly to the rear. In rhesus there is a slight tilt forward. Since all three Primates are ultimately derived from the same common ancestor, it is obvious that evolutionary divergence has affected limb proportions in quite different ways. Knowledge of the postural and locomotor habits of Man, chimpanzee, and rhesus, plus an understanding of the muscle-bone anatomy of each, permits us to form some educated opinions about the nature of the selective forces in evolution that resulted in such adaptive responses. For clearly these differences in relative bone lengths have adaptive value in each case.

The Mechanics of the Skeleton of a Quadruped

A very useful aid in comprehending the role of mechanical principles in the adaptive response of the skeleton to environmental change is to be found in a comparison of two temporal extremes in primate phylogeny—Man and the hypothetical ancestor of the Primates. It is a well-established fact that the Primates, like other orders of Mammals, represent one of many adaptive radiations from a terrestrial quadrupedal Insectivore. Although no complete skeletons of these Cretaceous placentals have been found as yet, it may be assumed that they were not significantly different from those of the living Tupaiidae, a representation of which is drawn in Figure 40. We may begin by observing the vertebral column, which has the shape of an arch resting near each end on "pillars"—the fore and hind limbs. Gregory has called this type of structure the "bridge-that-walks."[3] It is a suspension type of bridge in that it supports the weight of the thoracic and abdominal viscera. The individual vertebrae which constitute the building blocks of this bridge are so shaped that they form a sort of keystone arch (see Fig. 41). The more weight pendent from such a structure, the more firmly are the individual blocks locked in up to the breaking

[3] Gregory, W. 1937. *The Bridge-that-Walks:* The Story of Nature's Most Successful Design. *Natural History*, 39:33–48.

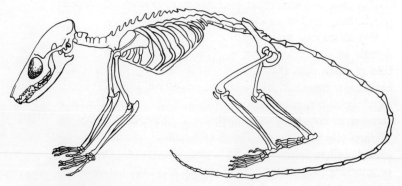

FIGURE 40. *The Skeleton of a Modern Tupaiid*, Ptilocercus (*Pen-tailed Tree-shrew*)

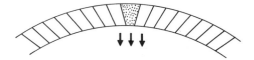

FIGURE 41. *The Architecture of the Verte-*
bral Column of Quadrupeds (exaggerated)

point of the material itself. Each portion of the column supports the weight of the viscera immediately below it, thus there
is an even distribution of gravitational pull along the entire
length of the column.

A frontal projection of the column beyond the front limbs
acts as a sort of crane which is attached at its end to the head
(or "grappling hook"). The crane (neck) raises and lowers the
head for feeding purposes. The head itself is attached to the
vertebral column at its most posterior extremity by a bony
articulation on either side of the *foramen magnum* (large hole)
through which the spinal cord leaves the skull and passes down
the length of the vertebral column. This joint forms a fulcrum
upon which the head may be raised or lowered. Obviously since
the entire weight of the skull is in front of the fulcrum there is
need for powerful musculature running from the back of the
skull over the fulcrum to the backs of the vertebrae in order to
counteract the pull of gravity. This is reflected in the large
nuchal crest running across the occipital bone of the skull to
which these muscles attach.

We notice that the orbits are directed laterally so that there
is little or no overlap of vision. This gives the animal a visual
field of more than 180 degrees without moving his head. The
braincase is very small relative to the size of the body. The entire
facial skeleton is situated well in front of the brain. The nasal
skeleton is very long, indicating in all probability highly developed olfactory senses. The jaws are long and narrow and
project well in front of the brain and eyes, so that in combat
or attacking prey neither of these vital structures are prone to
injury.

The two girdles, pectoral and pelvic, have two functions in
common. They serve as means of attachment of the limbs to

the axial skeleton and they transmit the weight of the body through the limbs to the ground. Each limb bears approximately one quarter of the body weight. The pelvic girdle has a third function, that of affording bony protection to the vital birth canal. The rib cage forms a sort of bony bellows that performs the tasks of inspiration and expiration. It also protects the lungs and heart and helps to support their weight. The tail, a posterior extension of the vertebral column, is used in balancing. We note that the abdominal viscera (stomach, liver, kidneys, intestines, spleen, etc.) are not encircled by a bony cage as is the thoracic viscera. The contents of the abdomen are supported below only by musculature such as the Rectus abdominis, Internal and External oblique, and Transversus, which extend from the ribs to the pelvis.

It is from this terrestrial quadrupedal type of mammalian bony architecture that Man's skeleton is derived. Let us imagine that the Insectivore skeleton, enlarged many times to approximate the size of the human skeleton, was suddenly called upon to assume an habitual erect posture. Is it adapted to this new orientation? In Figure 42A we have attempted to draw our ancestor in an upright position as if he had attained this state without going through millions of years of evolution. We observe, first of all, that the head hangs down upon the chest. It is difficult even for the powerful extensor muscles of the back of the neck to maintain the head in a horizontal position against the force of gravity. The head itself, a wonderfully equipped device for fighting, seizing prey, sniffing out spoor, and otherwise coping with conditions on the ground, is now far removed from its effective area of operation. The front limbs, now the upper limbs, have no longer any role in locomotion or body support, and are left free to discover some new part to play. The vertebral column, instead of lying at right angles to the pull of gravity, is now parallel to it so that the weight of the viscera is suspended from the upper vertebrae, thus exerting a force that would put tremendous strain upon the entire arch-shaped column. The keystone arch construction of the vertebral column is not only rendered useless, but faces stresses it cannot cope with.

As the viscera presses downward its weight is partly borne by

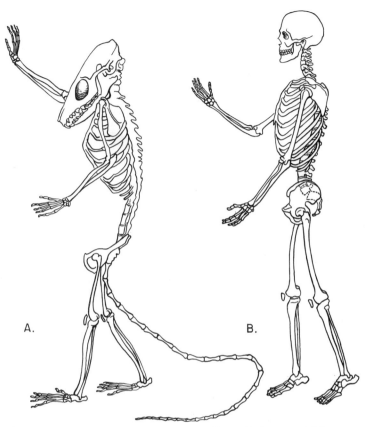

FIGURE 42. *The Skeletons of Man and an Insectivore in the Upright Posture*

the bony pelvis but most of it is thrust forward in the abdomen, exerting great pressure against the restraining abdominal musculature. The excessive demands placed upon this muscle complex find it ill-prepared to cope with them. The front and sides of the abdomen are not completely covered by muscle. There are certain "gaps," such as those at the sides just over the crest of each ilium, the canals in the groin through which the testes descend and which remain wide open in these primitive insectivores, the umbilicus, and the *fossa ovalis* located high on the front surface of each thigh. Too much pressure on these weak spots would result in an eruption of viscera from the abdomen (hernia).

Finally, we can envisage certain weaknesses that would develop in the hind limbs and feet as a consequence of their assumption of the entire weight of the body and the new method of locomotion, bipedalism. The architecture of the bones of the foot and the changes that took place over the course of evolution have been the subject of intensive study by Morton, culminating in his book, *Human Locomotion and Body Form.*[4] The locomoter apparatus of all Mammals has selective value of the highest order. Perhaps more than any other trait it must be well adapted to the environmental situation in which the animal finds itself. Failure to adapt means rapid elimination. For this reason the skeleton of the limbs and feet offer excellent clues to the method of locomotion and hence to many of the habits of the animal. A thorough exposition of this point is to be found in the study by Camp and Smith[5] of the evolution of the feet of horses. In Figure 43 we have presented drawings of the foot skeletons of Man, rhesus, and chimpanzee. Note the striking differences in shape and proportions. Each foot represented has different stresses placed upon it and each is called upon to perform somewhat different functions. Perhaps there is no better way to gain understanding of the relationship between foot structure and function than to spend a day at the zoo observing the ways in which these Primates use their feet. And while you are there, do not overlook the different methods of brachiation practiced by the gorilla, orang-utan, gibbon, chimpanzee, and various monkeys.

The Skeleton in Upright Posture

Having studied the skeleton of a generalized primitive Mammal in its natural posture and in an imaginary erect posture, let us now look more closely at the skeleton of Man, keeping in mind

---

[4] Morton, D. 1952. *Human Locomotion and Body Form.* Baltimore: Williams and Wilkins Company.

[5] Camp and Smith. 1942. Phylogeny and Functions of the Digital Ligaments of the Horse. *University of California Memoirs,* 13:69–123.

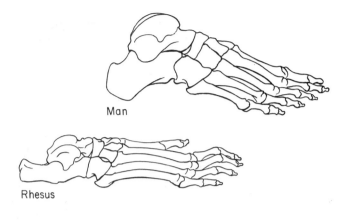

Man

Rhesus

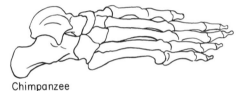

Chimpanzee

FIGURE 43. *The Skeleton of the Foot in Man, Rhesus, and Chimpanzee*

that the human skeleton is really that of a terrestrial quadruped which, over millions of years, has come to assume habitual erect posture. What architectural changes have been wrought and how well adapted is the human skeleton to this new orientation?

We begin with the skull (Fig. 44). It sits atop the vertebral column, the site of articulation and the foramen magnum being situated almost in the center of the base of the skull. The nuchal crest for attachment of the muscles of the back of the neck is only slightly elevated (in some skulls it is hardly discernible). The skull being well balanced upon the vertebral column, there is little need for powerful musculature to hold it up. The jaws and upper face are short and positioned under the very large brain case. There appears to be a reversal in relative sizes of the facial and neural components of the skull—the latter is now dominant. The orbits are located in front of the skull just below the frontal portion of the brain and are directed forward. The result is a considerable overlap of the two visual fields and hence stereoscopic vision. On the other hand there is a great reduction in the total field of vision when the head is fixed. In order to

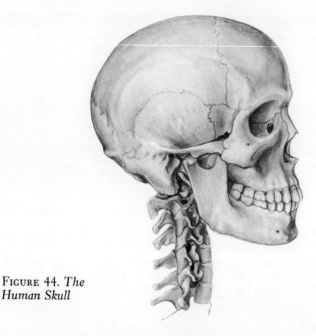

FIGURE 44. *The Human Skull*

achieve greater breadth of field the head must be rotated on the vertebral column. This is accomplished by the greater development of the *sternocleidomastoid* muscles which arise from the area of the sternoclavicular joints and are inserted into large processes (mastoid processes) on the base of the skull just below and behind the ear holes (external auditory meati). The prominent mastoid processes are the response of the bone to the strong pull of these muscles. Each muscle, acting independently, turns the head toward the opposite side. In our primitive Insectivore these processes are not present.

With the reduction of the snout, the nasal skeleton is considerably reduced in size, indicating a diminution in the powers of olfaction. The lower jaw (mandible) is not only greatly reduced in size but also bears a bony protuberance at its lower frontal extremity (chin). The muscles that act to close the lower jaw (Masseter and Temporalis) are correspondingly smaller and their sites of origin and insertion are not as readily discernible. The Masseter arises on the lower border of the zygomatic arch and inserts into the outer surface of the posterior corner (gonial angle) of the mandible. The Temporal muscle arises from the side of the skull in a sort of arc bounded by a faint temporal line of bone and inserts into the frontal projection (coronoid process) of the upper arm (ramus) of the mandible. If we compare these sites of origin and insertion with those of the Insectivore or any other Mammal we are struck by the relatively slight degree of prominence exhibited in Man. However, this is understandable when we realize that the jaws of Man are greatly diminished in size and require much less muscle pull to close them.

It is easy to see that the vertebral column, though composed of the same building blocks (vertebrae) as before, has assumed a different shape. Instead of an arch-like configuration it has developed curvatures resembling an S. In the neck region there is a forward convexity (lordosis). This becomes a backward convexity (kyphosis) in the thoracic area, a forward convexity in the lumbar region, and a backward convexity in the sacrum. These curvatures are accomplished by the simple expedient of alternating the keystone arch type of construction (see Fig. 45). The result is that the entire vertebral column can better withstand the weight of the head and viscera.

The shoulder girdle and upper limbs are relieved of all their former functions and must assume new ones. It is easy to see that with the head elevated far above the ground and the jaws reduced in size and placed under the eyes, the arms and hands are needed to bring food to the mouth. It is the pelvic girdle that finds itself in an anatomical and mechanical quandary. Not only must it transmit all the weight of the body to the two hind limbs and serve as the sole connection of the locomotor apparatus to the body, but it must continue to protect the birth canal while at the same time it must come to the assistance of the abdominal musculature in offering support to the viscera. This it has attempted to do in two ways. The sacrum, which in all other Mammals is a straight bone, has developed a pronounced kyphosis, so that its tip intrudes into the bony birth canal. Various ligaments reinforce the bottom of the canal, running from the sacrum to other protruding portions of the pelvis. In addition, the blades (ilia) of the pelvis, which are flat and lie in the same plane in all other Mammals, have become curved anteriorly, to-

A. Man   B. Insectivore

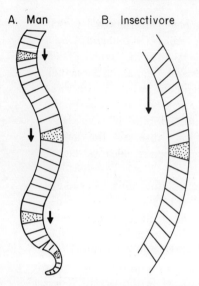

FIGURE 45. *The Architecture of the
Vertebral Column in Man and in
a Terrestrial Quadruped (exaggerated)*

gether forming a sort of pelvic basin and offering broader areas
of attachment to the muscles of the abdomen. Supplemental
support is afforded by two strong ligaments which run from the
upper anterior projections of the ilia to the top of the pubic
crest located low in the groin.

We have already discussed the relationship between the Gluteus maximus muscle and the bony sites of attachment on the
pelvis and femur. This muscle, which is most highly developed
in Man, and is a powerful extensor of the thigh, in the quadrupedal Mammal is a flat, thin sheet with weak insertion in the
greater trochanter and is basically an abductor of the thigh.

There are many other points of comparison between the human and the primitive mammalian skeletons which can best
be pursued by examination of the bones themselves. There is no
substitute for direct handling of such material. From our rather
superficial observations it is nonetheless quite apparent that
Man's skeleton is that of a terrestrial quadruped, secondarily

modified to the requirements of erect posture and bipedal locomotion. Have the modifications it has undergone during 70 million years of evolution adapted Man completely to his unusual stance and gait? According to Krogman, in an article entitled "The Scars of Human Evolution," not only is Man's skeleton inadequately adapted to upright posture, but Man himself is continuously paying a price for his evolution.[6]

What are some of the scars left by Man's unique evolutionary history? In order to turn his head and thus increase the field of his vision, he depends upon enlarged Sternocleidomastoid muscles which, in turn, have produced a prominent mastoid process. The latter is filled with numerous bone-lined cells which are focal points for infection spreading from the upper respiratory tract. Before antibiotics mastoiditis was a most serious affliction, often leading to drastic surgery and frequently to death.

The vertebral column, while modified into a series of curves, is still not an ideal design for supporting weight. As a result trouble develops at certain critical points of curvature, particularly in the lumbar region where backache is a common affliction. Slipped or herniated intervertebral discs are very frequent occurrences in Man. In middle and old age, the vertebral bodies become more brittle and the discs separating them lose their elasticity with the result that jumping piles them together and transmits shock to the skull or chips the individual vertebral bodies.

The abdominal musculature, though strengthened through the course of evolution, is by no means adequate to maintain pressure on the viscera. As the muscles lose their tonicity with age the viscera begins to overcome their restraining action and a "potbelly" develops. In addition, the "gaps" in the abdominal wall that we discussed above offer pathways of little resistance to the compressed viscera, resulting very frequently in inguinal, umbilical, femoral, and lumbar herniations.

The outlet of the bony birth canal, thanks to the inward curvature of the sacrum and the projections of bone into the canal for ligamental attachment, has become restricted in size

[6] Krogman, W. 1951. The Scars of Human Evolution. *Scientific American*, 185:54–57.

so that there is often interference with the passage of the head of the fetus during the birth process. This may necessitate surgical intervention. This apparent paradox—the restriction of the birth canal in an "effort" to provide bony support for the abdominal and perineal viscera—gives us occasion to speculate whether the evolutionary process may not indeed work at cross purposes in some instances. Many Mammals are revealed in the paleontological record to have become overspecialized in one trait or another, a process that may well have led to their extinction. Examples of such extreme specialization are the long, curved beaks of the *Drepanids* (Hawaiian birds), the long canines of the saber-toothed cats, the tremendous body size of the land-dwelling dinosaurs, and the gigantic antlers of the Irish elk.

As most of us can readily testify, Man's feet are but poorly adapted to their task of supporting the entire weight of the body and propelling it forward. The axis of gravity of the body which, in the quadrupedal monkeys, passed through the middle toe, and in the arboreal apes was centered midway between the second and the big toe, has in Man come to lie almost directly above the big toe. This emphasis on the big toe has resulted in its elongation relative to the other toes and in its close alignment with them (Fig. 46A). It therefore had to give up its prehensile abilities. Few people can pick up an object with their toes, but all apes can perform such a task. Viewed from the side the human foot possesses two axes, one passing through the metatarsal, the other through the tarsals. These axes cross each other to form the arch of the foot, a notably weak arrangement which often results in "fallen arches" (Fig. 46B).

We can, perhaps, speculate about the effect of upright posture on a mammalian type heart which was well adapted to pumping blood through arteries at its own level or below. The same kind of heart is now required to pump blood upwards into the arms and head, and at the same time blood must be returned, through veins straight up against the force of gravity. It is not unlikely that many cases of heart failure, varicositis, and other cardiovascular troubles are the consequences of the imposition of new tasks on a system designed for a pronograde body.

It is helpful to regard the changes that took place in the

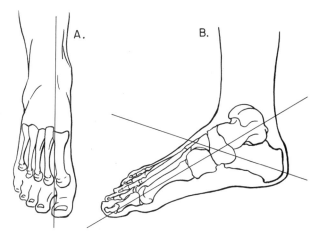

FIGURE 46. *The Human Foot*

human skeleton as a result of the assumption of erect posture in three different ways. Those changes which were the necessary and direct consequences of upright posture may be termed *primary* effects. They include the remodeling of the vertebral column and the modifications in the pelvis, limbs, and feet. As a result of these primary adjustments certain other modifications, called *secondary* effects, took place. Among these were the centering of the head upon the vertebral column, the reduction of the snout to give the head a spherical shape, the decrease in the size of the musculature attaching to the back of the head, and the increase in the size of the Sternocleidomastoid muscles for turning the head, with the attendant magnification of the mastoid processes. We shall call *tertiary* effects those changes which cannot logically be attributed to either primary or secondary effects, such as: the increase in the size of the brain, modifications of the dentition and occlusion, reduction of the brow ridges, development of a chin, formation of a nasal bridge, etc. Whether these architectural changes can be explained in terms of selection of mechanically better adapted variations, or on the basis of a complex of structures traveling together as a single functional or genetic matrix, it is impossible to say at present. Some causes may forever remain undiscovered. Nevertheless it is interesting and even stimulating to speculate on such matters, and we shall be bold enough to offer some thoughts of our own in a subsequent Problem.

If our analysis and classification of the structural differences between the human and primitive mammalian skeletons is correct, then we might expect to find fossil hominoid forms exhibiting characteristics that are morphologically intermediate between the two. In other words, early hominids should show less developed mastoid processes and more pronounced nuchal crests than modern Man, and the farther back in time we go the closer should these traits approach the primitive mammalian condition. In addition, those skeletal modifications which we have labeled primary effects should appear earlier in the fossil record than those which we call secondary. Similarly, secondary effects should make their appearance before tertiary effects.

The Teeth

Before we turn our attention to the fossil record itself, a final subject awaits our consideration—the dentition. Todd has defined teeth as "calcified papillae of the skin secondarily implanted in the bones of the jaws and subserving the purpose of mastication."[7] While this definition points the finger at the probable origin of the dentition—the placoid scales which covered the entire body of primitive cartilaginous fish—it hardly encompasses the teeth of Mammals nor the many other functions which teeth may fulfill. A survey of the Animal Kingdom shows that teeth are used for combat, seizing, holding and carrying, piercing, tearing, shearing, combing, cracking, grinding, and digging. In the adaptive radiations of Amphibians, Reptiles, and Mammals they have assumed many different forms as well as modes and rates of development. In spite of the truly vast literature dealing with the dentition we are left with many unsolved problems relating to its evolution. Perhaps we had best begin with what we know most about—the anatomy and morphology of the human teeth.

Man has a *diphyodont* condition, that is, he has two sets of

[7] Todd, T. An Introduction to the Mammalian Dentition. St. Louis: C. V. Mosby Company. p. 33.

teeth. One set, the primary or deciduous dentition, begins to erupt at the age of six months and is completely present in the mouth by the end of the third year. The second set, the permanent dentition, erupts from the sixth to the 18th year (or later). The primary dentition consists of 20 teeth, the permanent of 32 teeth. Mammals are *heterodont* and Man is no exception. By this we mean that Man's dentition is comprised of different kinds of teeth within each set. Since there is bilateral symmetry with regard to the dentition, we shall henceforth deal only with the upper and lower right quadrants of the mouth. Beginning with the midline and proceeding backward the primary dentition consists of two incisors, one canine (or cuspid), and two molars. This situation is represented as follows:

$$
\begin{array}{lccc}
 & i & c & m \\
\text{upper} & 2 & - 1 & - 2 \\
\hline
\text{lower} & 2 & - 1 & - 2 \\
\end{array}
$$

The usual practice is to employ lower case letters to indicate primary teeth and capital letters for permanent teeth. Subscripts and superscripts indicate whether the tooth is an upper or lower one; thus, i^2 represents an upper second (or lateral) primary incisor, while M_3 represents a lower third permanent molar. The permanent dentition consists of two incisors, one canine, two premolars (bicuspids), and three molars:

$$
\begin{array}{lcccc}
 & I & C & PM & M \\
\text{upper} & 2 & - 1 & - 2 & - 3 \\
\hline
\text{lower} & 2 & - 1 & - 2 & - 3 \\
\end{array}
$$

Each tooth consists of two parts, a crown and a root. The crown is the functional portion of the tooth which is present in the oral cavity. The root, consisting of one or more branches or bifurcations, is imbedded in a bony socket in the upper or lower jaw. A tooth is made up of four tissues: enamel, dentine, cementum, and pulp. Their distribution in a typical molar tooth is shown in Figure 47. The first three are hard tissues; the pulp is soft and provides blood and innervation to the tooth.

Incisors, as the name implies, are cutting teeth and possess a single straight edge. Canines are piercing teeth and have a single, more or less pointed, cusp. Premolars and molars are

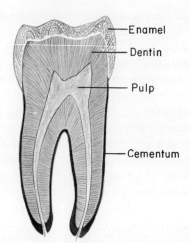

FIGURE 47. *The Components of a Human Molar*

multicusped teeth and are principally grinders. The cusps of the upper premolars and molars interdigitate (occlude) with those of the lower when the jaws are closed. The upper incisors generally overlap the lower in occlusion. Casts of the permanent dentition representing "excellent" occlusion are shown in Figure 48A. "Normal" or "good" occlusion is not the most frequent condition in modern Man. It is estimated by orthodontists that some 70 percent of the modern American White population has "malocclusion." An example of a typical malocclusion is shown in Figure 48B.

Incisors and canines, being of rather simple construction, are not as important in evolutionary analysis as are the premolars and particularly the molars. Multicusped teeth like the molars show a wide variety of crown configurations, especially on the occlusal surfaces, and these have been the subject of intensive study by zoologists, anthropologists, and geneticists. Drawings of the occlusal surfaces of M^1, M^2, M_1 and M_2 are presented in Figure 49. The various structures of the surface—cusps, fissures, ridges, pits, etc. are indicated. In dentistry the cusps are named according to their location with reference to the oral cavity. *Mesial* refers to the part of the crown nearest the midline of the mouth as we present forward along the dental arch; *distal* is the opposite; *buccal* indicates a structure on the cheek side of the tooth; *labial* is the lip side; and *lingual* is the tongue side. Cusps are thus identified as mesio-lingual, mesio-buccal, disto-lingual, and disto-buccal.

Zoologists and paleontologists use a different nomenclature, however, based upon the presumed phylogeny of the individual cusp. Both the dental and biological terminology for a typical upper and lower molar are illustrated in Figure 50. It has been well established that the individual morphological characteristics of the crown are under the control of heredity. Studies of monozygotic ("identical") and dizygotic ("fraternal") twins have revaled far greater concordances in dental traits between members of monozygotic sets than between members of dizy-

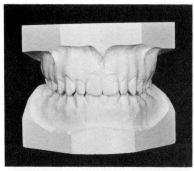

Normal   occlusion

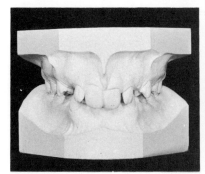

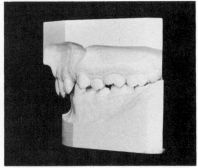

Malocclusion

FIGURE 48. *Excellent Occlusion and Malocclusion in Man*

Upper Right Permanent Molars

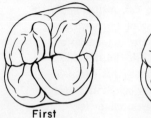 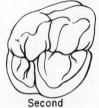

First   Second

Lower Right Permanent Molars

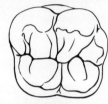 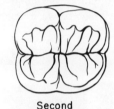

First   Second

FIGURE 49. *The Occlusal Surfaces of the First and Second Permanent Molars in Man*

gotic sets. The several structural elements that make up the occlusal surface of a premolar or molar are not inherited as a single entity but as separate and genetically independent traits. There are, therefore, thousands of possible combinations of these traits resulting in a wide range of premolar and molar types. Recently it has been demonstrated that the genetic control of morphological variability in the dentition can be utilized in the determination of zygosity of twins, a procedure which is less expensive and time-consuming than serological tests. An example of concordance and discordance in PM_1 in monozygotic and trizygotic triplets is shown in Figure 51.

The Functions of the Teeth

Since the dentition plays such a vital role throughout the life cycle of an organism it would follow that it would be a prime target of the selective forces of the environment and would indeed reflect the specific uses to which it was put. The unusual structure of the incisor teeth of the seal, in which the upper incisors are notched to receive the single edge of the lowers, is clearly an adaptation of what were once terrestrial mammalian teeth to the peculiar exigencies of a marine life. The powerful upper canines of the Javelina (a peccary of the American Southwest) are perfect tools for digging up the roots of desert plants. Rodents are characterized by chisel-like incisor teeth used in

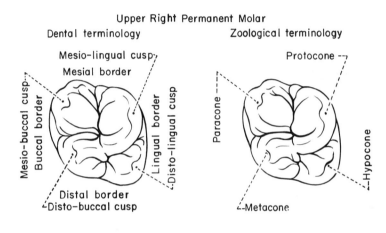

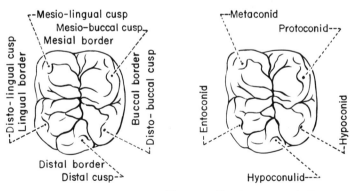

FIGURE 50. *Dental and Zoologic Terminology for Anatomical Features of Molar Teeth*

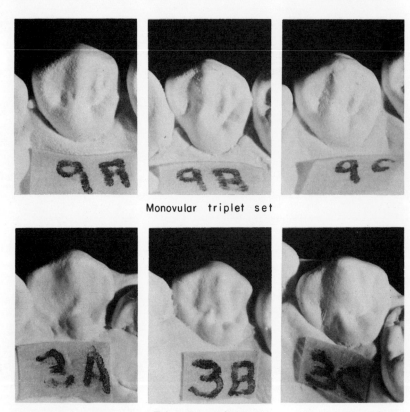

Monovular   triplet   set

Triovular   triplet   set

FIGURE 51. *The Morphology of the Lower First Premolar in Monozygotic and Trizygotic Triplets in Man*

gnawing; in fact some rodents (beavers) use their incisors to fell trees with which they then construct their dams. Many of the Insectivores and Prosimians have very narrow procumbent denticulated incisors used in grooming and combing their coats. In the higher Primates, particularly the anthropoid apes and Man, there is less tendency for specialization and the differences between them are of a more detailed nature. In the apes the incisors are more procumbent and there are gaps (diastemata) between the canines and the adjacent teeth to permit interlocking of the canines when the jaws are closed. In most of the higher Primates the canines project beyond the occlusal level of the rest of the teeth, but in Man they tend to be reduced to the same level (Fig. 52A). In the gorilla and orang-utan the molars increase in size from M_1 to M_3. In Man and the chimpanzee the

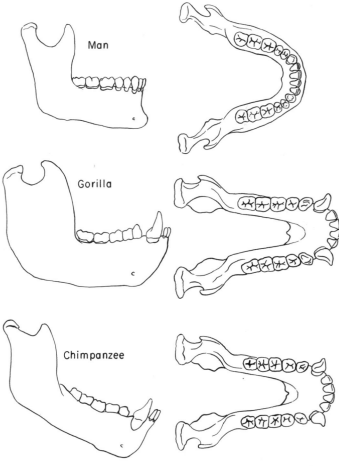

FIGURE 52. *The Occlusal Level and Dental Arch in Man, Gorilla, and Chimpanzee*

opposite trend is the case. The dental arch in the apes is U-shaped, with the canines projecting sharply at the base of the U. In Man, concomitant with his smaller jaws, the dental arch is parabolic (Fig. 52B).

The various morphological details of the bony girdles and limbs give, as we have seen, considerable insight into the postural and locomotor habits of the various types of Primates. The dentition, however, particularly among the higher Primates (anthropoid apes and Man), offers no substantial clues as to their dietary habits. Both apes and Man possess the masticatory apparatus to handle any kind of diet. That their diets are somewhat special-ized is undoubtedly not a consequence of their peculiar dental morphology nor, on the other hand, can their tooth structures be shown to be selected on the basis of their diets. Although our knowledge of the natural diets of the anthropoid apes is not complete, it can be said that the chimpanzee and orang-utan are mainly frugivorous, the gorilla primarily herbivorous, and the gibbon frugivorous, insectivorous, and carnivorous. Man, of course, is omnivorous. It would take more imagination than available evidence to claim any correlation between dental morphology and specific type of diet among these Primates. Anthropoid apes and Man have identical dental formulae: $2 - 1 - 2 - 3$. Their teeth can perform the functions of cut-ting, piercing, and grinding. Man's smaller canines and jaws, however, make him less effective in piercing and ripping coarser food. It is difficult to understand how the orang-utan molars, covered with many little fissures or "wrinkles" on their occlusal surfaces, subserve any masticatory function which cannot be per-formed equally well by the molars of the other apes and Man.

Morphologic Variability in the Human Dentition

This raises an interesting question which can only be met with speculation at the present time. If the morphological differ-ences in molar crowns of the degree exhibited among apes and men have little functional significance, how did they come about in the course of Primate evolution? In other words, if dental morphologic traits are not primary effects in the same sense as are pelvic, vertebral, and limb structural characters, could they be secondary and even tertiary effects? It is suggested that minor differences in cusp pattern, fissural arrangement, and extra cusps and tubercles may be pleiotropic "by-products." They may be traits of little or no adaptive value which are controlled by genes having other phenotypic effects which have high adaptive value. In such a case they are merely carried along, so to speak, on the heels of bodily traits which are positively selected and have the same genotype. Such an explanation, while not backed up with proof, is entirely in harmony with the genetic principles of pleiotropy and hereditary syndromes and relieves us of the necessity of finding functions for morphologic expressions where none may exist.

An interesting example of such a dental trait is the "Carabelli cusp," an extra tubercle or cusplet that is found on the mesio-lingual aspect of the upper first permanent molar. Occasionally, instead of a protuberance, there may be one or two pits or grooves at this location. The Carabelli trait is found not only in modern Man but also in fossil hominids and modern Primates. In modern Man there are marked differences in the frequencies of expressions. Mongoloids (Eskimos, American Indian, Chinese, etc.) have a very low incidence (0–8 percent) of cusps or tubercles and a high frequency of pits and grooves (ca. 75 percent). Whites have a high frequency of cusps and tubercles (ca. 50 percent) and a very low incidence of pits and grooves (ca. 11 percent). Many students of the dentition have attempted to ascribe functional significance to the Carabelli cusp. It is difficult, however, to explain its complete absence in some human populations if it truly has adaptive value. It seems much more likely that the Carabelli trait, which is undoubtedly inherited, is simply a "fellow-traveler" in a pleiotropic complex whose identity is not yet discovered. How else can we explain the existence of such a phenotypic trait as the ability to taste the synthetic compound phenylthiocarbomide, an ability which has been proven to be inherited as a simple Mendelian dominant. Could this trait in itself have adaptive value when the substance phenylthiocarbomide has never occurred in nature? Clearly we have simply stumbled upon a nonadaptive trait associated with some as yet unknown bodily character which has adaptive value. For example, recent work in Liverpool has shown a significantly high incidence of nontasters in patients suffering from adenomatous goiter, and a significantly high incidence of tasters with toxic diffuse goiter. It should be pointed out that there are differences in the frequency of tasters among the populations of Man, ranging from 98 percent in Navaho Indians and West Africans to 67 percent in Europeans and American Whites. Consistent differences in frequency of such traits as the Carabelli cusp and the PTC taster ability in populations of large size can hardly support an argument for genetic drift as a significant factor.

Dental Genetics

Thus far there are very few normal human traits for which the precise genetic mechanism is known. In the dentition, even though it is well established that the individual morphological structures of the crowns are under genetic control, we do not know the mode of inheritance of a single normal trait. The failure of attempts at genetic analysis are due, in large part, to the fact that any single morphological feature of the dentition has a continuous rather than a discontinuous variation. This merely means that any effort to classify the various expressions of a single trait is purely subjective, since one expression grades into the next almost imperceptibly. A good example is the well-known shovel-shape trait of the upper incisors, in which there are distinct ridges on both mesial and distal margins giving the back of the tooth the appearance of a shovel. This is a characteristic of very high frequency among the Mongoloid peoples but rather rare in Whites and Negroes except in cases of part Mongoloid ancestry. The trait is without question inherited but the difficulty in classifying its various types of expression has defied all attempts at genetic analysis. Correlation between arbitrary divisions of a continuous gradient and the underlying genetic components is largely fortuitous.

A serious criticism may be leveled at methods which seek to determine the mode of inheritance of dental traits which have a continuous variation. The shape of a structure, be it skeletal or dental, is the end result of a growth process involving both *direction* and *differential rates* of growth. Experimental genetics

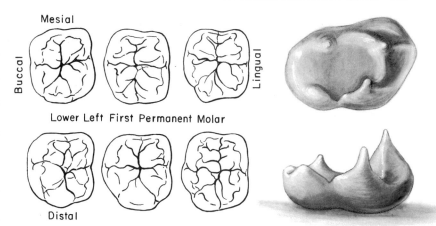

FIGURE 53. *Morphologic Variability of the First Permanent Molar in Apache Indians*

FIGURE 54. *The Crown of a Human First Permanent Molar before Calcification*

and embryology have shown that these growth processes are under the control of genes. In the case of the dentition the final configuration of the molar crown is the product of differential rates and directions of enamel deposition. The underlying surface of the crown, before the onset of calcification, shows very little variation among individuals. Apparently the genes that regulate the uplift of cusps in the precalcified tooth bud are remarkably alike throughout the human species and might be regarded as phylogenetically old and established. Those genes which regulate the rates of calcification are, on the other hand, extremely varied and are reflected in the great range of variation in pattern and configuration of the final occlusal surfaces, even within a single breeding population of Man. This may be illustrated in the case of a series of lower first permanent molars selected from the White River Apache Indians, a closely inbred population living on the Fort Apache Reservation in east-central Arizona (Fig. 53). Note the variety of expressions in fissural and cuspal patterns, as well as crown dimensions and proportions. In Figure 54 we have drawn a lower first permanent molar bud as it appears before initial calcification. It is one of hundreds of such teeth extracted from aborted fetuses of Whites,

Negroes, and Mongoloids. We have not seen a single variation among all these teeth from the morphological pattern represented in the figure. The same situation holds for the four types of primary molars.

Dental Morphogenesis

This brings us directly into a question discussed in Problem V: the embryological principle of recapitulation. In human ontogenesis the first eight weeks of prenatal existence are referred to as the embryonic period. This does not apply, however, to the dentition. Tooth development begins at the end of the embryonic period and beginning of the fetal period. It continues until the eruption of the third molar tooth at about 18 years of age. Thus the embryology of a single tooth encompasses a much greater period of time than does any other structure of the body and it takes place later in the ontogeny of the individual. Unfortunately we shall never know if the embryological stages through which a human tooth passes recapitulates the *embryonic* stages of ancient mammalian teeth, but there are some very interesting parallels to the postulated stages of evolution of the human dentition. While this is a subject that is at present being studied, it might be worthwhile to offer some illustrations of this phenomenon which, though not yet conclusive, are certainly provocative.

In our opinion the aspect of the dentition that is critical in evolutionary interpretation is its *morphogenesis* rather than its final morphology. As we indicated above, racial differences in tooth morphology *do not exist before the teeth begin to calcify.* In other words, among the various kinds of *Homo sapiens* ontogenetic divergence does not take place until late in tooth development. Moody (*Introduction to Evolution*) has pointed out that "the more closely related two animals are, the greater will be the proportion of their ontogenies exhibiting similarities."[8] On this basis we would expect the respective ontogenies of rhesus and human teeth to diverge at any earlier stage than do the human races. That this is so is suggested by the drawings in Figure 55. The upper second primary molars of rhesus and

[8] Moody, P. 1962. *Introduction to Evolution*, 2nd ed. New York: Harper and Row.

3 cusps
Precalcification stage

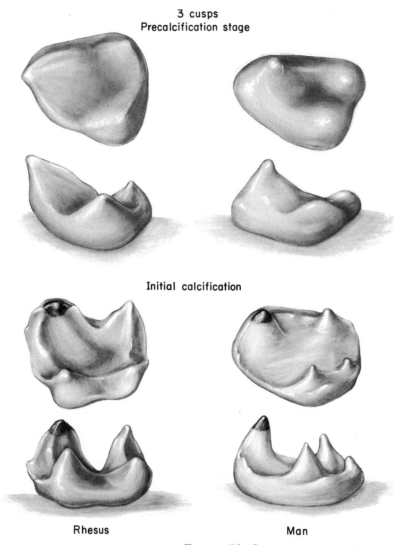

Initial calcification

Rhesus   Man

FIGURE 55. *Comparison of Molar*
Development in Rhesus and Man

Man are shown in an early, nearly equivalent stage of development in Figure 55A. Both are triangular in shape with three cusps of which the paracone (mesio-buccal cusp) is the most prominent. In a later stage of development (Fig. 55B), with calcification having commenced on the tips of the paracones, the rhesus and human molars show striking differences and can easily be identified. At this same stage it is impossible to distinguish a Negroid from a White or Mongoloid molar.

Dental Evolution

The theories of evolution of the mammalian dentition are many and extremely complex. We cannot attempt to deal with them here. An excellent review of the subject was provided by Krogman ("Anthropological Aspects of Human Teeth") in 1927.[9] More recently new ideas have been advanced by Butler ("A Theory of the Evolution of Mammalian Molar Teeth,") 1941,[10] Simpson ("Evolution of Mesozoic Mammals,") 1961,[11] and Vandebroek ("The Comparative Anatomy of the Teeth of Lower and Non-Specialized Mammals,") 1961.[12] Perhaps the most accepted theory is that known as the Cope-Osborn Theory of Trituberculy, first enunciated by Cope in 1874,[13] refined by Osborn in 1888,[14] and critically reviewed and revised by Gregory in 1934 ("A Half Century of Trituberculy").[15] We shall attempt to integrate some of the old ideas with some of the new in order to achieve a fairly coherent picture of molar evolution from the Reptile to the Primate. It must be understood, however, that there is probably no area in paleontology about which there is so little agreement among scholars.

The ancestors of the reptiles are known as *Cotylosaurs* or

[9] Krogman, W. 1927. Anthropological Aspects of Human Teeth. *Journal of Dental Research*, 7:33–53.

[10] Butler, P. 1941. A Theory of the Evolution of Mammalian Molar Teeth. *American Journal of Science*, 239:421–450.

[11] Simpson, G. 1961. Evolution of Mesozoic Mammals. In *The Evolution of Lower and Non-Specialized Mammals*, vol. 2:57–95. Brussels: Paleis der Academien-Hertogsstraar.

[12] Vandebroek, G. 1961. The Comparative Anatomy of the Teeth of Lower and Non-Specialized Mammals. *Ibid.*, vol. 2:215–320.

[13] Cope, E. 1874. On the Homologies and Origin of the Types of Molar Teeth of Mammalia Educabilia. *Journal of the Academy of Natural Sciences*. Philadelphia, Volume 8.

[14] Osborn, H. 1888. The Evolution of Mammalian Molars to and from the Tritubercular Type. *American Naturalist*, 21:1067ff.

[15] Gregory, W. 1934. A Half Century of Trituberculy. *Proceedings of American Philosophical Society*, 73:169ff.

stem-reptiles and originated in the latter part of the Carboniferous period about 250 million years ago. One of these early groups, the *Captorhinomorph Cotylosaurs*, gave rise to those reptiles called *Synapsids* who dominated life on earth until the end of the Triassic when the ruling reptiles took over. There were at least two major radiations of the Synapsids, one occurring in the late Carboniferous among the *Pelycosaurs* and the other among the *Therapsids* in middle Permian times. The essential features of these two radiations are presented in Figure 56. It can be seen from this outline, which represents the most recent thinking of Romer on the subject, that the key groups leading from Cotylosaurs to early Mammals are the *Sphenacodontia* among the Pelycosaurs and the *Theriodontia* among the Therapsids. The teeth of a typical captorhinomorph Cotylo-

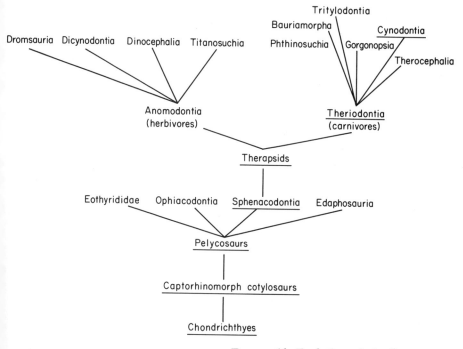

FIGURE 56. *Evolution of the Reptiles and Early Mammals*

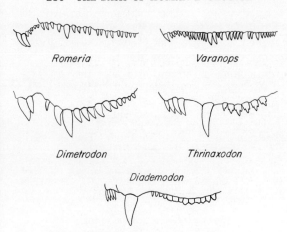

Romeria   *Varanops*

Dimetrodon   *Thrinaxodon*

Diademodon

FIGURE 57. *The Dentitions of Reptiles and Mammal-like Reptiles*

saur, *Romeria*, an early (*Varanops*) and a later (*Dimetrodon*)
Sphenacodont, and certain Cynodonts (*Thrinaxodon and Diademodon*) carnivorous mammal-like reptiles of the Theriodont
group, are shown in Figure 57.

As can be seen, the teeth of Cotylosaurs and Pelycosaurs
always consist of a single cone or cusp. In the former they are
spaced rather far apart; in the latter they are side by side in
the dental arch. Within the same animal the teeth show great
variations in size. Instead of being diphyodont, as are Mammals, the Pelycosaurs are polyphyodont; their teeth are continually being replaced as soon as they are shed. The replacement is
not, however, haphazard as was once believed, but is very
orderly, proceeding from back to front in alternate segments of
odd and even teeth. The result is that the Pelycosaur always had
functional segments of the dental arch present in both jaws and
on each side. (For an ingenious explanation of this phenomenon
see Edmund, 1960.)[16]

In the Therapsids we see the beginnings of heterodontia.
Among the Cynodonts the typical dental formula is:

[16] Edmund, G. 1960. Tooth Replacement Phenomena in the Lower
Vertebrates. *Contributions, Royal Ontario Museum, Life Sciences Division,* 52:1–190.

$$\frac{4 - 1 - 4 - 10}{3(4) - 1 - 4 - 10}$$

It is perhaps premature to call the first four cheek teeth "premolars" but they appear less advanced and smaller than the more posterior teeth. The incisors are well differentiated, the uppers curving inwards and the lowers being somewhat procumbent. The canines, both upper and lower, are long, stocky, and curved to the rear like sabers. There are prominent gaps between the canines and the incisors and premolars in the upper jaw and between the canines and premolars in the lower jaw. The molars have become elongated mesiodistally and compressed bucco-lingually and bear two small extra cusps, one in front and one behind the central cusp. This condition, in which three cusps appear in a mesiodistal axis, is known as *tricono-dontia*. Of the two accessory cusps there is some slight evidence that the posterior one was the earliest to appear. Triconodont molars are shearing rather than piercing teeth. In *Diademodon* and *Thrinaxodon* additional innovations are to be noted. The molars show a tendency to expand, the upper molars lingually, and the lower molars buccally, with the appearance of additional cusps on the expanded portions of the crown. At this stage the molars begin to assume grinding rather than shearing functions.

Presumably from various groups of cynodont Therapsids in Cretaceous times there radiated the many types of Mammals, of which three descendant subclasses survive: the Prototheria (monotremes), the Metatheria (marsupials), and the Eutheria (placentals). The immediate ancestor of both marsupials and Mammals is thought to have been the primitive *Pantotheria*, fossils of which have been found in North America, Europe, and Africa from middle and upper Jurassic horizons. Other early mammalian stocks were also present in the latter half of the Mesozoic, including *Triconodonta*, *Multituberculata*, and *Symmetrodonta*. The relationships between members of these groups and their phylogenetic positions are even more debatable than is Synapsid evolution and taxonomy. The earliest known pantotherian, *Amphitherium*, comes from the middle Jurassic of England. Its lower dentition has the formula: $4 - 1 - 4 \ (7\text{–}9)$. The incisors are small and slightly procumbent. The canine is long, double rooted, and also somewhat procumbent with little or no diastema between it and the other teeth. The premolars increase in size from front to back. They are single cusp teeth but are elongated mesiodistally by the posterior projection of the base of the crown which curves upward distally to form a sort of posterior cusplet. Encircling the lingual portion of the base of the crown is an enamel ridge or neck known as the cingulum. The molars are all of equal size and similar in morphology. They represent the most primitive type of *tuberculosectorial* pattern (Fig. 58). The anterior and larger portion of the crown, known as the trigonid, bears three cusps. The largest and apparently the oldest phylogenetically is the protoconid (mesiolingual cusp). The other two cusps, paraconid and metaconid, are situated on the lingual side of the crown, the former being most mesial. Projecting from the distal margin of the trigonid is a small heel or *talonid* bearing a small cusp, the entoconid (or perhaps hypoconid). The talonid is the sectorial, the trigonid the tubercular part of the crown, according to the nomenclature first introduced by Cope. Later Pantotherians show the same tuberculo-sectorial type of molar with some variations in the relative size, number, and disposition of the cusps.

Subsequent evolution of the molars toward the type found in modern Primates and Man involved the following steps. In the lower molars the paraconid became gradually reduced in size and finally disappeared. The metaconid moved forward to a position lingual to the protoconid, so that the trigonid bore only two cusps. The talonid increased in size and in number of cusps so that ultimately it bore three cusps (entoconid, hypoconid,

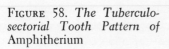

FIGURE 58. *The Tuberculosectorial Tooth Pattern of* Amphitherium

Paramomys maturus　　　　　　　　*Tetonius homunculus*

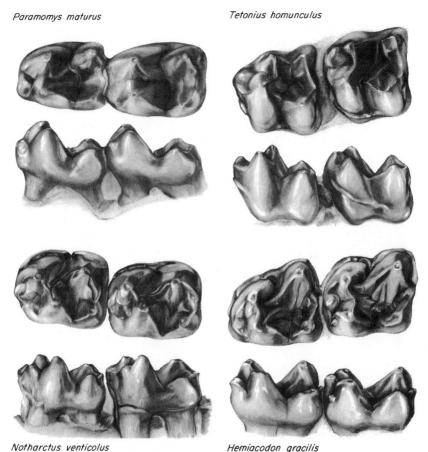

Notharctus venticolus　　　　　*Hemiacodon gracilis*

FIGURE 59. *The Molars of Fossil Tarsiers and Lemurs*

and hypoconulid). At first the talonid basin was lower than the trigonid basin and its cusps smaller, as in primitive Eocene tarsiers and lemurs (Fig. 59). Later, in the Miocene apes, the talonid attained the height and dimensions of the trigonid and the talonid cusps became equal in size. Since the Miocene there have been only minor changes in the molars of apes and Man. Essentially they have remained 4 – 6 cusped teeth, with only slightly projecting rounded cusp tips.

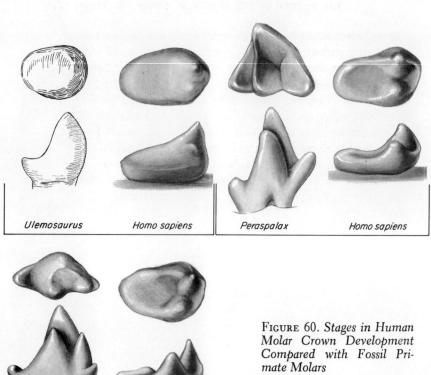

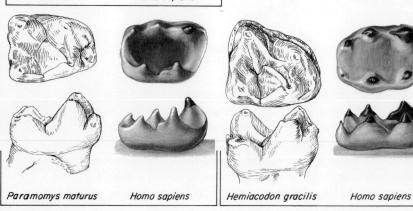

Figure 60. *Stages in Human Molar Crown Development Compared with Fossil Primate Molars*

Ulemosaurus   Homo sapiens

Peraspalax   Homo sapiens

Peramus   Homo sapiens

Paramomys maturus   Homo sapiens

Hemiacodon gracilis   Homo sapiens

If we select a few lower molar teeth to illustrate the basic evolutionary pathway toward modern human molars and place beside each a modern human tooth bud in a sequential stage of development (Fig. 60) the resultant analogy suggests very strongly that "ontogeny recapitulates phylogeny" in the dentition as in other characters of the body. Whether or not the ontogenetic sequence is a reliable criterion of the evolution of the human dentition is still a moot point. Nevertheless, there is disagreement in only one postulated stage of phylogenetic reconstruction—the triconodont condition. Man's molars, in their morphogenesis, do not pass through a triconodont stage.

THE FOSSIL EVIDENCE
FOR HUMAN EVOLUTION

Cried this pretentious Ape one day,
"I'm going to be a Man!
And stand upright, and hunt, and fight,
And conquer all I can."

        CHARLOTTE PERKINS GILMAN, *Similar Cases*

Introduction

Probably every city and town in the United States has its historical or pioneer society and museum—testimony to the great interest of our citizens in the early days of our country. The number of local archaeological societies and collections reflects a similar fascination with the prehistoric past when the White Man had not yet arrived. Each summer throngs of people visit those national parks and monuments where the ruins of pre-Columbian pueblos, villages, temples, burial grounds, and "forts" are carefully preserved and sometimes restored. In North and South America these vestiges of the cultures of early Man go back only a few thousand years at most, since there is every indication that Man himself did not enter these continents until about 20 or 30 thousand years ago. The earliest remains of such men clearly prove that he was not different in appearance from modern Man; in fact he was indubitably a member of the species *Homo sapiens.*

Here in the United States we are denied the great thrill of finding or viewing the fossil remains of our ancient hominid ancestors. This is a privilege reserved for the inhabitants of Europe, Asia, Africa, and perhaps Australia, where the major

217

steps in primate evolution leading to Man took place. Scattered over these continents are the mountain caves, the river terraces, and the gravel deposits where our early Primate forerunners lie covered by the accumulation of stones and sand over the past hundreds of thousands of years. Hundreds of such fossils have already been found and many more will yet be unearthed. The circumstances of the discovery of each fossil hominid make fascinating reading and viewing one of them at first hand creates a feeling for the immensity of evolutionary time and the agelessness of life that no amount of reading by itself can impart. The "romance of evolution" is to be found in the search by Dubois for the "missing link" in Java, in the discovery of *Gigantopithecus* among the fossil teeth in a Hong Kong apothecary shop, in the disclosure of the fraudulent nature of the Piltdown Man, and in the paleontological verification of many of Weidenreich's interpretations of human evolution. I have long been fascinated by Hrdlicka's detailed accounts of the circumstances surrounding the discovery of such fossil men as *Pithecanthropus*, Rhodesian Man, and various Neanderthaloids in his book *The Skeletal Remains of Early Man*.[1] Published in 1930, it does not, of course, deal with the many significant finds that have since come to light. For this one must go to the original sources, some of which are to be found in the list of suggested readings for this Problem. These interesting aspects of human paleontology must be omitted here for lack of space, but the reader is assured of most absorbing reading if he pursues the subject.

In the previous Problem we compared the quadrupedal skeleton of a terrestrial Mammal with the bipedal skeleton of Man. We inferred that the most important single event in Primate evolution that made possible Man's emergence from a Primate stock was the attainment of erect posture. Certain necessary changes took place in the mammalian skeleton as a consequence of and in correlation with the gradual adoption of this posture, and we have called them primary effects. Subsequent changes were called secondary and tertiary effects. We could draw these hypotheses without reference to paleontological evidence. In-

[1] Hrdlicka, A. 1930. The Skeletal Remains of Early Man. *Smithsonian Miscellaneous Collections*, vol. 83.

deed, as early as 1924 Weidenreich had proposed that the peculiarly human shape of the skull was the result of adjustment to erect posture.[2] In a later paper (1947), less than a year before his death, Weidenreich emphasized that there were two "specializations" in human evolution, the first a "general bipedal specialization" and the second a "particular brain specialization."[3] Although both are morphologically distinguishable, "it is impossible," he said, "to say which one set in first. Apparently they proceeded hand in hand . . ." Nevertheless, he regarded the bipedal specialization as typical of modern Man whereas the trend toward brain specialization is found also among the other Primates, though not to the extent it reached in Man.

In searching for factors responsible for the enlargement of the brain among Primates, Weidenreich reached the following conclusions:

If the phylogenetic enlargement of the brain constitutes a genetic change of the type—which undoubtedly is the case—this change alone is sufficient to transform "automatically" the entire skull with all its peculiarities. Since the enlargement of the brain appears as the inducing cause of other morphological alterations, the question is justified as to which general factor may now be made responsible for this enlargement. It can be reasonably assumed that the adoption of the upright posture was accompanied by characteristic changes in structure and proportion of the trunk and all constituents of the lower extremity, particularly also in the static and dynamic conditions of the spine. The increasing deflection of the base of the human skull which appears as the result of the special curvature of the spine supplied the possibility of widening the brain case and thereby the space to house the enlarged brain. It is rather difficult, of course, to distinguish sharply in this instance between cause and effect because each individual part concerned acts upon the other. But the enlargement of the brain is certainly in some way connected with the adoption of the erect posture and the corresponding transformation of the entire skeleton.[4]

[2] Weidenreich, F. 1924. Die Sonderform des Menschenschädels als Anpassung an den aufrechten Gang. *Zeitschrift für Morphologie und Anthropologie*, 24:157–189.

[3] Weidenreich, F. 1947. The Trend of Human Evolution. *Evolution*, 1:1–23.

[4] Weidenreich, F. 1941. The Brain and Its Role in the Phylogenetic Transformation of the Human Skull. *Transactions of American Philosophical Society*, new series, 31:321–442.

Weidenreich had cautioned that any theory of the origin of modern Man "has to be based on paleontological facts and only on them." Unfortunately he died just a year before the facts that substantiated the main tenets of his theory were unearthed in South Africa in the form of the numerous fossils of the Australopithecinae.

The Australopithecinae

The first representative of the Australopithecinae was discovered in 1924 by Dart at Taungs in Bechuanaland. Since that time many more fossils of this type have been discovered in various sites within a 400-mile range in the Transvaal region of South Africa, stretching from Taungs in the southwest to Potgietersrust in the northeast and including the cities of Pretoria and Johannesburg. There is every prospect that additional discoveries of these primitive hominids will be made in the future. By 1947 the fossil remains consisted of parts of skulls, jaws, teeth, fragments of long bones, and natural endocranial casts. At this point the English anatomist and anthropologist Le Gros Clark summed up his observations on the limb fragments as follows:

> A survey of the anatomical details of the *Plesianthropus* femur, . . . will make it quite clear that the bone is constructed almost entirely on the human plan. In other words, it is mechanically adapted for standing, walking and running in the erect position. It thus offers a complete contrast to the femur of the modern anthropoid apes. In the latter, the hind-limbs may be used as temporary struts on which these animals can occasionally balance themselves in an approximately upright position, but they do not permit of progression in the fully erect position characteristic of man.[5]

Comparing the evidence from the long bones with the morphological characteristics of the skull, Le Gros Clark concluded that:

> . . . it now seems clear that in human phylogenesis the evolution of the limb structure proceeded at a more rapid rate than that of the brain, since in these fossils the limb skeleton approxi-

[5] Le Gros Clark, W. 1947. Observations on the Anatomy of the Fossil Australopithecinae. *Journal of Anatomy*, 81: 300–332.

mates to that of *Homo* while the brain volume hardly surpasses the simian level.[6]

In the same year that Le Gros Clark was writing this a new Australopithecine discovery was made at Sterkfontein. It included, among other parts of the skeleton, an almost complete left half (os coxae) of a bony pelvis. In the following year another pelvis was found at Makapansgat by Dart and in 1950 a third was unearthed at Swartkrans. All were found in undoubted association with typical Australopithecine skull and limb fragments. These pelvic bones provided clear proof that the Australopithecinae walked erect, as Le Gros Clark had concluded from his study of limb fragments, and substantiated Weidenreich's claim of the priority of upright posture in the evolution of Man's skeleton.

Although some minor features of the Australopithecine pelvis show slight differences from that of modern Man (the sacral articular surface is relatively much smaller), the essential characteristics of its structure are beyond question hominid. In Figure 61 we present outline drawings of the three Australopithecine pelvic bones together with those of Man, chimpanzee, gorilla, orang-utan, and rhesus. The features which differentiate them from the monkeys and apes are shared by the human pelvis. There is greater breadth to the ilium with a marked backward projection that results in a deeper sciatic notch. The ilium is widely curved and terminates at its upper anterior end in a well developed spine (the anterior superior iliac spine). There is also an anterior *inferior* iliac spine situated just above the hip socket (acetabulum) which is entirely lacking in the lower forms. This spine marks the site of origin of the *Rectus femoris*, a muscle which extends the lower leg upon the thigh and hence is of great importance in erect posture and bipedal gait. In the anthropoid apes and in rhesus this muscle arises from a roughened ridge extending upwards from the superior margin of the acetabulum, but it is not as well developed as in Man and leaves no prominent spine. In addition the strong iliofemoral ligament arises from the anterior inferior iliac spine and inserts along the intertrochanteric line, preventing overextension of the trunk upon

[6] *Ibid.*

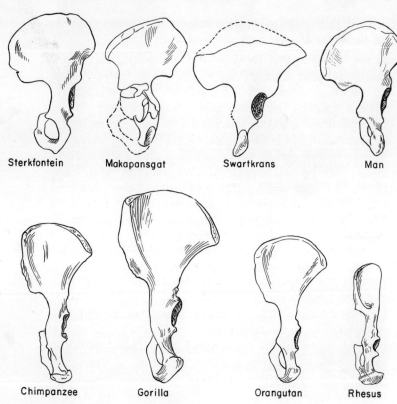

Sterkfontein   Makapansgat   Swartkrans   Man

Chimpanzee   Gorilla   Orangutan   Rhesus

FIGURE 61. *The Pelvic Bones of Man, Apes, Monkeys, and Australopithecines*

the thigh in the erect posture. In the apes and the lower Primates the height of the pelvis is very great relative to its breadth; in the Australopithecinae and Man the height is greatly reduced while the breadth is increased. The greater breadth and curvature of the ilium places the Gluteus maximus muscle in a position that is mechanically better adapted for extension of the thigh. Only in the lowest portion of the pelvic bone, the ischium, is the simian morphology retained (Straus, 1962).[7]

[7] Straus, W. 1962. Fossil Evidence of the Evolution of the Erect, Bipedal Posture. *Clinical Orthopaedics,* 25:9–19.

Although these early South Africans had come close to achieving the status of Man from the waist down, their upper limbs and skulls reveal a curious medley of hominid and ape-like characteristics. Before we examine them in some detail it might be wise to list the chief varieties of Australopithecinae as they are currently recognized. There are now 15 crania from the five Australopithecine sites, only three of which are relatively complete. The rest are in fragmentary condition. In addition, there are bits of jaws and facial skeletons which may represent as many as 100 individuals. Two of the sites, Taungs and Makapansgat, are at the extreme ends of the geographical range mentioned above; the other three, Kromdraai, Sterkfontein, and Swartkrans, are within a few miles of each other about 20 miles west of Johannesburg. There are many interesting problems presented not only by the skeletal anatomy but also by the variations in climate, faunal associations, and chronology of the five sites. The Australopithecinae may date from the late Pliocene or early Pleistocene but nothing more definite has been established at the present time. The five sites were not contemporaneous. For example, none of the fossil animals found at the Taungs site occurred at Sterkfontein. The former was occupied when the climate was very arid, the latter during very moist times. The cave at Kromdraai contained abundant remains of the horse, but none were found at Sterkfontein. The baboon, jackal, and dassie remains represent different species at these two sites. At Makapansgat the bones of animals not found in the other four deposits occurred: short-faced monkeys, a peculiar type of baboon, hipparion, chalicothere rhinoceros, elephant, giant giraffes, and a new type of pig. Study of these faunal associations has led to the tentative conclusion that the Makapansgat, Sterkfontein, and Taungs sites are the oldest, followed by Swartkrans and Kromdraai. Although the rather striking differentiation of faunal remains coming from the five sites would appear, at first glance, to suggest a wide separation in time among them, such is apparently not the case. Probably all the Australopithecinae lived in South Africa within a 200,000 year span of time. If this period is ultimately pinned down to the early Pleistocene then we are faced with a situation wherein very primitive hominids—the Australopithecinae—were contemporaries of morphologically more advanced forms—the Pithecanthropinae, who lived in Java and possibly even in South Africa (*Atlanthropus*). On the other hand this somewhat vexing problem would be removed if it is found that the Australopithecinae lived during the late Pliocene.

As nearly as can be estimated from the sizes of the limb bones and skulls, the Taungs, Sterkfontein, and Makapansgat individuals were of relatively small stature, probably less than five feet. Those of Swartkrans and Kromdraai were considerably taller and more robust, perhaps attaining the stature and weight of modern Man. Whether or not we are dealing with "samples of two successive populations" as Coon[8] seems to think, or with one considerably polytypic population, is a point that must await additional finds from South Africa.

The skulls themselves throw very interesting light on this early and crucial stage in human evolution. Lateral outlines of the skulls of *Plesianthropus transvaalensis* (Sterkfontein), *Paranthropus crassidens* (Swartkrans), *Australopithecus africanus* (Taungs), and *Paranthropus robustus* (Kromdraai) are presented in Figure 62 together with those of modern Man, *Proconsul africanus* (a Miocene anthropoid from East Africa), chimpanzee, and gorilla. Let us first examine these Australopithecine skulls in the light of the hypothesis advanced in the last Problem. In the many secondary and tertiary features of the skull are the Australopithecinae in an intermediate morphological position between early Primate quadrupeds and modern Man? In terms of brain size the maximum range, based on various estimations from reconstructions, is from 435 to 700 cc. In modern Man the maximum limits of normal brain size are 1050 cc. and 2000 cc. In this respect the Australopithecinae are not unlike anthropoid apes whose brain size falls into the 350–750 cc. range.[9]

The facial skeleton of Australopithecines projects forward (facial prognathism) but not nearly to the extent that occurs in *Proconsul* or even modern anthropoid apes. On the other hand they exhibit far more prognathism than *Homo sapiens*. A convenient measure of the degree of prognathism is obtained by the

[8] Coon, C. 1962. *The Origin of Races*. New York: Alfred A. Knopf, Inc.

[9] Schultz, A. 1962. Die Schädelkapazität männlicher Gorillas und Ihr Höchstwert. *Anthropologischer Anzeiger*, 25:197–203.

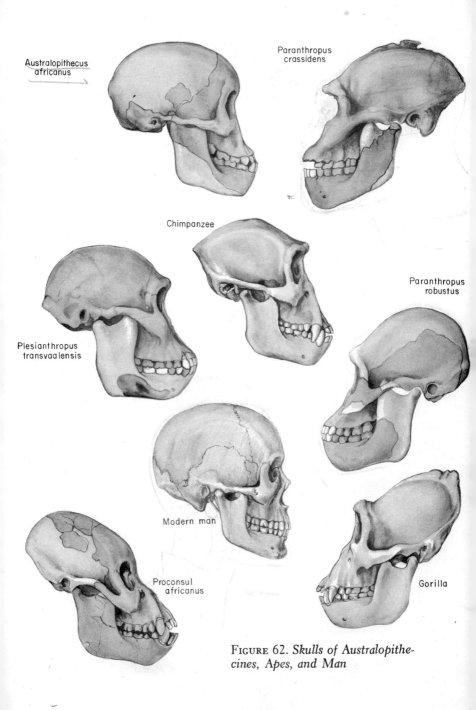

Australopithecus
africanus

Paranthropus
crassidens

Chimpanzee

Paranthropus
robustus

Plesianthropus
transvaalensis

Modern man

Proconsul
africanus

Gorilla

FIGURE 62. *Skulls of Australopithecines, Apes, and Man*

ratio of two dimensions, one from the anterior border of the foramen magnum (basion) to the root of the nose (nasion) and the other from basion to the most forward part of the bone between the two upper central incisors (prosthion). The relationship of the latter to the former gives an "index of prognathism." In some of the forms illustrated in Figure 65 approximate values for these indices are as follows:

Proconsul	1.70	Homo sapiens	1.00
Plesianthropus	1.40	Paranthropus robustus	1.36
Paranthropus crassidens	1.47	Primitive insectivore	1.53

It is apparent that the Australopithecinae are quite close to the prognathic condition of primitive Insectivores and considerably removed from the orthognathism of Man.

The brow ridges (supra-orbital eminence) are massive, not unlike those in chimpanzee and gorilla, but in the details of their architecture they are remarkably close to Man. Instead of a straight bar-like projection over the orbits they are rounded to follow the contour of the upper margins of the orbits and are somewhat depressed over the nasal region. There are several interpretations of the functional significance of the brow ridges. Some feel that they are correlated with the size of the jaws and act as a sort of buttress to reinforce the facial skeleton against the forces of the muscles of mastication. Others (Moss and Young, 1960)[10] claim that the position of the orbit relative to the frontal lobes of the brain is the determinant factor in brow-ridge size. If the orbit underlies the brain, as in Man, the portion of the frontal bone functionally related to the orbit does not need to project forward in order to enclose the orbit, but in such forms as the gorilla where the orbit lies well in front of the cerebral mass, the frontal bone is carried forward with the growth of the orbital contents and results in a prominent bony ridge. In terms of the latter interpretation the brow ridges of the Australopithecinae must be regarded as more primitive than modern

[10] Moss, M. and Young, R. 1960. A Functional Approach to Craniology. *American Journal of Physical Anthropology*, 18:281–290.

in the evolutionary road toward Man. The evolutionary interpretation of this trait is clearly dependent upon our understanding of its functional role in the growth and development of the head. It is undoubtedly a tertiary effect—a concomitant of other anatomical and physiological characters acting as a functional matrix or complex.

Compared with gorilla, chimpanzee, *Proconsul,* and a primitive. Insectivore, the Australopithecinae show a more prominent development of the forepart of the skull, an indication of the increase in size of the frontal lobes of the brain. The nasal bones are aligned in the same plane, as in all other Primates except Man. This results in the absence of a nasal bridge. The zygomatic arch is exceedingly broad and flaring in two of the *Paranthropus crassidens* skulls, indicating huge temporal muscles like those in anthropoid apes. This is confirmed by the presence of a sagittal crest running along the top of the skull in the midline to which the temporal muscles attach on each side. Similar crests are found in male gorillas and chimpanzees. On the other hand, the *Plesianthropus* skull lacks such a crest and shows a zygomatic development similar to Man.

The position of the foramen magnum, bounded on its lateral margins by the occipital condyles which articulate with the top of the vertebral column, is indicative of the degree to which the head is balanced upon the column in the upright posture although recently Biegert (1957) has suggested that its location may be more closely related to brain development than to posture.[11] As such it is a secondary effect. In primitive Insectivores and Mammals it is located at the back of the skull and is oriented backward and slightly downward. In modern Man the foramen magnum is situated almost in the center of the base of the skull and looks downward and slightly forward. In the Australopithecinae it is located about halfway between the center and posterior end of the skull and faces downward and slightly backward. In this respect it is roughly intermediate in the evolutionary progression toward the human condition. The position of the foramen magnum is correlated with the development of the nuchal crest, as was indicated in the previous Prob-

[11] Biegert, J. 1957. Formwandel des Primatenschädels. *Morphologisches Jahrbuch,* 98:77–199.

lem. In the Australopithecinae this crest is more strongly developed than in Man but is far less prominent than is found in the quadrupedal Mammal. The mastoid processes are distinct, but less prominent than in modern Man.

There are many other morphological aspects of the skull which might be considered, but discussions of these are to be found in great detail in numerous papers and monographs by Broom, Robinson, Dart, Le Gros Clark, Abel, Gregory, and others. The evidence of the skull, limb bones, and pelvis indicate very emphatically that each had undergone different rates of evolutionary development. In posture and gait the Australopithecinae had almost reached the status of mankind. In brain size they had a long way to go, but they had already departed significantly from the brain size of their Insectivore ancestors. The skull presents a medley of advanced, primitive, and intermediate characteristics. The snout is still prognathous but is considerably reduced in its protrusion. Supraorbital ridges and nuchal crests are prominent but not as much as in the anthropoid apes. The skull is rounder than in quadrupeds and its attachment to the vetebral column is more forward on the base. It is in the dentition, however, that the Australopithecinae have achieved hominid status.

The dental arch of the Australopithecinae is parabolic as in Man. The canines do not project beyond the level of the rest of the teeth, nor is there any diastema in either upper or lower jaw. In addition there is evidence of a more powerful development of the *Lateral Pterygoid* muscle which is responsible for lateral movements of the jaw. Wear facets occur on the tips of the canines rather than on the sides as in animals with projecting and interlocking canine teeth. The Australopithecine molars, both in the primary and permanent dentitions, are strongly "molarized," that is, bear a full complement of well developed cusps. The upper molars generally bear four cusps, the lower five. The lower first premolar is a bicuspid, with the lingual cusp smaller than the buccal. In general there is little difference in tooth size between the sexes. While the expert can quickly identify any of the teeth as belonging to Man or one of the anthropoid apes, it is only with difficulty that he could distinguish between those of Man and of the Australopithecinae.

The mandibles, unlike the dentition, reveal a more primitive character and can be easily distinguished from those of modern Man (see Fig. 62). Numerous mandibles have been recovered from the Australopithecine sites, including those of infants, adolescents, and adults. A considerable variation is exhibited both between age groups and between sites. Nevertheless a general description may be attempted. The body of the mandible is short and robust. The ascending portion (ramus) is relatively narrow, high, and slender. There is no chin. The body varies widely in thickness, from 20 mm. in an *Australopithecus prometheus* adult female to 35.6 mm. in the large *Paranthropus crassidens* male. This combination of short, thick body and tall, slender, and thin ramus is a distinguishing feature of the Australopithecine mandibles among those of other fossil hominids.

We have tried, somewhat unsuccessfully, to avoid extensive comparison between the Australopithecinae and the anthropoid apes. There is a long tradition in back of this practice. It is based upon the custom of comparing each new hominoid fossil find with the living anthropoid apes and with Man to determine which it most resembles. In the case of the Australopithecine and all the more recent hominid fossils this is unnecessary. It is far more likely that they are ancestors of Man rather than of the modern apes. It is true that the chronology of these primitive hominids is in some doubt; nevertheless we have nothing that is definitely on the phyletic line of Man which is either more primitive morphologically or chronologically earlier.

The Australopithecinae finds raise a number of problems, the answers to which are not yet forthcoming. Did they fashion artifacts? Did they have some form of articulate speech? Could they build fires? Did they consist of numerous distinct, non-interbreeding populations or were they one species with various partially isolated subspecies? And finally, did they pass their genes on to succeeding generations in an unbroken line leading to modern Man, or did they become extinct by catastrophe? There are still some students of human evolution who regard the Australopithecinae and most other fossil hominids as phylogenetic "dead ends," that is, as abortive attempts on the part of Nature to develop *Homo sapiens*. These questions we shall try to cope with in a later Problem. At present we must focus upon the morphology of fossil Man and leave the interpretation until "the evidence is in."

A somewhat more advanced morphological development is represented by two groups of fossil hominids from Java and China, the so-called Pithecanthropinae. These finds are more reliably dated and pertain to the middle Pleistocene, although some of the Java material may be as early as lower Pleistocene (see Table 1). The names of scholars most frequently associated with the Java finds are Dubois, von Koenigswald, and Weidenreich; for the Chinese material they are Pei, Black, and Weidenreich. Almost all other students of human evolution have, however, examined and interpreted these hominid remains. There is complete agreement that *Pithecanthropus* and *Sinanthropus* walked in the upright position. Indeed, bipedal locomotion had been achieved by the Australopithecinae and need not be considered as a useful criterion of phylogenetic status in the other hominids that will be discussed, since all of them were essentially like modern Man in this respect.

Hominid Fossils from Java

The four *Pithecanthropus* skulls are incomplete. Skulls I and II are represented only by calvaria (skull caps), skull III by parts of the parietal and occipital bones, and skull IV, *Pithecanthropus robustus*, by the posterior half of the skull plus parts of the maxilla and palate (Fig. 63). In addition there is a skull cap of a child, given the name *Homo modjokertensis*, which comes from a lower Pleistocene horizon. There were also fragments of four mandibles, labeled A, B, C, and D. The fourth, mandible D, has been given the name *Meganthropus paleojavanicus*.

There have been innumerable attempts at reconstruction of the entire skull from these fragments, all of which have led to estimates of the brain size of the Pithecanthropinae. Weidenreich has calculated it to be 935 cc. for skull I, 775 cc. for skull II, and 900 cc. for skull IV.[12] Most other authorities agree that the mean brain size was well below 1000 cc., thus putting it be-

[12] Weidenreich, F. 1943. The Skull of Sinanthropus Pekinensis. *Palaeontologia Sinica*, new series D. No. 10. Chungking: Geological Survey of China.

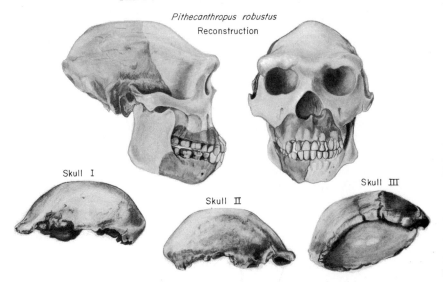

Pithecanthropus robustus
Reconstruction

Skull I

Skull II

Skull III

FIGURE 63. *The Skull of* Pithecanthropus robustus

low the lower limit for modern Man but significantly above the range of the Australopithecinae. Endocranial casts made from the various skull fragments have been studied in an effort to determine if the external convolutions of the *Pithecanthropus* brain resembled modern Man's and hence might furnish a clue to its intellectual capabilities. However, the markings on the internal surface of the skull do not accurately reproduce the external morphology of the brain, and these attempts have not led to reliable interpretations.

When viewed from above the *Pithecanthropus* skull shows deep postorbital constrictions, so that when placed on its occiput it looks very much like a Woodland Indian pot with flaring rim. This trait, typical also of the Australopithecine skulls, reflects the lack of development of the frontal and parietal lobes of the brain. All the skulls are *dolichocranic*, that is, are quite long relative to their greatest breadth. The opposite condition, *brachycrany*, is found only in recent human populations (see Figure 64 for a comparison of fossil and modern Man). From a lateral view the Java hominids exhibit heavy brow ridges,

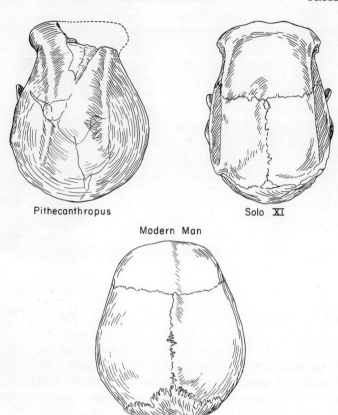

Pithecanthropus   Solo XI

Modern Man

FIGURE 64. *Superior View of the Skulls of Solo, Pithecanthropus, and Modern Man*

prominent nuchal crests, a sharply sloping occiput below the nuchal crest, and a very low forehead. The face is less prognathous than in the Australopithecinae but not as prognathous as in modern Man. Alveolar prognathism is particularly marked, that is the part of the bony maxilla between the nasal aperture and the upper teeth protrudes to a great degree. The temporal ridges are more pronounced than in modern Man and the zygomatic arches are considerably more flared outward, indicating a massive temporal and masseteric musculature. The ridges, however, are located well down on the sides of the skull unlike those in *Paranthropus crassidens* or the male chimpanzee and gorilla which meet in the midline on top of the skull to form a distinct crest. The mastoid processes show a range of development from slight to moderate, those on skull IV being rather heavy, but they do not attain the size of those of modern Man.

In frontal view the skull is keel-shaped, tapering to a midline prominence and sloping gradually toward the sides so that the greatest breadth of the skull occurs just above the mastoid process. In modern Man the greatest breadth is found high on the parietal bones. The facial skeleton must have been very broad, with wide orbits and nasal base. The nasal aperture was also of great width and its lower margin is rounded and trough-shaped, much as in anthropoid apes. The mandible lacks a chin and slopes backward rather sharply from its alveolar border. It is extremely thick. Mandible D, in particular, is thicker than that of any Primate, fossil or modern. Measured at various sites it ranges from 25.5 mm. to 28 mm., compared to a mean value of 13 mm. for modern Man and 24 mm. for the gorilla. The two premolars and first molar found in the mandible D fragment are also very large, exceeding in size those of any known hominid, past or present. From the large dimensions of mandible D Weidenreich considered it to belong to a "genuine giant form of early man."[13] Skull IV tells us something about the *Pithecanthropus* palate, which is very broad and lacks any of the rugosity which characterizes the modern human palate. In addition it is seen that the second upper molar is larger than either the first or third.

Hominid Fossils from China

Next to the South African Australopithecine sites the deposits at Choukoutien near Peking, China, were the most prolific source of early hominid fossils. From 1927 to 1937 the fragmentary skulls of 14 individuals were found, plus 14 mandibles and 148 isolated teeth. Probably 100 individuals in all were represented. Only five of the skulls are fairly complete calvaria with parts of the basilar portion still intact. Fragments of the facial bones be-

[13] *Ibid.*

longing to five or six of the skulls were also found. A few limb bones and fragments of mandibles complete the collection. *Sinanthropus pekinensis* was a middle Pleistocene contemporary of *Pithecanthropus*, the two populations being part of the so-called Sinomalayan fauna that occupied China, the Philippine Islands, Formosa, and Java during this period. Apparently there were land bridges that made these migrations possible. Included among the animals were *Stegodon, Elephas*, orang-utan, gibbon, tapir, and the Malayan bear.

The *Sinanthropus* skulls are quite similar to those of Java, differing only in certain morphological details. From above they present the same Woodland pot shape with marked postorbital constrictions. From frontal and lateral views there is more bulging of the parietal bones and a more prominent forehead than in *Pithecanthropus*, but the supraorbital ridges and nuchal crests are just as rugged. The mastoid processes are small and, as in the Java hominids, mark the area of greatest breadth of the skull. The fossa where the head of the mandibular condyle articulates with the skull is of unusual depth. The nasal aperture is very broad, as are the nasal bones. There is marked alveolar prognathism. The mandible is very rugged with a flaring of the posterior portion (gonial angle) where the Masseter muscle inserts. There is no chin, but the slope of the mandible in the midline is not as pronounced as in *Pithecanthropus*. The temporal ridges are prominent and the internal surface of the coronoid process of the mandible where the Temporal muscle attaches is very rugged.

Weidenreich has pointed out certain features of the *Sinanthropus* skulls which he considers to be characteristic of modern Mongoloid peoples. These include:

1. A midline crest or keel extending front to back on top of the skull.
2. The presence of separate "islands" of bone in the occipital region of the skull (called *Ossa Incae*).
3. Broad nasal bones (this may have been true also of *Pithecanthropus* but there is no direct evidence).
4. The face is very broad with the zygomatic bone facing forward rather than somewhat laterally, as in *Australopithecus* and modern Whites and Negroes.
5. The occurrence of shovel-shaped incisors (but von Koenigs-

wald has claimed that this trait is even more prominently present in isolated teeth from the *Pithecanthropus* sites).

6. Platymeria of the femur (a condition wherein the transverse diameter of the femoral shaft is greater than the antero-posterior diameter).

7. Marked flaring of the gonial region of the mandible.

For these reasons he concluded that *Sinanthropus* was an ancestor of *Homo sapiens* with particular phylogenetic ties to the Mongoloid race.[14]

There is overlap between the ranges of brain size between *Sinanthropus* and *Pithecanthropus*, with the former estimated at 850 to 1300 cc. In this trait the Choukoutien population bridges the gap between *Pithecanthropus* and modern Man. Out of 74 main characters examined by Weidenreich in both the China and Java fossils, only four are not held in common by the two groups.

The dentition of *Sinanthropus* was reported in a separate monograph by Weidenreich. In general it exhibits a strong *Homo sapiens* character. There are no diastemata; all the teeth are on the same occlusal level; the dental arch is typically parabolic; and the cusp patterns of the premolars and molars are arranged as in modern Man. In a few particulars the teeth are somewhat different: the lingual and buccal cusps of the premolar tend to be of equal size; the occlusal surfaces of the molar crowns show more wrinkling than is found in either modern or fossil man; and there is marked swelling around the bases of the crown (basal cingulum).

Solo Man from Java

Although Weidenreich felt there was a reasonable case for arguing the *Sinanthropus* ancestry of the modern Mongoloids, he was much more positive about the phylogenetic role of the Pithecanthropinae as the progenitors of the modern Australian aborigines. The evidence for this comes from additional fossils found in Java and in Australia. In geography, chronology and in morphological characteristics, these early hominids appear to offer some support for his hypothesis. The fossil hominids in-

[14] Weidenreich, F. 1951. Morphology of Solo Man. *Anthropology Papers*, American Museum of Natural History, Vol. 43, Part 3.

volved in this story are: *Homo soloensis* (Solo Man) and Wad-
jak Man of Java, and the Cohuna and Talgai skulls of Australia.
Our attention will be confined, at this point, to the Solo material.

From 1931 to 1933 Ter Haar and Oppenoorth unearthed
portions of 11 skulls from a terrace of the Solo River near
Ngandong in Java. The excavations were unusual in light of the
fact that as far as hominid remains were concerned only skull
caps and two tibiae (lower leg bones) were found scattered
throughout the deposit, but parts of whole skeletons of deer,
water buffalo, pigs, rhinoceros, hippopotamus, *Stegodon*, *Elephas*, panther, and tiger. The deer and pig are of types peculiar
to the Ngandong horizon which is dated as upper Pleistocene.
The description of the hominid material was undertaken by
Weidenreich, whose death occurred before its completion. The
unfinished manuscript was published posthumously under the
title "Morphology of Solo Man."

All of the skulls lack the facial skeleton but several have intact
occipital and basal regions. The cranial capacity (approximate
brain size) ranges from 1150 to 1300 cc., which is well within the
lower limits of the modern range and shows less variation than
the earlier *Sinanthropus* and *Pithecanthropus* skulls. The postorbital constriction is present but less strongly marked than was
the case in the China and Java material. The supraorbital ridges,
though massive, are less protrusive; this is correlated with the
slightly more prominent development of the frontal area. The
nuchal crest is still very rugged and the occipital bone below it
slants sharply forward and downward. When viewed from below
the ratio of the length of the projected skull outline in back of
the foramen magnum to the length in front is approximately
2:7; in modern Man this ratio is about 2:3 (see Fig. 65).
Thus the skull of Solo Man was not as well balanced upon the
vertebral column as is that of modern Man. The foramen magnum is still positioned in a downward and slightly backward
position. Variation is evidenced in the presence or absence of a
sagittal keeling effect and in the presence in at least one skull
(No. XI) of an os Incae. In some skulls the greatest breadth is
still at the base of the mastoid process, but in others (skulls V,

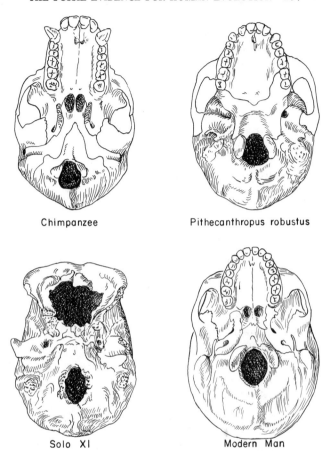

Chimpanzee

Pithecanthropus robustus

Solo XI

Modern Man

FIGURE 65. *Inferior View of the Skulls of Chimpanzee,* Pithecanthropus robustus, *Solo, and Modern Man*

X, and I) there is definitely more parietal expansion or bulging, a condition not found in the *Sinanthropus-Pithecanthropus* skulls. The temporal crest is distinctly observable but seems slightly lower on the sides of the vault. The mastoid processes are quite weakly developed. In general the Solo population seems slightly less primitive and closer morphologically to modern Man than either the *Pithecanthropus* or *Sinanthropus* groups. Unfortunately no teeth or mandibles were found, so that Solo Man must remain faceless until more complete material should be discovered.

Rhodesian Man

At Broken Hill in Northern Rhodesia in 1921 a miner found an almost complete skull in a cave located in a zinc and lead mine. It has been dated by means of analysis of lead and zinc content of the bone and archaeological associations as Upper Pleistocene, hence roughly a contemporary of the Javanese Solo Man. Rhodesian Man (Fig. 66) had an estimated brain size of 1325 cc. The entire skull cap could easily fit into the Solo Man population in its morphological characteristics. The facial skeleton affords us our first direct observation of this entire complex in early hominids. There is marked facial prognathism but the alveolar portion is not as protrusive as in *Pithecanthropus* or *Australopithecus*. The face is broad and high. There is a sharp anterior nasal spine, a feature lacking in apes and also apparently in the other early hominids, but the lower margin of the nasal aperture is still troughed rather than sharp as in modern Man. The zygomatic arches are neither as rugged nor as flaring as in the other types we have considered. The brow ridges are ex-

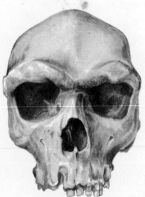
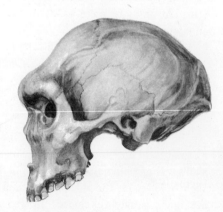

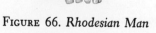

FIGURE 66. *Rhodesian Man*

tremely heavy but are arched over the orbits rather than extended straight across the midline. There is a slight convexity to the nasal bones to form a distinct nasal bridge. The palate is very broad and considerably larger in area than the modern palate. The mastoid process is relatively small. The foramen magnum is positioned farther forward in its relation to the total length of the skull, the ratio being about 1:2 compared with 2:7 in Solo Man. The left mastoid process is perforated on its anterior portion, indicating that Rhodesian Man suffered from mastoiditis resulting in an abscess which ultimately broke through the cortical bone at the base of the process. The teeth are considerably broken down, due to caries and wear, and there are evidences of periapical abscesses. Morphologically they cannot be distinguished from those of modern Man.

Other African Fossil Hominids

An almost identical type of skull cap (Fig. 67) was reconstructed from 27 fragments found by Singer and Jolly in 1953 near Hopefield, a village situated about 90 miles north of Capetown, South Africa, on Saldanha Bay. The hominid material was part of a huge deposit of animal bones and stone artifacts which date the finds quite reliably to the Upper Pleistocene. Carbon-14 dating places Saldanha Man and his culture at about 40,000 years ago, but other evidence points to an age of about 100,000 years. At any rate there seems to be agreement that it slightly antedates Rhodesian Man.

A third Rhodesian-like skull cap was discovered by Leakey in 1960 in the Olduvai Gorge southeast of Lake Victoria in Tanganyika. According to Coon,[15] who had only a photograph available, the calvaria is characterized by strongly developed supraorbital ridges, marked postorbital constriction, prominent nuchal crest, dolichocrany, and small mastoid processes. Associated with artifacts of the Chellean industry, it has been called the Chellean-3 skull. The age of the deposit (Bed II) where the skull was found has been estimated at 360,000 years by the Potassium-argon method of analysis. This would place Chellean-3 in the

[15] Coon, C. Op. cit.

FIGURE 67. *Saldanha Man*

middle Pleistocene and make him a contemporary of *Sinan-thropus* and the later Pithecanthropinae.

In the previous year (1959) Leakey and his associates had discovered even earlier hominid remains in Bed I of the Olduvai Gorge. They consisted of fragments of a child's skeleton together with scattered pieces of adult bones and, about five feet removed, a cranium, tibia, fibula, a few teeth, and fragments of a second cranium. The former are known as the Olduvai Child; the latter are given the name *Zinjanthropus*. Published accounts have appeared in the *Illustrated London News Nature* and *National Geographic*. Coon, who examined some of this material in 1961, concluded that "Zinjanthropus was an Australopithecine."[16] As to the Olduvai Child, he finds features which apparently link it to *Proconsul* as well as to the Australopithecinae but it is "at the same time both more dryopithecine and more human than any Australopithecine yet found." Recently, however, grave doubts have been cast upon the accuracy of the Potassium-argon dates assigned to the various beds of the Olduvai Gorge. Straus and Hunt (1962) state:

Because some of the Olduvai Gorge dates are inconsistent, some must be inaccurate; they may all be. Until further tests determine which materials give dependable dates, we do not know which dates are accurate. Until this is learned, the indicated ages must be taken *cum grano salis*. . . . The ages of *Zinjanthropus* and other hominid fossils from Olduvai Gorge thus are *sub judice*.[17]

[16] *Ibid*.
[17] Straus, W. and Hunt, C. 1962. Age of Zinjanthropus. *Science*, 136:293–295.

Clearly these interesting fossils cannot be integrated into the story of hominid evolution until more thorough study has been undertaken. They may be of early Pleistocene age and thus contemporaries of the Australopithecinae.

In 1954 and 1955 Arambourg found a large deposit of animal bones in a sandpit near Oran in Algeria.[18] Included in the faunal remains were a parietal bone, some isolated teeth, and three mandibles. The early Middle Pleistocene date was assigned on the basis of the type of fauna. Named *Atlanthropus* by Arambourg, the mandibles, of which number III is almost completely intact, are not much alike. Mandible III lacks a chin and has a very high ramus, with a deep mandibular notch. It is, next to *Meganthropus paleojavanicus*, the largest hominid mandible yet discovered. The coronoid process is much higher than the condyle. In mandible II there is a slight suggestion of a chin. Both mandibles I and II are considerably smaller than III. The occlusal surfaces of the premolars and molars bear an unusual number of wrinkles and there are traces of a cingulum around the bases of each tooth. *Atlanthropus* is almost certainly a Pithecanthropine.

Other African finds of hominid fossils are too fragmentary or too chronologically dubious to be dealt with in this account. Recently discovered fossils still await careful examination and publication. Brief descriptions of their nature, circumstances of discovery, and possible significance have been provided in Coon's *The Origin of Races*.

Early Pleistocene Man

At this point it might be wise to review what has been covered. In the early part of Pleistocene, perhaps as much as one million years ago, hominids who had attained upright posture existed in South Africa and Java. In certain other features, notably the dentition, they bore close resemblance to modern Man. In other respects they showed varying degrees of primitiveness. Their brains were small, well below the minimum normal limit for modern Man, and their skulls were unusually long relative

[18] Arambourg, C. 1955. A Recent Discovery in Human Paleontology: Atlanthropus of Ternifine (Algeria). *American Journal of Physical Anthropology*, new series, 13:191–202.

to their breadth. There were very heavy brow ridges, strongly developed nuchal crests, small mastoid processes, pronounced postorbital constrictions, low foreheads, rugged sites of attachment of the Temporal and Masseter muscles, flat nasal bones, broad faces, and a tendency toward a midline sagittal crest on the top. The skulls were poorly balanced on the vertebral columns, judging from the posterior location of the foramen magnum. The jaws, as well as the crania, were thick and heavy with complete absence of a chin. The faces were markedly prognathous, particularly in the alveolar region. The nasal apertures were broad, lacked an anterior nasal spine, and had guttered lower margins.

The Javanese hominids continue through the middle Pleistocene. In China a population closely related morphologically and chronologically existed in the region near present-day Peking. In Africa the Australopithecinae, who were apparently scattered throughout much of Tanganyika and Rhodesia, were succeeded by a larger-brained population, as represented by the Chellean-3 skull of Middle Pleistocene age.

The Upper Pleistocene in Java found a population with a brain size well within the modern normal range but in other cranial features they were only slightly advanced over the preceding *Pithecanthropus* population. In South Africa the Chellean-3 type continued into the Upper Pleistocene as Rhodesian and Saldanha Man. The differences between the South African and Javanese hominids of the Upper Pleistocene, as represented by cranial morphology, are of a very minor nature. They were less primitive than their early Pleistocene predecessors but their skulls could never be mistaken for those of modern Man. Reports of the two Upper Pleistocene finds come from China. One, found in Szechuan province in 1951 was described by Pei and Woo and called the "Tzeyang Paleolithic Man."[19] It apparently is within the range of *Homo sapiens* in cranial morphology. The other was discovered in Kwangsi province in a cave near Liukiang and reported by Woo in 1959. It too is modern in type, with certain Mongoloid characteristics.

[19] Pei, W. and Woo, J. 1957. Tzeyang Paleolithic Man. *Institute of Vertebrate Paleontology Memoirs*, No. 1.

Early European Hominids

Thus far we have discussed only African and Asiatic hominid fossils. What was happening in Europe that might throw light upon human evolution? To date there has been only one discovery of early Man of undoubted Lower Pleistocene age in this continent. The two finds that pertain to the Middle Pleistocene were made before 1936 and since that time nothing further has been uncovered. The famous *Heidelberg jaw,* found in the mauer beds of the River Neckar near Heidelberg in 1908, is dated by Zeuner to the Mindel Glaciation and given an age of 450,000 years. The mandible was completely intact with its full complement of teeth. It is very large, with an exceedingly wide ramus. It lacks a chin and has a very shallow notch between the condyle and the coronoid process. The teeth are entirely hominid, lacking a diastema and canine protrusion above the occlusal level. Heidelberg Man was thus a contemporary of the Australopithecinae in Africa and the first Pithecanthropinae of Java.

The two Middle Pleistocene fossils from Europe are the *Steinheim* and *Swanscombe* skulls. The former was found in 1933 in a gravel pit a few miles north of Stuttgart. Its faunal associations indicate an age of about 250,000 years, placing it in the second or Mindel-Riss Interglacial. Its brain size has been variously estimated from 1100 to 1175 cc. Its supraorbital ridges are large but not as heavy as those noted in previously discussed crania. The mastoid processes are small and the occiput is rounded rather than sharply inclined. The sides of the skull do not slant inward toward the top but are more or less parallel so that the greatest breadth is not at as low a level as in the Java or China hominids. The face is not strongly prognathous except in the alveolar portion. There is a pronounced depression at the root of the nose, as in modern Man, but only a slight nasal bridge. In general, the Steinheim skull is such an interesting combination of early and late hominid features that von Koenigswald has stated: ". . . by underplaying its Neanderthal characteristics, we can easily change it into *Homo sapiens*; by exaggerating these characteristics we can turn it into "extreme"

Neanderthal man. However, the *sapiens* characteristics . . . seem to be the more pronounced of the two."[20]

The Swanscombe skull is most unusual in several respects. It consists of three bones—an occipital and two parietals. The occipital bone was found in 1935 by a dentist named Marston in the gravels of the 100 foot terrace of the Thames River during the course of excavations in the Barnfield Pit at Swanscombe. In 1936 Marston found a left parietal bone as the excavations proceeded. Then, in 1955, a right parietal bone was found at the same site. All fitted perfectly together. Like Steinheim, the Swanscombe skull has been assigned to the Mindel-Riss Interglacial. Although the critical areas of the skull—frontal bone, face, and mandible—are missing, the morphology of the back, sides, and base is typical of *Homo sapiens*. Only the thickness of the bones suggests a primitive characteristic. The apparent discordant note sounded by the Swanscombe skull has led Le Gros Clark to the following precaution: ". . . this isolated discovery pointing to the existence of *H. sapiens* in Europe during the second interglacial period needs to be confirmed (just because it *is* an isolated discovery) by the accession of further, and more complete material."[21]

The Neanderthaloids of Europe

When we turn to the Upper Pleistocene period in Europe we are confronted with more fossil hominid material than the accumulated finds of Lower and Middle Pleistocene from Asia, Africa, and Europe. The term *Neanderthaloids* is given to these early Europeans after the site in the Neander gorge near Düsseldorf where in 1856 a skull and most of the bones of a skeleton were dug out of an old cave. Whereas at one time any primitive hominid skull found in Europe was apt to be termed Neanderthaloid, the term finally came to be used to designate only those skulls which displayed a certain complex of morpho-

[20] von Koenigswald, G. 1962. *The Evolution of Man.* Ann Arbor: University of Michigan Press.
[21] Le Gros Clark, W. 1955. *The Fossil Evidence for Human Evolution.* Chicago: University of Chicago Press.

logical characters. Neanderthaloids, in the morphological sense, have been found as far east as Central Asia and as far south as Israel and Iraq. All of them are of Third Interglacial or early Fourth (Würm) Glaciation age (see Table 1). Since the Third Interglacial period had a duration of 60,000 years it is probable that the Neanderthaloids were in Europe as early as 175,000 years ago and survived until about 90,000 years ago. After the first phase of the Würm Glaciation their remains are not found. Much stress has been placed upon the chronological division of the Neanderthaloids, those of the Interglacial phase being termed "Early" and those of the Würm Glaciation "Late." In addition, various students of this group have emphasized the morphological differences that distinguish the Early from the Late Neanderthaloids. There is general agreement that the *chronologically earlier* Neanderthaloids are *morphologically closer* to Homo sapiens. This somewhat paradoxical situation has lent itself to some rather interesting and sometimes bizarre interpretations on the part of human paleontologists. One theory holds that the Early Neanderthaloids evolved into the Classic Neanderthaloids in Europe whereupon the latter became extinct by one means or another. A second contends that the fate of both groups in Europe remains a mystery at the present time but that Neanderthaloids in Western or Central Asia evolved into modern Man. A third hypothesis would have the Early Neanderthaloids radiating into two branches, one leading to the Classic Neanderthaloids in Europe and the other into Homo sapiens in the Near East. One of the obstacles to the consideration of Europe as a site of evolution into modern Man is the fact that no fossil hominids "intermediate" between Neanderthaloids and Homo sapiens have been found there. The latter "suddenly" appear throughout Europe at the end of the Würm Glaciation.

Neanderthaloids are usually pictured as standing with knees slightly bent and shoulders thrust forward. Early studies of the original Neanderthal and La Chapelle aux Saints long bones had concluded that these early Europeans were unable to completely extend the tibia upon the femur. More recent examinations of these and other Neanderthaloid skeletons by Straus and Cave

(1957),[22] Arambourg (1955),[23] and Patte (1955),[24] have confirmed that the Neanderthaloids had completely erect posture.

The literature describing the various Neanderthaloid finds of Europe is most voluminous and no good purpose would be served by reviewing each of them here. We shall confine ourselves to a consideration of the main characteristics of each of the two groups as exemplified by a "type" specimen. For the Early Neanderthaloids the *Saccopastore* skulls may be considered as representative, although it is of the utmost importance to keep in mind that among both the Early and the Classic Neanderthaloids there is considerable variation. The *Circeo* skull may be regarded as the "type" Classic specimen.

The two Saccopastore skull fragments were found in a gravel pit near the Ponte Nomentano in Rome in 1929 and 1935 and were described by G. Sergi in a series of publications.[25] They were found with the bones of such Pleistocene Mammals as rhinoceros, hippopotamus, and elephant. Sergi judged Saccopastore I to be the skull of a female, age about 30 years, and Saccopastore II to be that of an adult male. The former is almost complete, lacking only the mandible and both zygomatic arches. The latter consists of the facial skeleton and the entire base of the skull. The Saccopastore people lived in caves at the base of hills overlooking the Tiber River valley toward the close of the Riss-Würm Interglacial.

In 1936 excavations at Saccopastore continued and near the site where the second skull was found a sealed cave was discovered. On the floor of this cave was a circle of stones on which lay a fairly complete skull surrounded by the bones of deer, oxen, horses, elephants, leopards, lions, and hyaenas. A mandible was also found, but it represented a second individual. The Circeo remains, as they are called, represent a population that lived about 70,000 years ago during the Würm Glaciation.

[22] Straus, W. and Cave, A. 1957. Pathology and posture of Neanderthal man. *Quarterly Review of Biology,* 32:348–363.

[23] Arambourg, C. 1955. Sur l'Attitude, en Station Verticale, des Néanderthaliens. *Comptes rendus des Séances de L'Académie des Sciences,* 239:804–806.

[24] Patte, E. 1955. *Les Néanderthaliens.* Paris: Masson et Cie.

[25] Sergi, S. 1948. The Palaeanthropi in Italy: the Fossil Men of Saccopastore and Circeo. *Yearbook of Physical Anthropology,* 4:57–65.

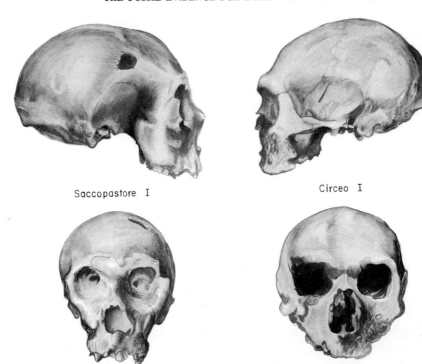

Saccopastore I

Circeo I

FIGURE 68. *The Saccopastore and Circeo Skulls*

Hence, in the same locality at what is now the city of Rome, we find a succession of Early and Classic Neanderthaloid populations. The Circeo fossils have been described by Blanc and Sergi.[26]

In Figure 68 are presented front and lateral drawings of the Saccopastore I and Circeo skulls. The cranial capacity of Saccopastore I is somewhat less than 1200 cc. The skull is relatively broad, bordering on brachycrany (round-headed). The supraorbital ridges are slight in front but toward the sides are more prominent resulting in a postorbital constriction that is less marked, however, than was observed in the skulls previously dis-

[26] Blanc, A. and Sergi, S. For papers on the Mt. Circeo fossil see references in Sergi, S., 1948, *Op. cit.*

cussed. The nuchal crest is well developed and the occiput below it is not as rounded as in modern Man. The mastoid processes are slight and there are distinct bulges in the parietal bone so that the maximum breadth of the skull occurs at a much higher level than in earlier hominid types. The nasal aperture is broad and its height is relatively low. The nasal root is broad with only a slight inclination of the nasal bones to form a low bridge. The forehead rises rather steeply and falls well within the range of modern Man. The face is only slightly prognathous and there is no alveolar protrusion. The orbits are high and rounded in Saccopastore I but are broad and more "primitive" appearing in Saccopastore II.

The Circeo skull is definitely long-headed, with a pronounced occipital "bun," a more rugged nuchal crest, and an infranuchal occipital region that slants sharply forward. The forehead is low and terminates anteriorly in a heavy supraorbital ridge. The sides of the skull slope inwards and upwards, much as we have observed in earlier forms, so that the greatest skull breadth is measured low on the temporal bone. The cranial capacity is about 1550 cc. Compared to the Saccopastore skulls the Circeo facial skeleton is broader and relatively shorter, with wider orbits and broader nasal bones. The position of the foramen magnum in both the Saccopastore and Circeo skulls is much the same, described by Sergi as indicating "that the head must have been held erect as it is in present-day man." The dental arch of the Circeo skull is U-shaped, according to Sergi, while that of Saccopastore is parabolic.

These are, in general, the basic differences in cranial morphology that appear to separate the Third Interglacial from Würm Glaciation Neanderthaloids. The reader will gain some insight into the nature of these differences as well as the range of variation exhibited by each group by study of Figures 69 and 70. In the former we have drawn in lateral outline the skulls of Early Neanderthaloids of Europe (*Ehringsdorf, Saccopastore*) and the Near East (*Galilee, Skhūl* V), and those of some Classic Neanderthaloids of Europe (*Gibraltar, La Chapelle, Spy*, and *Circeo*) and the Near East (*Tabūn* I). In the latter (Fig. 70) some of these skulls are drawn from a superior view.

One of the most important Neanderthaloid sites consisted of

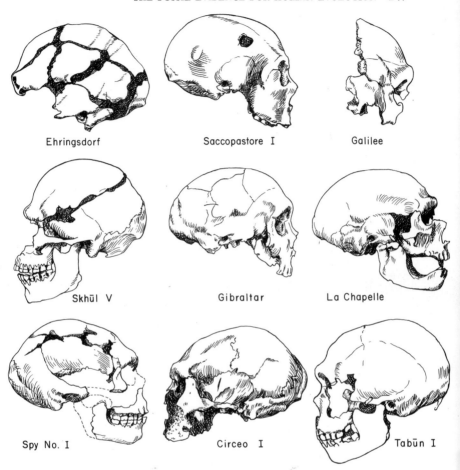

Ehringsdorf Saccopastore I Galilee

Skhūl V Gibraltar La Chapelle

Spy No. I Circeo I Tabūn I

FIGURE 69. *Lateral View of Neanderthaloid Skulls*

deposits in two caves on the western slope of Mount Carmel in Palestine, Mugharet es-Skhūl and Mugharet et-Tabūn. The *Skhūl* hominid material consisted of seven skulls ranging from a few fragments to a nearly complete specimen (*Skhūl* V). Including the rest of the skeleton there were the remains of at least ten individuals. The *Tabūn* cave contained the skeleton of an adult female with a badly crushed but almost complete skull and the

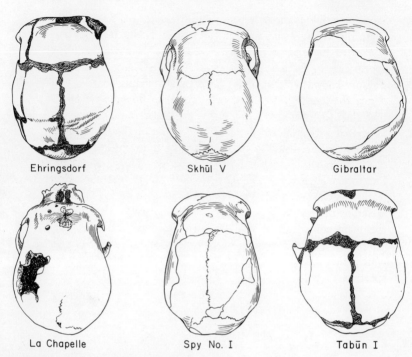

Ehringsdorf   Skhūl V   Gibraltar

La Chapelle   Spy No. I   Tabūn I

FIGURE 70. *Superior View of*
Neanderthaloid Skulls

mandible of an adult male. The artifacts found in association
with the two populations were practically identical except for
certain minor differences. On the basis of archaeological analysis by Garrod and faunal examination by Bate it was decided
that the *Tabūn* population slightly antedated the *Skhūl* people.
Both groups lived in the latter part of the Third Interglacial and
were roughly contemporaneous. A thorough description of the
Mount Carmel fossils is to be found in the monograph by Mc-
Cown and Keith.[27] These authorities considered the *Tabūn* to be
considerably more primitive in their total morphological configuration than the *Skhūl* inhabitants even though the time
differential is probably very slight. A very striking feature of the

[27] McCown, T. and Keith, A. 1939. *The Stone Age of Mount Car-*
mel. London: Oxford University Press. vol. 2.

Skhūl mandible is the presence of a distinct chin, a feature lacking in the *Tabūn I* mandible but present in *Tabūn II* (Fig. 71).

Toward the end of the Pleistocene *Homo sapiens* made his appearance in Europe, Africa, and Asia. In Europe over 160 sites are known which contain his skeletal remains. In Asia and Africa they are not so numerous, owing no doubt to the fact that there has been less systematic exploration and excavation associated with building and industry. Some of the best known of these sites are listed in the table on the following page.

Although all the material from these late Upper and Post-Pleistocene sites are of undoubted *Homo sapiens* morphological status, they show a wide variability such as is to be found in the skeletons of modern Man himself. Apparently the ancestors of the main subspecies of Man—Mongoloid, Caucasoid, and Negroid—had begun to establish themselves in the continents in which they now predominate—Asia, Europe, and Africa, respectively.

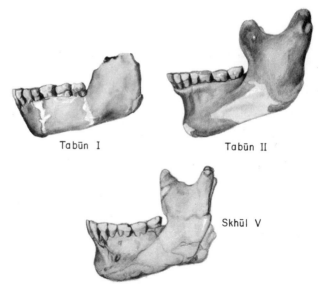

Tabūn I   Tabūn II

Skhūl V

FIGURE 71. *The Mandibles of the Mount Carmel Skulls*

Europe

Oberkassel	In Germany, near Bonn
Chancelade Combe Capelle Cro-Magnon La Madaleine	In France, near Dordogne
Brno Predmosti	In Czechoslovakia, Moravia
Nagy-Sap	In Hungary
Bichon	In Switzerland, Neufchatel
Grotte des Enfants	In Italy, Grimaldi
Kent's Cavern	In England, Devon

Africa

Mechta al-Arbi	In Algeria, Constantine
Florisbad	In Orange Free State
Elmenteita Gamble's Cave	In Kenya
Cape Flats	In Cape Province

Asia

Upper Cave of Choukoutien	In China, near Peking
Hotu Cave	In Iran, Mazandaran
Jebel Qafza Mugharet al-Wad	In Palestine

The Problem of Pre-Pleistocene Hominoid Evolution

We have now briefly surveyed the important fossil material that can be regarded as hominid and which must be phylogenetically interpreted in a way that is consistent with the basic principles of evolution as we attempt to reconstruct the pathway that led to modern Man. It should be noted that they all pertain to the last one million years, since the beginning of the Pleistocene, and that the earliest specimens—those of the South African

Australopithecinae—had by this time achieved upright posture and probably (as we shall see in the next Problem) some rudiments of culture. Obviously there must have been a considerable period of time leading up to this development and following the point where the hominid line first diverged from its Primate stem. There is increasing evidence that the ancestors of Man began to pursue their own evolutionary destiny some time during the Miocene Epoch, which began 26 million years ago. There is, then, a 25 million year period that we have not yet even touched upon during which Man developed from some kind of terrestrial or arboreal ape, no longer represented among the living Primates, to a terrestrial biped with a relatively expanded brain, man-like dentition, and a very simple cultural inventory. It may seem surprising that in this vast expanse of time not one fossil has been found which primatologists agree is a representative of the hominid line! True, there are fossil Primates discovered in Asia, Africa, and Europe which are dated to the Miocene and Pliocene Epochs, but scholars generally consider most of them to represent lines of adaptive radiation that became extinct. It seems most peculiar that we find the skeletal remains of the evolutionary failures and that of the very successful phyletic line leading to modern Man not a single fossil has been discovered from a 25 million year period.

Perhaps the elimination of all Miocene and Pliocene fossil apes from a position on Man's ancestral line arises from the point of view with which we approach our examination. The usual custom is to compare the dentition of the fossil suspect with those of the living apes or Man; if it appears to have closer morphological resemblance to one of the former it is promptly disqualified from ancestral hominid status. This strict adherence to an orthogenetic conception of the evolutionary development of the dentition is based upon the very reasonable observation that the teeth have, in all animals with dentitions, a number of most important functions. They would therefore have high adaptive value. Since dental morphology and function are closely interrelated, any fortuitous change in morphologic characters not consistent with the functional demands of the environment would seriously disturb the animal's state of adaptive equilibrium with the environment. This would be true up to the

point where a change in posture and locomotion, such as occurred in the hominid line, began to reduce the functional role
of the dentition. With the head held far from the ground, with
the upper extremities freed from locomotor responsibility, and
with an omnivorous diet requiring less and less tearing, piercing,
and grinding as methods of preparing food were devised, the
teeth rather rapidly lost their former functional importance.
They were no longer needed as weapons for fighting, catching,
or killing prey. Indeed, their position above the ground and in a
reduced snout made them ineffectual for these purposes. For
these reasons they were not primary targets of the selective forces
of a changing environment, nor even secondary targets. As we
have already pointed out, the hominid dentition is a tertiary
effect in evolution. The minor morphological changes it underwent as the early hominid line gradually assumed the fully erect
posture and complete bipedal locomotion need not have been a
direct response to environmental pressures in the same sense that
the limb bones, pelvis, vertebral column, and skull reflected
primary and secondary effects of this new postural orientation. It
may therefore be a misconception of the adaptive significance of
the dentition that has led us to deny rank in the hominid phylogeny to any of the Miocene and Pliocene fossils thus far discovered.

Parapithecus and Other Eocene Hominoids

Let us now turn our attention to some of these fossils. They
have been listed in Figure 11 (Problem II). Perhaps the earliest
representative of the Hominoidea is *Parapithecus*, the sole surviving part of which is a mandible discovered in a Lower Oligocene deposit in Egypt and first described by Schlosser in 1911
(Fig. 72). This animal was the size of a squirrel. Its dental

FIGURE 72.
Parapithecus

formula apparently was: 2 – 1 – 2 – 3 (but 1 – 1 – 3 – 3, according to Schlosser). The canine was short and spatulate rather than long and tusklike, and projected only slightly above the occlusal level of the rest of the teeth. It had a small basal cusp and a pronounced lingual cingulum. Straus, however, (as cited in Coon, 1962, p. 194) claims that the canine is really a premolar, thus making the dental formula 1 – 1 – 3 – 3, and considers *Parapithecus* to be an "aberrant tarsier" if a Primate at all. The premolars were bicuspid, the buccal being most prominent, and had lingual cinguli. The molars bore five cusps, two on the trigonid and three on the talonid. The paraconid, typical of prosimians, was absent. The cusps were low and rounded and the occlusal surfaces were unwrinkled. The molars each had an external cingulum at the base of the crown. The fifth cusp, the hypoconulid, was well developed and situated in the center of the distal portion of the tooth. The mandible itself converged from the two rami toward the center or symphysis, much as is found in tarsiers, and had a fairly short ramus with a coronoid process that extended high above the condyle—another primitive characteristic.

The possible affinities and phylogenetic position of *Parapithecus* have been much debated. Schlosser considered it as a representative of an ancient group of monkeys with relationships to the Eocene Anaptomorphs (infraorder Tarsiiformes) but not on the line leading to the Anthropoidea. Gregory, on the other hand, claimed that *Parapithecus* was "structurally ancestral to the whole anthropoid-man series."[28] Mollison felt that it was ancestral to the Cercopithecoids,[29] and Remane and Le Gros Clark considered it ancestral to the Hylobatidae (gibbons) and not on the line leading to the other hominoids.[30] In the latest study undertaken of this specimen Kälin holds to the hypothesis

[28] Gregory, W. 1951. *Evolution Emerging.* New York: The Macmillan Company. 2 volumes.

[29] Mollison, T. 1924. Zur Systematischen Stellung des Parapithecus Fraasi Schlosser. *Zeitschrift für Morphologie des Anthropoidengebisses,* 24:205–210.

[30] Remane, A. 1921. Beiträge zur Morphologie des Anthropoidengebisses. Archiv für Naturgeschichte. 87:1–179. Also, Le Gros Clark, W. 1949. New Palaeontological Evidence Bearing on the Evolution of the Hominoidea. *Quarterly Journal of the Geological Society,* 105:225–264.

that *Parapithecus* represents that transitional stage in Primate evolution when the forerunners of the superfamilies Cerco-pithecoidea and Hominoidea radiated out from a prosimian stem.[31] A diagrammatic representation of some of these theories is presented in Figure 73.

The fragments of Upper Eocene mandibles found in Burma, named *Pondaungia* and *Amphipithecus*, are hardly sufficient to warrant the formulation of any substantial judgment about their affinities. Both may represent transitional stages between the prosimians and the Anthropoidea. Le Gros Clark has suggested that the cercopithecoid and hominoid lines may have separated as early as the Upper Eocene, on the basis of his analysis of *Amphipithecus*.[32]

Oreopithecus

Since 1872 the Upper Miocene and Lower Pliocene lignite beds of Central Italy have yielded fossils of a Primate now known as *Oreopithecus bambolii*. Recently (1956–1958) Hürzeler found additional specimens, including an almost complete skeleton.[33] Study of this material has resulted in much controversy over the position of *Oreopithecus* in Primate phylogeny. Butler and Mills (1959)[34] undertook a comparative study of the dentition and concluded that:

1. *Oreopithecus* was not on the phyletic line of any of the living monkeys.
2. It had a number of primitive characters shared with tarsioids, such as

[31] Kälin, J. 1961. Sur *Parapithecus* Schlosser. In G. Vandebroek (editor), *The Evolution of Lower and Non-Specialized Mammals*, 193–200.

[32] Le Gros Clark, W. 1960. *The Antecedents of Man*. Chicago: Quadrangle Books.

[33] Hürzeler, J. 1956. *Oreopithecus*, un point de repère pour l'histoire de l'humanité à l'ère tertiare. *Cen. nat. Rech. Sci. Coll. int.*, 60:115–121. Also, 1958. *Oreopithecus bambolii* Gervais. A Preliminary Report. *Verhandlungen der Naturforschenden Gesellschaft*, 69:1–48.

[34] Butler, P. and Mills, J. 1959. A Contribution to the Odontology of *Oreopithecus*. *Bulletin, British Museum (Natural History)*, vol. 4. No. 1.

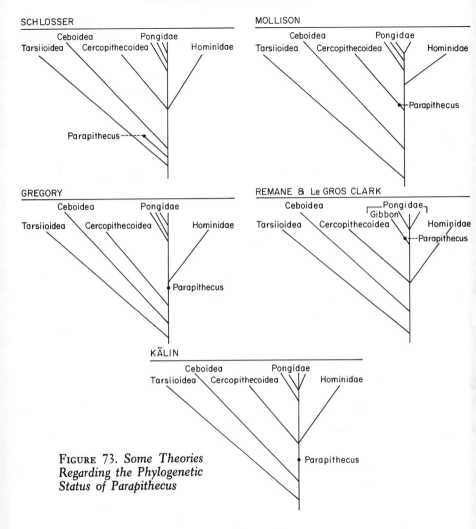

FIGURE 73. *Some Theories Regarding the Phylogenetic Status of Parapithecus*

a. high crown-relief
b. V-shaped protocone
c. well-developed conules
d. clearly differentiated cingulum
e. presence of a paraconid on the first lower molar
f. weakly developed hypoconulid on the lower first and second molars

3. It had a number of specialized dental characters which probably arose after *Oreopithecus* had diverged from the primitive
monkey stem.

4. "*Oreopithecus* is the terminal form of an independent phyletic line which extended back probably into the Oligocene."

In 1960 Schultz published his observations on the skelton of
Oreopithecus.[35] It would appear that *Oreopithecus* did not walk
erect—a possibility Straus (1957)[36] held open—but was an arboreal brachiator, about the size of a chimpanzee, but not a
particularly efficient brachiator. Schultz felt that it was a
hominoid rather than a cercopithecoid, but after eliminating it
from the hominid and gibbon line was uncertain as to its
affinities with the remaining Pongidae. It seems most probable
that *Oreopithecus* represents one of the hominoid groups that
migrated from East Africa in middle and late Miocene times
(see below). Its location and its peculiar combination of primitive and specialized characters would appear to eliminate it
from the direct line leading to Man.

The East African Miocene Hominoids

One of the two most prolific sites of fossil hominoids belonging
to the Miocene epoch is located in Kenya, East Africa. There
Hopwood in 1933, Leakey and MacInnes in 1943, and the
British-Kenya Miocene Expedition in 1947 found rich fossil-
bearing beds. They have been described by Le Gros Clark and
Leakey in a series of British Museum publications (*Fossil
Hominids of East Africa*, 1951).[37] The hominoid material is
divided into three groups or "genera": *Limnopithecus*, *Proconsul*, and *Sivapithecus*. *Limnopithecus* is almost certainly an early
member of the Hylobatinae on the basis of its dentition. Two
varieties of these gibbons were found, one as large as the mod-

[35] Schultz, A. 1960. Einige Beobachtungen und Masse am Skelett
von Oreopithecus. *Zeitschrift für Morphologie und Anthropologie*,
50:136–149.

[36] Straus, W. 1957. Oreopithecus bambolii. *Science*, 126: 345–346.

[37] Le Gros Clark, W. and Leakey, L. 1951. The Miocene Hominidae
of East Africa, *British Museum Fossil Mammals of Africa*, No. 1.

ern *Hylobates,* the other the size of the siamang gibbon. The discovery of these forms, according to Le Gros Clark, offers convincing support for the reconstruction of the evolutionary line of the gibbons leading from the Upper Eocene *Parapithecus* through an Oligocene fossil from Egypt named *Propliopithecus,* to the East African Miocene *Limnopithecus.* Other gibbon-like fossils, *Pliopithecus antiquus* from the Miocene of Europe, *Hylopithecus* from the Lower Pliocene of India, and *Pliopithecus posthumus* from the Middle Pliocene of Mongolia, may represent migrations of the apes from East Africa (see Fig. 74). One of the most interesting aspects of gibbon evolution has been brought out by a study of the limb bones of *Limnopithecus.* They are clearly not adapted to brachiation. Apparently this form of locomotion, which the modern gibbons practice with a

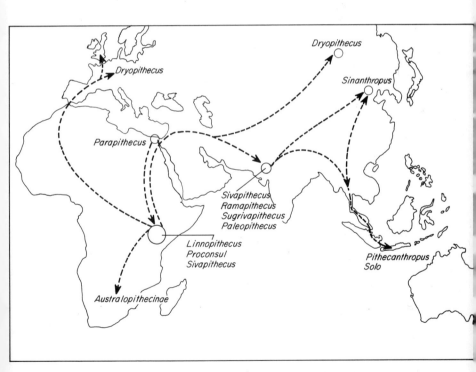

FIGURE 74. *Migration of Miocene Apes from East Africa*

high degree of speed and precision, was a late specialization in this line. The gibbons of the Miocene epoch were terrestrial quadrupeds, perhaps not to the same degree as the modern baboons but more so than the macaques.

Of more direct significance for hominid evolution were the East African Miocene apes known as *Proconsul,* represented by three "species": *P. africanus, P. nyanzae,* and *P. major.* The best preserved of these fossils was the skull of *Proconsul africanus* (Fig. 75). Evidently this group of apes was equal in size to the modern siamang gibbons. *Proconsul nyanzae* was as large as a chimpanzee and provided the greatest number of remains. The largest of the *Proconsul* apes was *P. major,* a form as large as the modern gorilla. In addition to fragments of mandibles and facial bones, there were a number of limb and foot bones found, not, however, in direct association with the cranial portions but probably belonging to *Proconsul nyanzae.*

The *Proconsul* finds are of great importance for a number of reasons. The bones of the limbs and feet tell us that these creatures, though equal in size to the modern apes, were not brachi-

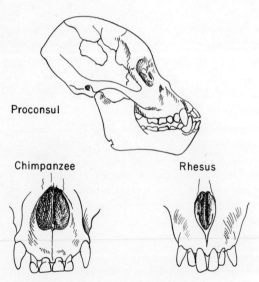

Proconsul

Chimpanzee   Rhesus

FIGURE 75. *The Nasal Aperture in Chimpanzee and Rhesus Monkey*

ators but were quadrupedal in locomotion. Perhaps they were equally at home on the ground and in the trees as are the Old World monkeys of today. This is precisely what we learned from the paleontological evidence in the gibbon line. From this point of view, *Proconsul* could well have been the basic form from which there radiated lines leading to brachiating forms (the Pongidae) and to erect bipedal forms (the Hominidae). The skull of *Proconsul*, in certain respects, fits in with this assessment of phylogenetic position. It presents no supraorbital ridge, has extremely pronounced facial prognathism, procumbent incisors, absence of a chin, and rather delicate, thin bone. The mandible, as seen from above, converges toward the symphysis. As might be expected with a form in which the snout lies well in front of the brain, the canines are long and tusk-like and there are marked diastemata on both sides of each canine in upper and lower jaws. The nasal aperture is unlike that of any of the Hominoidea in appearance; it converges downward to a point in the midline as in the Cercopithecoidea (see Fig. 75). The upper molars have marked internal cinguli and the lowers have prominent external cinguli—a characteristic, as we have seen, of the early prosimians. Thus *Proconsul* is an interesting combination of old and new characters. Since East Africa in the Lower Miocene was apparently the focal point of rapid radiation of these hominoid forms, it is quite possible that the *Proconsul* populations could have given rise to at least two diverging phyletic lines, one leading toward the Pongidae, the other to the Hominidae.

Included among the finds in Kenya were a fragment of a maxilla and some premolar and molar teeth. Their large size and distinctive morphology excluded them from being assigned to either *Limnopithecus* or *Proconsul*. Since they resemble material found in the Siwalik Hills of India, they were given the name *Sivapithecus africanus*.

The Hominoids of the Siwalik Hills in India

The other important source of hominoid fossils was the Siwalik Hills of India, where Pilgrim, Gregory, Lewis, and de Terra, in a series of expeditions (1910–1935), uncovered a number of fossil teeth and fragments of jaws from Lower and Middle Plio-cene horizons. Gregory and Lewis have recognized a number of genera among these fossil hominoids, each of which includes a number of species.[38] The various genera are the following:

Dryopithecus	Bramapithecus
Sivapithecus	Paleopithecus
Sugrivapithecus	Paleosimia
Ramapithecus	

Other Dryopithecine material has been found sporadically in Europe, where it comes from Middle Miocene and Lower Plio-cene deposits, and in China from Lower Pliocene beds in Yun-nan Province. All of this material has been given the family name *Dryopithecinae* after the original discovery in France in 1856 of a mandible called *Dryopithecus fontani*.

The Siwalik fossils have been the subject of much controversy since their discovery and subsequent descriptions. The focal point of the discussions has been aptly summarized by Le Gros Clark (1949):

. . . the question naturally arises whether any of them have any special significance for the evolutionary origin of the Ho-minidae. On the basis of inferences which may be drawn from comparative anatomy, and also from the palaeontological evi-dence of the early hominid types so far known, it is certainly reasonable to seek for the precursors of the human family among these fossil types, particularly since the great variability which they manifest in the size and proportions of their teeth make it fairly easy to envisage the modifications which might be necessary for the development of a dentition of the hominid type.[39]

Those who would take the Dryopithecinae off the direct line leading to Man apparently do so on the basis of the well-developed, projecting canines, claiming that this is a pongid specialization. To this argument Le Gros Clark replied:

[38] Gregory, W. and Lewis, G. 1938. Fossil Anthropoids of the Yale-Cambridge India Expedition of 1935. *Carnegie Institute of Washing-ton Publications*, No. 495.

[39] Le Gros Clark, W. 1949. New Palaeontological Evidence Bearing on the Evolution of the Hominoidea. *Quarterly Journal of the Geo-logical Society*, Vol. 105, Part 2.

Such a view . . . does not give due regard to the possibilities of retrogressive evolution and, indeed, the morphology of the canine tooth in modern Man (including its shape, its tendency to project beyond the level of the adjacent teeth, its relatively long root, and its late eruption) is strongly indicative of such a retrogression. The robust and projecting canine in primitive hominids such as *Pithecanthropus robustus* is also in harmony with the view that the canine of *Homo sapiens* is the result of a secondary reduction in size.[40]

I am entirely in agreement with the view that the so-called "specializations" of the Dryopithecine dentition need not eliminate these fossils from consideration as directly ancestral to Man. The term "retrogression," however, bears with it the same sort of connotations as does the word "orthogenesis" implying an orderly, straight-line evolution. As the teeth became gradually relieved of their adaptive functions they were likewise morphologically "liberated" from the direct pressure of selection, both positive and negative. This led to variability "with impunity." True, they would follow the reduction of the snout and become reduced in size (a consequence of selection) but the details of their crown morphology could have been of little adaptive significance. In hominid ancestors we could therefore expect an increased range of morphological variability together with a steady reduction in size.

On the basis of the available fossil evidence it would appear that East Africa in Miocene times was the center of rapid evolutionary development for certain cercopithecoid populations, giving off many lines of adaptive radiation. Some of these lines were ultimately to lead to the modern Pongidae and Hominidae. From East Africa in Upper Miocene times there was a series of emigrations to Europe and Asia. That of the gibbons is best documented, but other hominoids likewise emigrated, establishing themselves in the Siwalik Hills of India among other places. The gibbons failed to survive in Africa, but the hominoids established homelands in both Asia and Africa. In the Pliocene epoch there was a cauldron of evolutionary activity in India which may have given rise to several hominoid lines. In Africa we have clear evidence of hominids (Australopithecinae) appearing at the

[40] *Ibid.*

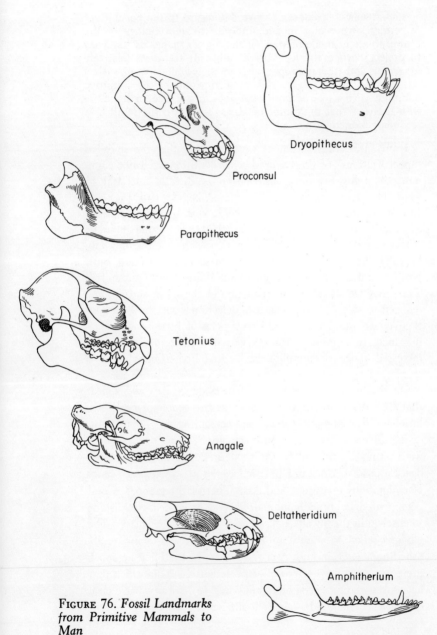

Dryopithecus

Proconsul

Parapithecus

Tetonius

Anagale

Deltatheridium

Amphitherium

FIGURE 76. *Fossil Landmarks from Primitive Mammals to Man*

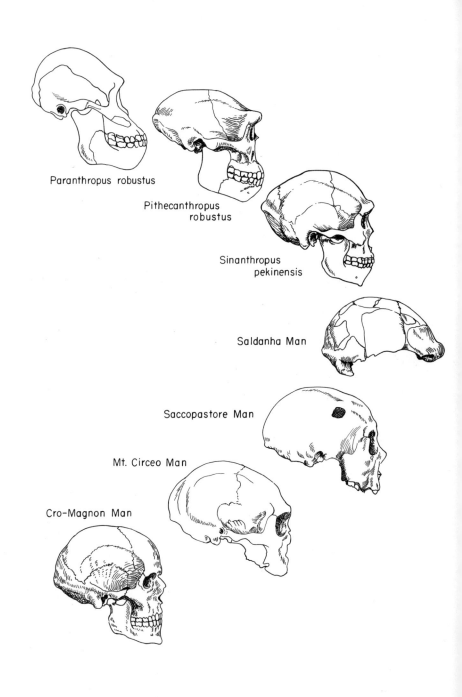

Paranthropus robustus

Pithecanthropus robustus

Sinanthropus pekinensis

Saldanha Man

Saccopastore Man

Mt. Circeo Man

Cro-Magnon Man

dawn of the Pleistocene, and in Southeast Asia the Pithe-canthropinae are found sometime in the Lower Pleistocene. Whether the latter originated from the Pliocene center in the Siwalik Hills and the former evolved in Africa is a moot point. There are too many gaps in the fossil record to allow us to do more than point out these possibilities.

In its bare outline, the morphological stages leading from a cercopithecoid base to the emergence of *Homo sapiens* can be traced with some assurance. The morphological details, the chronological timetable, and the geographical routes of migration and centers of development—these cannot be filled in without a great deal more evidence. At the rate at which new fossil discoveries are being made there can be every expectation that this will be forthcoming. In terms of the *morphological stages* leading to modern Man the fossils listed below (and drawn in Fig. 76) will provide a reasonable picture until the gaps in our record are narrowed by new finds:

> *Amphitherium*—a Middle Jurassic stem mammal (panto-therian)
> *Deltatheridium*—an Upper Cretaceous insectivore
> *Anagale*—a Lower Oligocene tree shrew
> *Tetonius*—a Lower Eocene tarsier
> *Parapithecus*—a Lower Oligocene hominoid
> *Proconsul*—a Lower Miocene hominoid
> *Dryopithecus*—a Middle Pliocene hominid
> *Paranthropus robustus*—an Upper Pliocene or Lower Pleisto-cene hominid
> *Pithecanthropus robustus*—a Lower Pleistocene hominid
> *Sinanthropus pekinesis*—a Middle Pleistocene hominid
> *Saldanha Man*—an Upper Pleistocene hominid
> *Saccopastore Man*—a Third Interglacial hominid
> *Mt. Circeo Man*—a Würm I Glaciation hominid
> *Cro-Magnon Man*—a Late Würm Glaciation *Homo sapiens*

THE DEVELOPMENT OF HUMAN CULTURE AND ITS BIOLOGICAL IMPLICATIONS

Looking to future generations, there is no cause to fear that the social instincts will grow weaker, and we may expect that virtuous habits will grow stronger, becoming perhaps fixed by inheritance.

CHARLES DARWIN, The Descent of Man

Introduction

With any other animal but Man we could now say that we have reached the point where a reconstruction and interpretation of its evolutionary pathway is in order. We have reviewed the subjects of geochronology and geographical distribution, the basis of evolutionary theory, the current status of genetics and its applications to and modifications of Darwinian evolution, the nature of the skeletal and dental evidence, and the important fossil material relating to Primate evolution. However, Man, though an animal, is a unique kind of animal. He alone in the Animal Kingdom has produced a culture, and the development of this culture has had a profound effect upon his biological evolution. No real understanding of human evolution is possible without taking into account the nature of Man's cultural evolution and the interactions between Man and his culture.

What is culture? Linton (*The Study of Man*, 1936) has defined it as "the total social heredity of mankind."[1] A distinction is thereby drawn between what man has inherited *biologically* (*via* genes) and what he has inherited *socially* (*via* writing, speech, and imitation). His blood groups, skin color, eye color, tooth morphology, and growth rates are more or less determined for him at the moment he begins life by virtue of the fact that certain of his parents' genetic material has been united in a single cell—the zygote; but his language, gestures, dietary habits, tools, habitation, cosmetic practices, religion, way of life, values and motivations, and theoretical and practical knowledge—these are acquired from the world around him after birth and long after the major portion of his biological growth and characteristics have been achieved. Culture is accretive; everything that has been acquired by all the preceding generations is available to the new generation which, in turn, adds something of its own to the total cultural inventory. The biological inheritance of one generation is limited, however, to the genetic content of the immediately preceding generation, and the genetic bequest to the following generation cannot be consciously added to or modified. Culture is limited to Man. Many other animals have been observed to learn from their environments and to modify their behavior accordingly. There are, however, very definite limits to the degree to which they can learn, retain, and initiate patterns of behavior. In effect, then, we can say that Man is not qualitatively different in this respect from other animals but quantitatively there is a tremendous gap between him and the rest of the Animal Kingdom.

As biologists we are frustrated by the fact that the story of evolution must be pieced together from fragments of only one system of the organism—the skeleton. Those whose interests are focused upon the reconstruction of Man's cultural evolution are beset by similar difficulties. The evidences of early Man's behavior consist of only a small number of products of that behavior—the stone, bone, and shell artifacts which have resisted

[1] Linton, R. 1936. *The Study of Man*. New York: D. Appleton-Century Company.

the forces of erosion over thousands of years. As the paleontologist calls upon his knowledge of the anatomy and physiology of living forms to aid him in interpreting the phylogenetic meaning of morphological differences in bones and teeth, so the archaeologist must rely upon the social scientist's understanding of the dynamics of modern society and culture in order to reconstruct the context in which these artifacts once were operating. There is much in archaeology that is unknown, and there is much that will never be known. Nevertheless some of the main features of cultural evolution can be reconstructed with a good deal of confidence. Here too there is a vast literature that has accumulated, including many attempts at presenting syntheses of cultural evolution as it progressed in different regions of the world. Here we can only touch upon some of those events which have particular pertinence to Man's biological evolution and to an understanding of how culture has interfered with the principles of evolution as they apply to Man.

The Earliest Evidence of Human Culture

We first glimpse Man as an upright creature with ape-like face and human-like dentition at the dawn of the Pleistocene epoch. It is precisely at this geological date that the archeologist has observed the first objects that can be classified as either made or used by "Man." From the oldest glacial gravels of England and France stones have been collected which some archaeologists insist bear scars that could only have been purposely inflicted upon them, presumably of course by Man. They have been called "eoliths" and comprise the only evidence of "human" culture during the first 500,000 years of the Pleistocene. Whether or not early hominids chipped off edges of these river pebbles to make them adaptable for use in hammering, cutting, or piercing, there can be little doubt that he picked up and used suitably shaped stones for one purpose or another.

The first definitely man-made artifacts come from the Middle Pleistocene of Europe, Asia, and Africa. Generally they are found in open gravel deposits and are not associated with either hominid bones or other signs of hominid presence or habitation. One important exception is the cave at Choukoutien where hundreds of stone artifacts were found associated with the remains of *Sinanthropus*. From the Middle Pleistocene on innumerable sites have yielded assemblages of stone tools. The story of cultural evolution during the Middle Pleistocene and up to the very end of the Würm Glaciation rests upon the analysis of the kinds of implements found in these sites. This is reflected in the name "Paleolithic Age" (Old Stone Age) given to this period, and in the divisions of this period into Lower, Middle, and Upper Paleolithic.

The Traditions in Stone Working

Stone artifacts have been classified in various ways, according to (1) shape, (2) technique used in manufacture, and (3) type of material. The techniques employed in fashioning stone implements are often referred to as "traditions." Three major traditions have been defined for the Lower and Middle Paleolithic: the *core*, the *flake*, and the *chopper-chopping tool*. The core tradition is characterized by the flaking off of opposite sides of a pebble and tapering it down toward one end so that the result is a pear-shaped implement with an untouched end for grasping and two flattened faces, sharp along their margins, for cutting edges. They have been called "bifaces," "hand-axes," and "coup-de-poing." Apparently these tools had multiple purposes. The flake tradition was more sophisticated in that a sharper and longer cutting edge was produced, sometimes by preparing a "striking-platform" at one end of the pebble and then striking it at such an angle that large flakes, often running the length of the stone, were detached. The remaining core could then be used for cutting or scraping. Both the core and flake traditions were widespread throughout Europe, Africa, and Southwestern Asia. Throughout the rest of Asia the third tradition was practiced in early Paleolithic times—the chopper-chopping tool. It produced heavy broad tools with adze-like cutting edges as well as implements with pointed ends. Such tools were found in the cave at Choukoutien.

At many sites tools of different traditions may appear in the same assemblage. Although many names have been assigned to these assemblages on the basis of typology, frequency dis-

tributions of the different kinds of tools, locality, and stratigraphy, they are of interest only to the specialist. The most
generally used terms for the stone cultures or "industries" of
Pleistocene Man, with their approximate chronology, are presented in Table 5.

TABLE 5. *Stone Cultures of Pleistocene Man*

	Glacial Chronology	Core Tradition	Flake Tradition	Mixed Core and Flake
Lower Paleolithic	Gunz-Mindel Inter-glaciation	Abbevillian (Chellean)	Clactonian	
Middle Paleolithic	Mindel Glaciation	Acheulean I	Levalloisian I	
	Glaciation	Acheulean II	Levalloisian II	
	Glaciation	Acheulean III	Levalloisian III	
	Glaciation	Acheulean IV	Levalloisian IV	
	Glaciation	Acheulean V	Levalloisian V	
	Glaciation	Acheulean VI	Levalloisian VI	
	End of Riss Glaciation	(Micoquian) Acheulean VII	(Tayacian) Levalloisian VII	
Upper Paleolithic	Riss-Würm Inter-glaciation to Würm II Glaciation	(Micoquian)	(Tayacian)	Mousterian Acheulian-Leval-loisian-Mous-terian Mixtures
	Würm II through Würm III	Blade Tradition		

We do not know where the fourth stone tradition had its
origin but it first comes to our attention in the Mt. Carmel
caves associated with the remains of *Skhūl* and *Tabūn* populations. Presumably it is as old as the Riss-Würm Interglaciation,
but only in the Near East. Blade tools did not make their appearance in other parts of the world until the end of the
Würm II Glaciation, about 50,000 years ago. Unlike the previous traditions, the blade tool is the flake that was detached

from the core. It requires careful preparation of the pebble, both on its sides and at one end where a striking-platform must be made. One quick blow on the platform detaches a flake whose length and shape has thus been predetermined. Wherever the tradition started (Garrod thinks it was in Central Asia or the Middle East),[2] the method spread westward from Palestine into Europe and Africa. This new methodology was adopted by the practitioners of the core and flake traditions in various ways and to varying degrees, with the result that sites throughout Europe and Africa during the last phases of the Würm Glaciation show various combinations of tool types and traditions. Some of the important cultures of this period in Europe, Western Asia, and North Africa are presented in Table 6.

TABLE 6.   *Late Paleolithic Cultures*

Approximate Dates	Europe	Western Asia	Egypt	Africa
50,000 years ago (Würm II)	Chatelperronian	Wad F	Khargan	
	Middle Aurignacian	Wad E Wad D		
25,000 years ago	Gravettian	Wad C (Atlitian)		Aterian
20,000 years ago	Solutrean			
	Magdalenian I			
15,000 years ago to 10,000 years ago	through		Sebilian I	
	Magdalenian VI		Sebilian II	Capsian
			Sebilian III	

SOURCE: R. Braidwood, *Prehistoric Man*, 2nd ed., 1951. Chicago: Chicago Natural History Museum Press.

Late Stone Age Cultural Achievement

Stone artifacts constitute almost the sole direct evidence of Man's cultural activities up until about 50,000 years ago. Then

[2] Garrod, D. 1938. The Upper Palaeolithic in the Light of Recent Discovery. *Proceedings of the Prehistorical Society of London*, new series, 4:1–26.

other kinds of materials and artifacts other than tools begin to appear in the various sites. Bone, horn, antler, shell, and teeth show unmistakable evidence of Man's handiwork. In addition to a wide assortment of tools such as harpoons, knives, projectile points, spear-throwers, and arrow-shaft straighteners, there were indications of Man's interest in aesthetic expression and religion. Incised decorations on bone and antler tools were beyond all utilitarian needs and took the form of animals, plants and simple geometric figures. To this period of Man's cultural development belong the famous cave paintings and stone sculptures of pregnant females. The former, found on the walls of caves in southern France and northern Spain, are too well known to require description here. It is argued, with a good deal of logic, that these paintings are manifestations of the beliefs of early Man in "compulsive" or "sympathetic" magic. The figures drawn are those of animals which provided food—bison, cattle, horses, bear, pig, deer, and rhinoceros. They are depicted in various stages of the hunt, often with arrows or spears embedded in their flanks. This, plus the fact that the paintings are located deep in the innermost recesses of the caves where the pictures could be viewed only with great difficulty, would indicate that the very act of showing a successful hunt was the important thing; it would "compel" the gods to grant a similar result in actual reality.

The small figurines of women, in which the extremities are almost entirely neglected while the breasts and swollen abdomens are overemphasized, may be examples of the same effort by early Man to control forces he could not understand or regulate. The depiction of pregnant females may have been thought to compel the supernatural powers to bless the group with plentiful offspring (or game). For this reason these sculptures are called "fertility" or "Venus" figures. In addition to weapons, figurines, and paintings, there were large numbers of utensils such as fishhooks, needles, pins, buttons, and toggle pins. The discovery of beads, combs, and pendants give ample evidence of prehistoric Man's interest in personal adornment.

A further indirect indication of early preoccupation with religion is the occurrence, for the first time, of the custom of interment of human remains. Some of the Neanderthaloids are found in intentional burials, their skeletons either flexed or extended, sometimes with bones of animals arranged nearby in a way suggesting the modern custom of some primitive peoples of providing the dead with food for the journey into the "other world."

In Africa the blade tradition was utilized to produce very small tools and weapons known as "microliths." This type of industry proved very popular, for the idea spread to all parts of Europe by the end of the Paleolithic Period.[3]

Who were the men who produced the various cultures which archaeologists have uncovered from Middle and Upper Pleistocene deposits? We know that *Sinanthropus* produced chopper-chopping tools and that the Ngandong deposits of Java in which Solo Man was found yielded a bone spearhead, some flaked tools, and many small stone "balls." In Europe we have only one site in which tools are associated with hominid remains as early as the Second Interglacial period—that at Swanscombe where stone axes and flakes of the Middle Acheulian type were found with the skull fragments. At the Fontechevade cave in France early Neanderthaloids produced a rather poor stone industry known as *Tayacian* in the flake tradition during the Third Interglacial period. In Asia the Mount Carmel population also manufactured *Tayacian* implements. In Europe there can be little reason to doubt that the Neanderthaloid peoples were responsible for the assemblages of tools that were blends of Acheulian, Levalloisian, and Mousterian industries. Whether they also produced the earlier Abbevillian, Clactonian, Acheulian, and Levalloisian sites of the First and Second Interglacial periods is very much a moot question.

In Africa, where much less archaeological work has been carried out, the prehistoric cultural picture is more obscure. The possibility that the Australopithecinae made tools and used fire has been argued strongly by Dart and his associates. They claim that the deposits in which the Makapansgat skull and pelvis were found show clear evidence of fire hearths and the use of the long bones of animals as tools—hence the name *Australopithecus*

---

[3] Braidwood, R. 1951. *Prehistoric Men*, 2nd ed. Chicago: Chicago Natural History Museum Press.

"*prometheus*."[4]   Others   (Oakley,   1954;[5]   Washburn,   1957;[6] Singer, 1956;[7] Straus, 1954[8] and 1957[9]) are just as vehement in their denial that the charred areas are anything but the result of fortuitous grass fires, and the fractured bones represent any more than the remains of accumulated repasts of hyaenas. The answer to the question of *Australopithecus'* fire- and tool-making abilities, while of great significance for human evolution, must be held in abeyance until more acceptable evidence is produced.

Saldanha Man of South Africa was a follower of the core tradition, making hand-axes, cleavers, choppers, and knives. He was probably the last producer of an Acheulian industry (Stellenbosch V) in South Africa. Rhodesian Man, on the other hand, was associated with a stone industry of the Levalloisian type. In terms of the European cultural periods, the Saldanha culture was Middle Paleolithic while that of Rhodesian Man was Upper Paleolithic. The stone artifacts found in Bed II of the Olduvai gorge along with the Chellean-3 skull were made in the core tradition as the name implies. In Bed I, which yielded the remains of *Zinjanthropus* and the Olduvai Child, a number of crude Chellean type tools were found, but not in direct association with the hominid bones.

We have certain clues to another facet of early Man's cultural behavior. Very likely he was a cannibal. This conclusion is based upon a number of circumstances surrounding the nature and disposition of his fossil remains. In the cave at Choukoutien the *Sinanthropus* skulls lack either the basal portion or the

[4] Dart, R. The Makapansgat Australopithecine Osteodontokeratic Culture. *Proceedings of the Third Pan-African Congress on Prehistory*, p. 161–171. Also, 1960. The Bone Tool-Manufacturing Ability of Australopithecus Prometheus. *American Anthropologist*, 62:134–143. See also Dart, 1958. Bone Tools and Porcupine Gnawing. *American Anthropologist*, 60:715–724.

[5] Oakley, K. 1954. Dating of the Australopithecines of Africa. *American Journal of Physical Anthropology*, 12:9–23.

[6] Washburn, S. 1957. Australopithecines: the Hunters of the Hunted? *American Anthropologist*, 59:612–614.

[7] Singer, R. 1956. The "Bone Tools" from Hopefield. *American Anthropologist*, 58:1127–1134.

[8] Straus, W. 1954. Fire and the Australopithecines. *Science*, 120:356–357.

[9] Straus, W. 1957. Hunters or Hunted? *Science*, 126:1108.

frontal area. As von Koegniswald[10] has pointed out, some of them when placed upside down on a table resemble bowls and may have been used as such, much as certain modern individuals use the tops of skulls found in excavations as ash trays. The fact that the skulls were found in a cave with a disproportionately small number of infracranial bones, suggests that *Sinanthropus* was sometimes decapitated by his fellow man and the head brought into the cave where it was fractured to get at the brain for food. This theory is reinforced by the later Solo finds in Java. Here skull caps and only two tibiae were found. There is unquestionable evidence, according to Weidenreich, of "violence to the living individuals."[11] The condition of the skulls and the fact that they were collected in one area with little sign of the remaining skeletons may indicate the proclivity of Solo Man for supplementing his diet with the brains of his neighbors. Cannibalism was obviously practiced by certain Upper Paleolithic men, and of course we are well aware that the practice has survived to the present day, primarily ritualistic rather than dietary, among certain primitive tribes.

Pleistocene Man as a Cultural and Social Animal

We can attempt, from the meager evidence of but a segment of the total social heredity of Man throughout the entire Paleolithic period, a reconstruction of the social and cultural nature of hominid existence. It must be assumed that at the very beginning of Man's cultural development he used his upper limbs, now freed from locomotor and weight-bearing responsibilities, to explore the properties of the natural objects around him. He would lift branches, twigs, stones, and animate objects to test their weights. He would throw such objects, noting the relation between shape, size, weight, and force of propulsion and the distance, line of flight, and final impact achieved. Qualities such as flexibility of different kinds of wood and hardness and friability of the several kinds of stone would gradually be impressed upon him by continual conscious and accidental experimentation. Probably the conscious working of bone, stone, and wood into

[10] von Koenigswald, G. 1951. In *Introduction* to Weidenreich, F. *Morphology of Solo Man.*

[11] Weidenreich, F. 1951. Morphology of Solo Man.

crude hand implements for cutting, scraping, and splitting occurred soon after the erect position and bipedal locomotion
became the habitual mode of posture and movement in our very
early ancestors. Let us reflect upon the profound effect of this
new terrestrial orientation. How could an animal with reduced
snout, no fangs, lowered olfactory acuity (Jahn and Wulff,
1950),[12] relatively slow bipedal gait, and no claws, survive?
How would he catch the fast-moving quadrupeds upon which he
must depend for meat? How could he avail himself of the fish
which abounded in the streams and lakes? And how would he
defend himself against the attacks of carnivores? Without a
thick coat of fur how would he keep warm and protect his newborn and young children against the damp cold weather?

The acquisition of upright posture rendered this Primate
hors de combat. He was shorn of the weapons, agility, speed,
acuity of senses, and bodily protection which had hitherto allowed him to compete successfully with other members of the
Animal Kingdom and to adapt to his total environment. No
longer could he withstand the direct forces of the natural environment. The equipment so carefully developed over hundreds
of millions of years of evolutionary selection was "suddenly"
stripped from him. As a result we might expect that he would
become helpless in the face of new adaptive requirements and
suffer the fate of catastrophic extinction common to all species
whose range of bodily characteristics left no individuals capable
of meeting new environmental demands.

Not being able to adapt *biologically* to the new environment
brought about by his erect posture and bipedal gait there was
but one course left to Man. He could adapt *culturally*, by erecting a barrier between himself and the selective forces of the
natural environment. His survival and continued successful
adaptation to the world around him became a contest between
his ability to build and continually heighten this barrier and the
effectiveness of negative selection on the part of nature. The
evolution of Man is not so much a story of biological adaptiveness but of cultural development. Other phyletic lines stand or

[12] Jahn, T. and Wulff, V. 1950. Chemoreception. Chapter 12 in
Comparative Animal Physiology. Philadelphia: W. B. Saunders Company.

fall upon their ability to *bend with* the winds of a constantly changing environment. The hominid line based its fate upon *diverting* these winds with a wall of culture.

It is idle to speculate about how Man first came to know, build, and use fire, but we can reasonably infer the effects fire had upon his existence. He could now keep warm in winter and afford his offspring the protection needed against damp and cold. Perhaps through repeated accidents, *à la* Charles Lamb's famous account of the origin of roast pork, he found that fire could render meat more palatable and more suitable for infant diet. A similar series of fortuitous events would teach him that burned flesh would resist decomposition better than raw, so that the food supply afforded by such large animals as mammoth and rhinoceros could be made to last for a longer period of time. The earliest evidences of fire hearths are found in caves where Man could find sustained refuge from the weather and deposit his family and meager possessions with some safety while he was absent on the hunt.

With the discovery that stone and wood objects thrown through the air could be effective extensions of his arms, Man's efficiency in capturing small animals was greatly increased. Likewise, a long branch held in the hand could extend the striking range of his arm. Learning that such a branch, when suitably trimmed and straightened, could be accurately thrown and when sharpened inflict fatal wounds upon animals was a momentous event in early hominid life. Eventually it was found that attaching a jagged piece of stone to the end of the stick would result in penetration of hides, even of elephants. I have seen stone projectile points imbedded in the bones of mammoths who once roamed the savannah lands in what is now southern Arizona. Gradual refinements in the methods of working flint and other stone materials resulted in longer, sharper, and more effective spear points.

Other stone implements such as scrapers, knives, hammers, and chisels, gave primitive Man increased ability to fashion wood and bone into a variety of utilitarian forms. He could now butcher and skin the animals he caught, using the furs and hides for garments and footwear. In addition to meat we can assume that he gathered such edible foods as nuts, berries, fruits, roots, insects, and mussels. Until the very end of the Pleistocene epoch Man's subsistence was by what is called "hunting and gathering." In Upper Paleolithic times his cultural inventory had increased to the point where he had developed the tools and skills for retrieving food from the streams and lakes, and the presence of large harpoon heads indicate that he ventured after larger sea animals. The deposits of this period show increasing numbers of bone utensils from which we know that he had advanced from simply throwing animal skins around his body to the actual cutting and sewing of hides for use as clothing.

It took at least 500,000 years for Man to progress from the very crudest non-artifactual elements of culture to the point where he had an extensive inventory of bone, stone, shell, and wood implements, fire, clothing, and some simple articles of self-adornment. Similar stages of cultural development could be observed at the beginning of the twentieth century among such primitive peoples as the Australian aborigines, the Pygmies of the Malay and Bataan peninsulas, the Seri Indians of the Gulf of California, and the Bushmen of the Kalahari Desert in South Africa. We are apt to look upon such primitive cultural levels as "barbaric," "savage," "simple." Yet, as I am writing this, the newspapers have announced that a group of our astronauts have been sent to the jungles of Panama to "learn" how to survive should their future space craft inadvertently land them in this type of environment. Our Neanderthaloid ancestors would have had a chuckle over our helplessness under these conditions.

The rate of cultural inventions approximates a geometric type of acceleration. Each innovation speeds up the invention of the next. At first this was so slow that thousands of years would pass before there was a perceptible change in the shape of a stone scraper or a slightly different method of chipping flint. With the introduction of the blade tradition into Europe from the Middle East, plus other techniques and ideas of which we have no records, there was a marked impetus in the rate of invention and within the relatively short span (50,000 years) of Upper Paleolithic times the culture of Man achieved a high degree of sophistication compared with that of the Lower and Middle Paleolithic. As we shall see, the acceleration in cultural accretion increased enormously in the Post-Glacial period until today additions to our knowledge and technology occur at a rate too rapid even to calculate—perhaps dozens every minute throughout the world. Whereas the cultural epochs of the Paleolithic are measured in tens of thousands of years, today we pass from one Age (Atomic) to another (Space) in a matter of a few years.

What little we can say about Pleistocene Man's social life is based mostly upon analogies drawn from the lives of primitive peoples observed only 50 or 100 years ago. Early Man, as a hunter and gatherer, lived in small groups of perhaps 50 to 100 individuals. These groups occupied definite territories over which they roamed in systematic seasonal migrations based primarily upon the availability of different kinds of food. In a limited area no food supply would support a large population, and with no means of preserving foodstuffs over long periods of time there was need for almost daily forages in quest of animals and edible plants. Such a life allowed little time from the relentless pursuit of food, and required strong physiques, acute senses, and a thorough knowledge of the terrain, the habits of the animals, and the locations of other sources of food. Habitations consisted of open camp sites with perhaps crude structures like the lean-to of the Sakai of the Malay Peninsula. In winter available caves and rock shelters were used. Floods, drought, storms, and insect infestations could mean sudden death for the entire band. Invasions of the territory by other bands could mean drastic reduction in the adult male hunters or capture of women and children leading to the ultimate extinction of the group. Friendly contacts with other bands could have led to a system of direct barter and the exchange and passing on of bits of new information or technical know-how. It could also lead to the *exchange of genes through interbreeding*. The wide range of similar tool assemblages throughout large areas of Europe, Africa, and Asia are mute but sufficient evidence that bands of Paleolithic men were not living a completely isolated existence.

Language

We have stated that culture is socially inherited, that it is transmitted from generation to generation not by genes but by word of mouth and imitation, thereby implying that the presence of culture connotes the ability to produce articulate speech. It is hard to imagine how early Paleolithic Man could have functioned and endured, generation after generation, if children could acquire the necessary skills and knowledge to survive only by imitation and empiricism. There have been many investigations in comparative anatomy to determine whether speech is a matter of organ morphology or brain development. Some claim that various oral, pharyngeal, and laryngeal changes had to take place before speech was possible (DuBrul, 1958),[13] while others maintain that the development of a "speech center" in the brain is the important factor that forms the "Rubicon" between articulate and nonarticulate animals. Perhaps the difficulty lies in differentiating between "speech sounds" and "speech." The hundreds of languages in the world today all constitute speech. But each employs different kinds of sounds to achieve articulate speech. In some languages certain organs of speech are emphasized in producing the sounds while in others the emphasis is shifted to different parts of the speech apparatus. In English, for example, we make very little use of sounds produced by vibrating the uvula or passing air through the nose. Instead we make much use of the lips, tongue, and dento-alveolar part of the mouth. In some African languages extensive use is made of clicking sounds as meaningful "phonemes." The vocal cords are alternately constricted and relaxed to produce laryngeal "stops" as in Northern Chinese and certain African languages. There are no organs that have the primary function of producing speech. Speech makes use of organs whose main job is breathing, swallowing, and mastication; these include: lungs, larynx, pharynx, the arytenoid cartilages, tongue, palate, nose, teeth, and lips. They are all present in many other animals besides Man, although in somewhat different forms and spatial relationships. Nevertheless they can be made to produce a wide assortment of sounds. Evidently the ability to assign meanings to these sounds and to arrive at mutual understandings regarding them is a property of the brain. In animals other than Man this property is lacking.

[13] DuBrul, E. 1958. *Evolution of the Speech Apparatus.* Springfield: C. C. Thomas.

The question then arises: At what point in hominid evolution did the Primate brain begin to acquire the ability to mediate the production of meaningful speech sounds, to retain the experiences of life in the "memory," to call upon such information stored away in the brain upon a given stimulus, and to originate stimuli which result in either overt or covert (thinking) behavior? We can meet this question only with pure speculation. It seems most likely that Man could not have produced, sustained, and augmented culture without the ability to transmit his experiences and knowledge to his offspring other than by example. This means speech. If he had articulate speech then he possessed a brain far advanced over those of other Primates as early as the beginning of the Pleistocene epoch. And yet, as you will recall, the brain size of Lower Pleistocene and many Middle Pleistocene hominids was well below the lowest limits of normal brain size in modern Man. Apparently, as far as size or volume of the brain is concerned, the distribution curves for *Homo sapiens* and, say, *Pithecanthropus* or *Sinanthropus* are significantly different, although there is considerable overlap. Yet *Sinanthropus* (surely) and *Pithecanthropus* (probably) produced culture and were presumably nonpathological individuals and functionally well-adapted to their environments. It would seem that, from the evolutionary point of view, brain size and brain quality (physiological functioning) were not correlative developments. The ability of the brain to permit speech and culture evidently was achieved long before its volume reached the status found in modern Man. Invariably the question arises in class: could a *Pithecanthropus* child, born and raised in the modern world, have developed into an efficient member of the society? My suggestion is that he would have fared no better or no worse than a randomly selected infant born of *Homo sapiens*.

A Theory of the Evolution of the Human Brain

If innate capacity and not sheer size is the critical point in the divergence of the hominid from the typical mammalian brain, how could this have come about? By applying some of the principles of evolution discussed in a previous Problem we should be able to construct a reasonable hypothesis. We may begin with the simple but fundamental fact of variation. Among the hominoid Primates who were beginning to acquire the habit of walking erect there was a range of variation in the biochemical properties of the brain making for greater or lesser facilitation of nerve impulses. The nature of conduction of nerve impulses is an extremely complicated subject and one which is currently under intense investigation. We can only briefly touch upon some important highlights, with full cognizance of the fact that in this field, too, there is much that cannot yet be explained.

The nerve cell is composed of a cell body and processes (neurites). The long single processes are *axons,* the numerous short ones are *dendrites.* The axons, or nerve fibers, serve to transmit impulses from one nerve cell to others, whereas dendrites receive impulses from other nerve cells. The point where the tiny branched ends of the various axons are intermeshed is called the *synapse.* Generally synapses are polarized; impulses can travel across them in one direction only. A resistance, however, is encountered by a single impulse when it reaches the synapse so that usually it will not be able to cross. It requires several impulses in fairly rapid succession to "break down" the synaptic resistance so that one impulse can jump the barrier to the adjoining axon. Once the synapse has been crossed, succeeding impulses follow with no difficulty as long as the interval between them is not too great. If a delay occurs between the first crossing and the arrival of the second impulse, the resistance at the synapse rises to its original level. The tendency for repeated impulses to lower the synaptic resistance until finally the passage of succeeding impulses is achieved is known as *facilitation.* Two important characteristics of facilitation should be noted. One is the fact that individual synapses have different levels of resistance. The other is the observation that continual passage of impulses over a particular synapse will permanently lower the resistance of that synapse. Synaptic transmission is a most complex phenomenon and several factors are involved, none of which are entirely understood. We shall concern ourselves only with one of these factors in order to suggest, in a simplified way, how the evolution of the peculiarly human brain *may have occurred.*

When an impulse arrives at a synapse one of the events that

is thought to occur is the liberation, at the ends of the fiber, of acetylcholine, a chemical which is closely associated with the passage of the impulse across the synapse. The larger the concentration of acetylcholine, the greater the facilitation. When an impulse fails to cross the synapse to the efferent fiber the enzyme cholinesterase rapidly hydrolyzes the acetylcholine, thus raising the resistance at the synapse. If the second impulse arrives before the acetylcholine has been completely hydrolyzed it may cause the production of sufficient acetylcholine to effect stimulation of the connecting nerve fiber. There is, then, a sort of balance between the rate of impulses and the concentration of acetylcholine. We know that the amounts of acetylcholine and cholinesterase in nerve tissue vary greatly in different mammals and invertebrates, in different parts of the nervous system, and between individuals of the same species. It may well be that specific concentrations of these substances in the brains of early hominoids were more conducive to greater facilitation and hence acquired high adaptive value. Positive selective forces may have acted rapidly to favor those erect walking hominoids whose synapses permitted easier passage to nerve impulses, thereby allowing them to establish more neuron pathways in the brain. In more practical terms this would mean that one such hominid could pick up and throw pebbles repeatedly without storing in his brain the various impressions of weight, force of throw, distance, and perspective upon which he might draw for future use and without which learning is impossible. Another might be able to retain such experiences in his "memory" and when the proper stimulus is repeated draw upon this stored information for the proper response.

Admittedly this is too simple and hypothetical an explanation of the mechanism of brain development, but basically it must be near the truth. There was nothing miraculous about the acquisition of human intelligence. The basis for selection may have been a combination of physical, chemical, and electro-chemical phenomena, but whatever may prove to be the case the same biological principles were involved that operated to transform the tiny *Cotylosaur* into the giant *Allosaurus*. In view of the great changes wrought by the adoption of erect posture—changes which rendered these hominoids physically unable to cope with their environment—the rate of evolution of the brain must have been extremely rapid. It would seem, then, that the trinity of qualities which above all separate Man from the rest of the Animal Kingdom—upright posture, culture, and speech— was present early in the Pleistocene, about one million years ago. The physical attainment of erect posture must have come first, perhaps by relatively small evolutionary steps over a long span of time. The secondary and tertiary effects brought about by this new posture created an imbalance between the organism and its environment. This disequilibrium placed a high premium upon the rapid development of the central nervous system which now became the crucial adaptive mechanism of the entire organism. The biochemical and electrophysical modifications of the brain made possible the development of culture and articulate speech, probably simultaneously.

From this point of view, the hominid skeletons of the Pleistocene that we have been discussing were those of Man. The Australopithecinae, it is true, have not been found in definite association with cultural material, but this negative evidence cannot be interpreted as positive indication that these early hominids were without culture. It seems to me that we can expect clear-cut evidence before very long that the Australopithecinae were culture-bearing, though in a most rudimentary way. The widely-scattered and profuse remains of this hominid throughout South Africa indicate his successful adaptation to the environment. Could this have happened if the erect, bipedal Australopithecinae were without language and culture?

The Changes in Evolutionary Forces Wrought by Early Cultural Development

In terms of Man's biological evolution, the history of culture during its Paleolithic phase represents the early stages in the erection of a barrier between Man and his natural environment. At first this barrier was very weak and consisted of but a few elements—fire, wooden clubs, caves, animal skins, and crude jagged river pebbles. Some of the selective forces of the natural environment—"the slings and arrows of outrageous fortune," so to speak —were thereby diverted from direct contact with Man. Cold weather, rain, and snow need no longer drive him away from his territory or exact a high toll of infant deaths. Similarly, armed with clubs and stones he could meet with some success in obtaining meat and furs. The early barriers could not have been very effective, however, and we can assume that many bands of these early men failed to survive.

A start had been made and the barrier slowly but steadily strengthened as new additions and refinements augmented the cultural inventory. By the time of phase 3 of the Würm Glaciation Man's culture enabled him to exploit many facets of his environment in the quest for food, shelter, and clothing. Existence was still harsh, but the likelihood of band survival was greatly increased, as the great number of Upper Paleolithic sites testifies.

A most significant change had now occurred in the relationship of Man to his environment. Whereas in other animal species evolution was the product of the interactions between the natural environment and the population, in the case of Man it involved interactions between the population and both the natural environment and the very culture it had produced. Culture itself, as part of the environment of Man, began to exert selective pressures upon him. For example, an individual born with a hereditary condition slightly affecting eyesight, hearing, or neuromuscular coordination, would be an inefficient hunter and a poor risk in combat. No woman would pick him as a mate lest she and her family starve to death. Such an individual would be negatively selected *by his culture* and his genes would not be passed on to the next generation. A high premium must have been placed upon excellent physiques and hardy constitutions by Paleolithic cultures as well as by the natural environment. Those of inferior biologic endowment, if allowed to escape the negative forces of natural selection, might well have been eliminated by the culturally conditioned pressures of sexual selection. How well the individual could adapt to the culture produced by his own kind must have been an important criterion of biologic survival in Paleolithic times. In modern "Paleolithic" bands (Eskimo and Bedouin) only good hunters can afford to have more than one wife, so that there would be a tendency for able-bodied, intelligent men to have a greater influence upon the genetic composition of the succeeding generation. In an aboriginal group in northern Australia consisting of four bands totaling 393 people, Sharp found 20 percent of the matings to be polygynous (more than one wife per man) but 20 percent of the individuals over 25 years of age had no mates.[14] Not only can the culture operate selectively in various ways upon the population, but the latter, in turn, effects changes in the culture, as we have observed. Gillin emphasizes this aspect when he points out that "the individual of strong personality, good intelligence, or more than average physical attributes has a greater opportunity for influencing the culture and changing the customs in a band-type society than in a larger group with more complicated culture."[15]

We have indicated that from the very beginning there is no reason to believe that the small bands of Paleolithic hunters and gatherers lived in complete isolation, even though they probably had well demarcated territories within which they lived. Exchange of genes undoubtedly took place in the form of raids to capture women, splitting off of bands because of factional disputes or overcrowding, and merging of bands when populations were depleted in number. True, such interbreeding was undoubtedly confined to contiguous bands because the sole mode of travel was by foot. Nevertheless genetic interchange could have been accomplished by a chain-like type of process, becoming attenuated as it reached farther from the center. We have witnessed the spread of tool traditions across whole continents. While in many cases this was the result of word-of-mouth dissemination of ideas, there is no reason to believe that individuals, and indeed whole bands, could not have migrated great distances during the vast periods of time available in the Pleistocene. We need only reflect that within a very few thousand years, beginning about 20 or 30 thousand years ago, almost every nook and cranny in North and South America was explored and inhabited by small bands originating in Asia, crossing the Bering Straits, and, in successive generations, spreading eastwards and southwards. It is difficult to conceive of a human

[14] Sharp, R. 1940. An Australian Aboriginal Population. *Human Biology*, 12:481–507.
[15] Gillin, J. 1948. *The Ways of Men.* New York: D. Appleton-Century Company.

population, made up of individuals with the curiosity, imagination, and intelligence that produced culture, that did not constantly seek contact with others of its kind. I have stressed this point because it is important to recognize that the very nature of Man and his rapidly growing culture precluded, almost from the outset, the kind of reproductive isolation which could lead to speciation.

From the beginning of the Pleistocene, almost a million years ago, Man was destined, because of his cerebral development, to remain a single species, *Homo sapiens*. On the other hand, because for most of this million year period he lived in *relatively* isolated small bands and because large areas containing many bands were more or less separated by water barriers, mountain ranges, and deserts, we might expect that local and regional variations would arise. This is precisely what happened. Before new cultural advancements made large-scale travel necessary and feasible, genetic differences became established on a continental basis. Mongoloids differentiated in Asia, Negroids in Africa, and Caucasoids in Southwest Asia and Europe. But within each major genetic variety of *Homo sapiens* there are detectable minor sub-subspecies or races, such as the Nordic, Alpine, Mediterranean, and Armenoid types of the Caucasoid "sub-species." All these genotypic and phenotypic varieties of Mankind are living reminders of the unique biological and cultural events that characterized our evolutionary history during the Glacial Age.

We must now turn to a consideration of the cultural evolution of the last 10,000 years. Along with the cultural assemblages of the Upper Paleolithic period are found the skeletons of modern type Man. Whether these Solutrean, Aurignacian, and Magdalenian men represented "on the spot" evolutionary descendants of Neanderthaloids, or whether they, like the blade tradition, spread into Africa and Europe from some Asiatic center, replacing the Middle Paleolithic Neanderthaloids, is a moot question. At any rate, modern or "neanthropic" Man was "on stage" 50,000 years ago and the succeeding events are focused not on skeletal changes but on cultural development. In various parts of the world there were quite different ways in which culture changed. In some areas technology advanced rapidly, in others the social or religious aspects of culture underwent intensive development. Unfortunately those of us who are members of "western civilization" are apt to measure cultural achievement primarily in terms of technology and to regard those peoples who advanced very slowly along these lines as "backward" or "primitive." Indeed, I have been guilty repeatedly of referring to such folk as "modern primitive peoples." The habit is difficult to break. However, if we insist on ranking cultures, we should at least take into account other aspects of culture, such as social organization, aesthetics, political organization, and marriage regulations. Among the Australian aborigines, for example, technology remained at a Middle Paleolithic level until modern times, but the complexity and formality of their kinship regulations almost surpass our understanding. Our story would be unnecessarily complicated if we were to attempt to trace the manifold lines of cultural development as they unfolded in the different areas of the world. Instead we shall pursue the particular stages that led to our own western civilization.

Agriculture and Its Effects Upon Cultural Evolution

About 10,000 years ago a most significant discovery was made. It was observed by Man, perhaps independently in such places as the Indus Valley in India, the Nile Valley in Egypt, and in Central America, that the seeds of plants and grasses, when accidentally dropped on barren soil, would propagate. Once the role of seeds in plant production was empirically understood it was a relatively simple step to plant domestication. The practice of agriculture spread rapidly from the tropical valleys of the world to the temperate zones. From the eastern and southern shores of the Mediterranean it entered Europe and soon became an indispensable part of the cultures of the peoples of this continent. Hunting and gathering of food were relegated to a minor role in the quest for subsistence. Food production, beginning with the domestication of cereal grasses (wheat, rice, barley, oats, corn), penetrated all parts of the world where soil and climatic conditions permitted. The effect of agriculture upon Man's culture, society, and biology was profound. Oddly enough, the period marking the transition from a hunting and gathering economy to a food producing one has been called the *Neolithic* or "New Stone Age" because of the fact that new techniques of working polished stone were added to the old core, flake, blade, and chopper-chopping tool traditions. It was because of agriculture, however, that we speak of the "Neolithic Revolution."

In a very general way let us examine the immediate cultural and social consequences of plant domestication and then turn to the indirect effects. The operations involved in agriculture include clearing the land of trees, preparing the soil, planting the seeds, cultivating the earth during plant growth, irrigating when necessary, harvesting the crop, clearing the field of stalks, and then turning the soil in preparation for the next planting. In the temperate zones this is a seasonal task, beginning early in Spring and ending in Fall. It requires the continuous presence of the farmer and hence his proximity to the field. The roving habits of hunting and gathering bands had to be given up and means found for permanently inhabiting a single location. Men must live as close to their cultivated land as would permit walking to and from the field within a single day. On the other hand, if each family lived in the center of its field in relative isolation from others, it would become vulnerable to attack. Families therefore clustered together in single habitation sites—the first villages. Their fields surrounded them, but all were within walking distance. For this reason these early villages were limited in size, but probably permitted a greater concentration of people than did the former hunting territories of the bands. Braidwood and Reed have estimated the population density in this early phase of village life in the Near East at 2500 per 100 square miles.[16] The earliest known village site is that of Jarmo in northern Iraq with a radiocarbon date of 4750 B.C.

More or less permanent occupation of a site meant the construction of larger and more stable structures than mere rock shelters. Braidwood and Reed have estimated that Jarmo consisted of about 25 huts at any one time during its 250 years of existence. If each hut contained one family, and if the average size of a family was six persons, then we arrive at a population of

[16] Braidwood, R. and Reed, C. 1957. The Achievement and Early Consequences of Food Production. *Cold Spring Harbor Symposia on Quantitative Biology*, 22:19–31.

about 150 for Jarmo. Unexcavated sites of contemporaneous villages near Jarmo suggest that an average distance of about 2.5 miles separated early villages in the Near East. The building of permanent individual family homes, the working of the same field year after year, and the subsequent reduction in the mobility of the population, meant that there was the time and the place for the accumulation of personal as well as real property. The concept of ownership must have been a direct outgrowth of agriculture and settled village life.

In a hunting and gathering economy the adult male played the dominant role because of his superior physical strength, but in agriculture there are tasks in which women and children can participate on an equal footing. This apparently led, in many instances, to increased importance of women in the economic life and even to their dominance of the local society in some groups (viz. Menang Kabau of Sumatra, Iroquois and Hopi of North America).

Since harvesting generally takes place but once a year and provides more food than can be consumed before spoilage, and because there had to be some way to make this surplus last until the next harvest, ways had to be devised to preserve and store food. The invention and development of ceramics was the response to this need. Clay when burned lasts indefinitely and can hold water if fashioned into bowls and pots. At first pottery was molded by hand and every household had its potter, usually the woman. Not only could a pot be used for storing and cooking food, but it presented a broad surface upon which designs could be incised, molded, painted, or applied. In brief, pottery offered an admirable means for the expression of Man's aesthetic drive. Undoubtedly it did not take long for Man to discover that when grain was left very long in a pot or other kind of container it would ferment and produce a liquid which induced very pleasurable sensations. Needless to say there was no pronounced lag in the spread of this cultural innovation.

Agriculture provided a better guarantee against starvation throughout the year than did the former hunting and gathering pursuits, but it failed to supply the necessary proteins. Hunting was never entirely abandoned if there was game in the vicinity, but it was an unreliable source of meat. Perhaps these early villagers first thought of raising their own animals when they observed wild pigs, sheep, goats, cattle, and fowl grazing in their fields. It was no difficult feat to build stockades and traps around these animals after they had become used to Man's presence in the near vicinity. The stubble from the harvested crops provided excellent food for these captive animals and cost nothing but the labor of cutting it. The domestication of animals was an early consequence of the domestication of plants and relieved Man finally and completely from the daily hand-to-mouth struggle that had been his lot during the previous one million years of his existence.

There were many other consequences of plant domestication that followed each other in chain-like succession. Only a few more need be mentioned to fully appreciate the nature of this cultural revolution. Farming activity engaged the full attention of the entire family during the Spring, Summer, and Fall, but outside of a few chores connected with the care of the stock, the long Winter months left Man with a good deal of leisure time for contemplating Nature, for expressing his artistic inclinations, and for experimenting with new techniques and materials. Linton once wrote that Man differs from all other animals in his capacity for boredom.[17] First, however, he had to have the free time to become bored. After that his active brain kept him constantly exploiting the world around him. Some individuals became more expert than their neighbors in making pottery, others devoted themselves to perfecting tool-making skills, and still others learned to construct better houses than anybody else. The products of such "specialists" came in demand by those not as skillful and soon groups of artisans were relieved of the usual duties of farming and tending the flocks and herds. Their pots, tools, houses, and decorative arts were exchanged for farm and dairy products. Thus the various crafts arose, eventually leading to labor "guilds" and finally to modern labor unions.

We have seen that even in Paleolithic times there was evidence of some conception of, and preoccupation with, supernatural powers. If our reconstruction of the meaning of the cave paintings, the burials, and the Venus figures is correct, then early Man

[17] Linton, R. *Op. cit.*

believed that superorganic beings held control over various natural phenomena and could be influenced to bring about results favorable to Man. Let us examine this important concept in more detail. In the hunting and gathering type of life that characterized the entire Paleolithic period, the very existence of a band depended each day upon the whimsies of Nature. The inexplicable absence of game from its customary haunts, the sudden storm that washes out the plants and trees used for food, the lightning that strikes and kills members of the band, and the many other catastrophic blows of Nature that threatened the safety and food supply of the band—these were events which primitive Man could neither explain nor control. And yet it was vital that they be predicted and controlled if Man was to free himself from constant anxiety and despair, and gain a measure of mastery over his environment. It would never do to leave to chance alone the occurrence of natural events which could seriously affect the welfare of himself, his family, and his group. He therefore invented supernatural beings who did have control over those elements of the environment upon which his safety and well-being depended. By endowing these beings or "spirits" with his own personality traits of avarice, jealousy, love, ambition, kindness, trickery, etc., Man was thus enabled to understand, approach, and influence them to the end that he could exercise some control, albeit indirectly, over vital natural phenomena. A well-known example of this human device is the bear cult as it was practiced among many tribes of northern Europe, Asia, and North America until quite recently (Hallowell, 1926).[18] To these people the bear was an important source of food and clothing and its presence was therefore essential. In each group a supernatural "owner" or "master" of the bear species was conceived and regularly propitiated, in one way or another, in order to influence, beseech, or coerce him to make bears plentiful on earth. Among the Ainu of Hokkaido vestiges of this cult still survive. Archaeological remains in New York State give evidence of the existence of the bear cult among the prehistoric Indian cultures of the "Late Woodland" horizon

[18] Hallowell, A. 1926. Bear Ceremonialism in the Northern Hemisphere. *American Anthropologist,* 28:1–175.

(Ritchie, "Archaeological Evidence for Ceremonialism in the Owasco Culture," 1947).[19]

Actually there could have been little in the natural environment of Paleolithic Man that was understandable to him in terms of prediction and control. Therefore, in order to gain ascendancy over Nature he had to "invent" numerous deities whom he could understand and manipulate. That portion of Man's natural environment over which he had no direct control we might term the "sacred," while that part of his world of which he had knowledge and control might be called the "profane"—a dichotomy first proposed by the French sociologist Durkheim in a somewhat different application. Obviously early Man's world was overwhelmingly "sacred" and as such was controlled by many different supernatural beings. Even today, among groups whose technological development has hardly emerged from a Neolithic stage, we find well populated pantheons consisting of spirits or gods with various specific functions and with whom each society is in continual communication.

With the leisure time afforded by plant and animal domestication Man could examine Nature and its behavior in more detail, and his fertile mind developed more ingenious ways of predicting and controlling those elements of vital importance to his well-being. He found, for example, that by careful examination of the entrails of animals he could "predict" the fortunes of war or the auspicious time for planting or harvesting. Some were more concerned with the movements of the heavenly bodies and soon found significant "correlations" between the phases of the moon and the proper time to sacrifice to certain gods. The contemplation of Nature led, on the one hand, to its better understanding by Man and, on the other hand, to a more elaborate and formalized approach to the supernatural. Hence science and religion were conceived and nurtured under the same roof. It was only when both reached adulthood that they turned upon each other. As was the case with artisans, a class of specialists called "shamans" or "priests" arose whose knowledge of the

[19] Ritchie, W. 1947. Archaeological Evidence for Ceremonialism in the Owasco Culture. *Researches and Transactions of the New York State Archaeological Association*, 11:55–75.

techniques of prediction of future events, the characteristics of the gods, and the varied ways of communicating with these gods, made them an indispensable segment of each social group.

The barrier that Paleolithic society was erecting between itself and the onslaughts of the natural environment rapidly reached new heights as the rate of cultural development became accelerated during the Neolithic period. The greater assurance of a steady food supply, the stability of a more settled village life, and the protection of better clothing, housing, and food preparation—all of these achievements made life less precarious and undoubtedly reduced the number of infant and child deaths. More people could reach the age of reproduction and pass their genes on to the next generation. Inevitably the population increased to the point where the effects of genetic drift were gradually reduced and no longer figured prominently in Man's biological evolution. This of course applied only to those societies which actually entered upon a full-blown Neolithic type of cultural existence. For many bands throughout the peripheral areas of the world life continued with only slight changes up to the present day and genetic drift continued to exert profound but little analyzed effects. Birdsell, however, has made a thorough analysis of the possible role of genetic drift in the evolution of the modern Australian aboriginal tribes, concluding that certain kinds of traits are more affected by drift than others in populations "under Australian conditions."[20]

It would appear, then, that under Neolithic cultural conditions, certain important evolutionary trends, begun in Paleolithic times, were intensified. The population size of human groups began to increase, thus reducing the effectiveness of genetic drift as an evolutionary agent. The expanding cultural inventory warded off more and more the direct selective forces of the natural environment, so that physical fitness and constitutional hardiness gradually came to have less importance as adaptive criteria. Culture began to encroach upon Nature as the significant world in which Man was to operate. It exerted its own kinds of selective forces aimed not at the bodily character-

[20] Birdsell, J. 1950. Some Implications of the Genetical Concept of Race in Terms of Spatial Analysis. *Cold Spring Harbor Symposia on Quantitative Biology*, 15:259–311.

istics of Man but at his qualities of intelligence, social adaptability, and personality. After all, a man need not be physically strong or vigorous to be a skilled potter or priest.

The impetus given to Man's cultural development by the invention of agriculture rapidly gained momentum. The domestication of oxen, camels, horses, and other large animals led to the discovery of better means of plowing and transportation. Man's world began to expand, and contacts between peoples increased. Rafts, canoes, and dugouts enabled him to cross bodies of water and travel along rivers, carrying the food and manufactured products of his villages to places where they were in demand and where he in turn could obtain articles sought by his own people. The dissemination of ideas as well as material goods broke down cultural isolation, while the greater ease of transport and personal mobility increased contacts between peoples widely separated. Reproductive isolation, never complete nor continuous in Paleolithic times, was removed as a means of genetic differentiation except among groups in remote areas of the world.

The Age of Metal

The discovery of metals and their obvious advantages made stone almost immediately obsolete for the production of weapons and utensils. Peoples with easy access to ore deposits became the targets of migrations and raids by those less fortunately situated. Extensive trade routes were established to secure raw copper and tin or the articles manufactured from them. The alloying of copper and tin to produce bronze further intensified this trade. Soon villages grew into towns, and towns into urban centers of many thousands of people who need no longer till the fields or tend the herds. Population grew by leaps and bounds, both in rural and urban areas. The invention of the wheel revolutionized transportation on land, and the construction of large ships meant that there was now ready access to the most remote coasts and continents. Bronze had hardly supplanted copper, tin, and stone, when iron entered the scene and rapidly became the metal without which no society could compete successfully with its neighbors.

The growth of large population centers and the development of land and sea routes brought people into even closer contacts with each other. Ways had to be devised of organizing social groups so that they could exist in harmony and act as effective units economically, politically, and defensively. The highly individualistic life of the band, wherein each individual had great freedom of choice, had to give way to increasing regulation of personal behavior for the greater cohesion of the society. Such regulations became so numerous that only specialists could know them all. With the invention of writing such rules of behavior could be inscribed permanently on clay tablets and papyrus sheets. Thus arose the codification of rules and regulations governing all forms of social behavior of which the famous Hammurabi Code (about 1950 B.C.) is our earliest example. The trend toward more and more restrictions of individual freedom of behavior was an inevitable consequence of the increasing size of population units and complexity of culture. The trend continues to the present day at an ever increasing rate.

Less than two hundred years ago new cultural forces were unleashed which further changed the basis of Man's biological evolution and removed it even farther from the principles which had, until the beginning of the Pleistocene epoch, governed the phylogenesis of all forms of life. These forces, beginning with the Industrial Revolution, and their evolutionary meaning for Mankind today and in the future, will be discussed in the next Problem.

Biological and Cultural Status of Modern Man

Man is the only animal that laughs and weeps; for he is the only animal that is struck with the difference between what things are, and what they ought to be.

WILLIAM HAZLITT, *Lectures on the English Comic Writers*

I have sedulously endeavored not to laugh at human actions, not to lament them, nor to detest them, but to understand them.

SPINOZA, *Tractatus Politicus*

Introduction

From the meager clues that have filtered down through the corridors of Time we might select a few momentous "events" that must have been critical in the evolution of the human species. They are:

1. The adaptive radiation of hominoids about 26 million years ago in East Africa, one line of which ultimately was to lead to modern Man.
2. The assumption of erect posture and bipedal gait among the members of this line about 1 million years ago.
3. The apparently simultaneous selection of physiological attributes of the central nervous system, permitting the development of culture and the acquisition of articulate speech.

299

4. The beginnings of cultural intervention in the normal selective processes of the natural environment, about ½ million years ago, and the formation of small, relatively isolated bands.
5. Plant and animal domestication, resulting in increased population size (about 10,000 years ago) with a subsequent lowering of the effects of genetic drift.
6. The discovery of metals (about 5,000 years ago), resulting in increased communication between societies, the reduction of isolating mechanisms, and the beginnings of large urban centers.

This brings us to the last 200 years or so of Man's existence. It might be wondered how, in such a brief period of time, representing but eight generations, the mode of human evolution could have been even more profoundly altered. Paleontology and geochronology have accustomed us to thinking in terms of relatively minute evolutionary changes over vast stretches of time. When we recall the biological mechanisms of evolution, involving the selection of adaptive portions of the range of phenotypic variations by a slowly changing natural environment, we become conscious of their limited application to the peculiar conditions of human evolution. Over the past 1 million years culture began to replace Nature as Man's environmental milieu. Unlike Nature, culture was created by Man. While Nature undergoes changes in an apparently haphazard fashion and at different, unpredictable rates, culture changes in a single direction—greater complexity—and at a constantly increasing rate of acceleration. We have seen that when the natural environment changes too rapidly it outstrips the potentialities of the species (its existing range of variability) to adapt, with the inevitable result that the species is condemned to extinction. The cultural environment, on the other hand, changes with ever increasing rapidity, but included in its expanding developments is the very means by which the human species may survive without phenotypically adapting. Let us examine this phenomenon more closely.

Cultural Changes Brought About by the Industrial Revolution

The term "Industrial Revolution" is given to the rapid succession of cultural innovations brought about by the discovery that iron could be successfully smelted by the use of coke, a by-product of coal, to produce steel. The story of steel and its influence upon the life of man has been recounted in many books and in many ways. It ushered in the ages of Machinery, Industrialization, Transportation, Communication, Trade, Power, Warfare, and Manufacture on a scale that even today is difficult to comprehend. New sources of power were found, such as coal, gas, oil, steam, water, electricity, and atomic energy. The discovery that electrical impulses could be sent through insulated wires led to the telephone and telegraph. Soon this was superseded by wireless techniques and the invention of the radio tube whereby speech sounds could be transmitted. Radio and television made communication over vast distances instantaneous. The power released from oil via the gasoline engine replaced the less dependable source provided by steam. Ships and trains, driven by oil-burning diesel engines, could traverse oceans and continents in a few days. Gasoline engines were utilized in small vehicles so that each individual or family could become a highly mobile unit. Electricity could be manufactured from water power and stored and transported by transformers to supply energy hundreds of miles from its source. The speed of travel was fantastically increased by the development of jet engines and rockets, so that Man can now look forward within a very few years to traveling through the atmosphere much faster than sound. Already he has demonstrated his ability to travel around the earth at a speed of 18,000 miles per hour, and to send satellites to the sun, moon, and the far distant planets.

The Industrial Revolution had immediate and dramatic effects upon the daily lives of people. Instead of spending his entire life roaming an area perhaps no larger than the island of Manhattan, a man may now leave his home in New York City on a Monday morning, have his next meal in London, spend the next day in Rome and the following day in Calcutta, transact some business in Cape Town, South Africa, stop off in Rio de Janeiro to visit friends, and return to New York—all in less than one week. A hundred years ago it took his grandfather several months and innumerable hardships to make the trip from New York City to the West Coast by wagon train. Modern Man can visit all the continents of the world and never alter his dietary habits. He is served food that can be preserved for years or transported fresh from thousands of miles away.

It is difficult to realize that Man's present modes of habitation had their origin in the rock shelters, lean-tos, and caves of Paleolithic times. Relatively few people are engaged in the direct tasks of food production. Most of the population of western civilization will live and die without having raised a single vegetable, milked a cow, or fed a pig. The activities of the great majority of men are only very remotely connected with the quest for food; whereas only 10,000 years ago every man spent almost all his waking hours hunting game, gathering fruits and plants, and searching for new sources of food. No one builds a fire in his house to keep warm; he turns up the thermostat and obtains the desired temperature uniformly throughout all the rooms. In hot summer weather an air conditioner and refrigerator keep the house cool and comfortable. Whether it rains, snows, or blows up a tempest makes no difference to modern Man. He gets into his automobile *inside* his house, turns up the heater because the day before his radio told him the temperature would be 35 degrees above zero Fahrenheit, turns on the radio so that he can find out what has happened throughout the world in the last 12 hours, and drives to his place of work several miles away. Having arrived he parks his automobile in an underground lot in the same building in which he will work, eat his lunch, and communicate with business associates by local and long distance telephone.

Modern Man can now engage in combat with others of his kind in a far more sophisticated and effective way. In the far distant Paleolithic past, band warfare was conducted with stones, spears, and flint knives. Casualties were often limited to two or three wounded men. Twenty years ago a single explosion destroyed an entire city and killed thousands of people instantly. Today the atomic bomb of the type that leveled Hiroshima and Nagasaki is obsolete and relatively ineffective. A few hydrogen bombs will not only wipe out the principal urban centers of a nation but will so contaminate the atmosphere with radioactive particles that no life will be able to survive except in concrete shelters dug deep into the ground. Animal life will perish and plant life will be rendered lethal as food. A major war today would banish from the earth all forms of life, except perhaps for a few primitive bands of people inhabiting the peripheral margins of the continents.

The Effects of Advances in Medicine

Not only has human culture developed to the point where it can obliterate instantly all the products of two or three billion years of biological evolution, but it has also, somewhat paradoxically, achieved means of keeping the human individual alive and functional far beyond the usual life span allotted him during the Paleolithic and Neolithic periods. A large number of significant inventions and discoveries in the health sciences have not only given Man the power to ward off disease, heal the sick, and provide livable environments for the disabled, but they have brought him close to the secrets of life itself. We can confidently expect that before long Man will himself be able to create life. Indeed, just three days ago as I am writing this, a Chicago newspaper reported that two biochemists had produced live viruses in their laboratory. The advances in medical science have important implications for the present and future course of human evolution. They include: anesthetics, vaccinations, drugs, antibiotics, synthetic hormones, vitamins, X-ray, metallic and plastic implants, prosthesis, transfusion, oxygen masks and tents, surgical instruments, radioactive isotopes, analgesics, and organ transplants.

Let us examine the significance of these great medical achievements on the individual life cycle:

1. Both mother and fetus receive regular medical care and supervision. The mother's diet is carefully regulated to insure her own health and the viability of the fetus.

2. Obstetrical care minimizes the dangers of childbirth. If the normal birth process threatens either mother or infant, a Caesarian section can be performed. If the infant is born prematurely, special techniques are applied to increase its chances of survival and normal development. When there is serologic incompatibility between mother and fetus, transfusions of new blood can save the newborn baby, as in erythoblastosis fetalis.

3. Defects and congenital malformations can be recognized at birth and remedial and ameliorative measures can often be taken to minimize their effects, as in cleft palate, cardiac or intestinal anomalies, and club foot.

4. Diseases of infancy can often be prevented or their effects lessened by medication.

5. Developmental defects can be treated or ameliorated during childhood, as with congenital dislocation of the hip, myopia, and partial anodontia.

6. New environments can be created for those with constitutional defects or deficiencies so that they can continue to function and lead almost normal lives. Immunity against various infectious diseases can be conferred in many instances and their deleterious effects alleviated in others.

7. Prosthetic devices enable those who suffer the loss or crippling of limbs to perform functions hitherto denied to them. Plastic surgery restores to almost normal appearances external features which have been mutilated by disease or accident. In some cases loss of sight can be restored by transplantation of eyes taken from a dead person. Impaired hearing can be alleviated by a variety of amplifying devices.

8. Life itself can be prolonged by surgery, medicine, nutritional supervision, therapy, prosthesis, and institutional care.

Not the least significant accomplishment is artificial insemination, whereby a couple need not be childless if the husband is sterile and the wife wishes to give birth to her own child.

Thus a protective blanket of modern culture has been thrown over human society, warding off the selective agencies of the natural environment and providing optimum environments for the successful development of Man from "germination to termination." Figuratively speaking, we might phrase the implications of this phenomenon in terms of the probability of a human zygote reaching the age of reproduction. Among Paleolithic women perhaps only 10 percent of all pregnancies resulted in viable individuals who attained the age of about 20 years. In modern times probably 60–70 percent are successful pregnancies in this sense. Penrose (1959) is more conservative in his estimation. He states:

Even in highly civilized countries, like the United Kingdom or the United States, nearly half of all zygotes formed are unfit in the crude sense of failure to reproduce and it may be assumed that this failure is, to a significant degree, attributable to the genes carried by them. By piecing together evidence from many sources, I have estimated that early prenatal loss accounts for at least 15%; then 3% of the remainder are stillborn, 2% are counted as neonatal deaths and 3% more die before reaching maturity. Of the survivors, 20% do not marry, and, of those who do, 10% remain childless.[1]

These figures cannot be verified. They are suggested only to emphasize the indisputable fact that the uncertainties of human ontogenesis have been sharply curtailed by the development of human culture. Among all the modern embryos, fetuses, infants, and children who would have died had they been conceived and reared under Paleolithic conditions there are undoubtedly some with genotypes predisposing to constitutional and phenotypic weaknesses and disabilities. Under our modern conditions of nutrition, clothing, medicine, and housing they are permitted to live, to function normally (in many cases), and to reproduce. In this way their defective genes are passed on to the next generation. It is very important to emphasize that not all such individuals who would have failed to survive in a primitive society are genetically poorly endowed. Nor is it true that all pregnancy terminations and infant and childhood deaths can be attributed to defective genetic constitutions.

In a Paleolithic society death could come to an individual at any time before the reproductive period because of either genetic or environmental causes. If his genotype was defective, containing one or more mutants, he might be eliminated in early embryonic life if the mutants were involved in the processes of mitosis or cellular differentiation. Or, if he possessed mutants affecting the vital organs, death might be delayed until later in prenatal development. Other mutants might permit a successful prenatal existence but result in constitutional weaknesses or predispositions to disease that lowered his resistance to some infections or failed to provide him with immunity to others. And

[1] Penrose, L. 1959. Natural Selection in Man: Some Basic Problems. In Roberts, D. and Harrison, G., *Natural Selection in Human Populations*. London: Pergamon Press.

finally, his genetic constitution might result in poor neuromuscular coordination, subnormal eyesight, defective hearing, flat feet, violent allergic reactions, or other debilitating conditions. If such were the case he would be a poor risk as a husband and a liability to a small group that depended upon mobility and physical dexterity for survival. Undoubtedly such individuals had less opportunity to contribute their genes to the succeeding generation than those better endowed genetically. On the other hand there can be little doubt that many who were genetically fit were eliminated by warfare, accidents, famine, and disease. The important point is that culture today permits many with genetic defects to live and reproduce who under a Paleolithic type of existence would have either died early in life or failed to reproduce had they lived.

The Age-group Composition of Human Populations

Although we have no direct evidence of the composition of a Paleolithic or Neolithic population, some insight may be gained by an examination of modern peoples living under rather primitive conditions here in the United States. In Arizona the Papago, Pima, and Apache Indians live on reservations which, until very recently, had few or very inadequate medical facilities. Roads were few in number and often impassable during the Winter months or because of flash floods. The only hospital available to the more than 9000 Papago Indians was off the reservation and accessible only by horse and automobile. The Fort Apache Reservation had one hospital but this was reached only with great difficulty over rugged terrain by the Indians living in the western half of the reservation. Only the Indian Hospital at Sacaton was strategically located in the Pima Indian Reservation. Approximately 20,000 Indians live on the three reservations—Papago, Pima, and Fort Apache. The mere fact that there are hospitals staffed with doctors and nurses, roads, horses and automobiles, schools, trading posts, and telephones precludes equating their way of life with either Paleolithic or Neolithic societies. Nevertheless, compared with the surrounding villages and cities of our western civilization, the Arizona Indian is still carrying on a "primitive" existence.

Among the Papago Indians 46.4 percent of the total live births occur in hospitals, compared with 91.6 percent of White births in the United States. The remaining 53.6 percent of Papago babies are born at home, unattended by either a doctor or nurse. Among the Apache 33.2 percent are born without medical attention of any kind. Only 8.3 percent of the Pima births are unattended, this being related to the central location of the Sacaton hospital. In the White population of the United States only 1.5 percent of the total births are unattended. Needless to say, gynecological and obstetrical care has been practically unheard of among these Indians until the past ten years. We would anticipate, therefore, that fetal mortality rates among the Indians is extremely high in comparison to those of American Whites. It is estimated (Potter, 1961) that 20 percent of all American White pregnancies terminate in abortion. This is, of course, a conservative figure since many pregnancies end in early abortion before a doctor is consulted. My own embryological investigations would indicate that a figure of 30 percent would be very conservative. Among American Indians the fetal death rate must be considerably higher, but there are no direct data to confirm or deny this claim.

It is in the postnatal death rates that the comparison between Indians and Whites points up the discrepancy in hospital and medical service availability. In 1952 the infant mortality rate for all Indians in Arizona was 115.8 per 1000 live births. The greatest killers of Indian infants are gastroenteritis, influenza, pneumonia, and tuberculosis, all of which can be overcome with proper and readily available medical attention. The comparison is by no means complete if we look only at infant mortality rates. In Table 7 we see the mortality rate per 1000 population for the different age groups in Arizona Indian and other populations. It becomes clear that populations with relatively poor medical services have exceedingly high mortality rates in all age groups up to 55 years as compared with the United States where there is maximum availability of modern medical services. The highest death rates in the period from birth to 55 years of age are found among the Egyptians and Papago Indians.

The age-group composition of a population is dependent not only on mortality rates but also upon birth rates and the flow of

TABLE 7. *Mortality Rates Per 1000 Population in Selected Countries and Tribes by Age Groups*

Age Group	Population						
	U.S.	Egypt	Apache	Pima	Papago	Japan	Fiji Islanders
5–14	.6	4.8	2.1	1.8	4.8	1.7	1.8
15–24	1.08	4.9	4.2	3.2	4.9	4.3	3.2
25–34	2.4	8.4	5.4	4.5	8.4	6.0	4.5
35–44	3.18	11.1	8.1	6.6	11.1	6.6	6.6
45–54	8.7	14.1	13.2	12.3	14.1	10.3	12.3
55–64	19.38	20.5	31.0	32.0	20.5	___	30.3

SOURCE: Kraus, B. *Indian Health in Arizona*, 1954.

immigrants and emigrants. In 1950 the birth rate for the total United States population was 24.1 per 1000, and for the Southern Arizona Indians about 36 per 1000. In the period from 1900 to 1950 the United States population increased 100 percent while that of the United States Indians increased 48 percent. Thus, in spite of a much higher mortality rate from infancy to middle age the Indian population, because of its high birth rate, was enabled to increase. The greater increase in the United States population as a whole was due to low mortality rates and the influx of immigrants even though the birth rate was not as great as that of the Indians.[2]

The study of age-group composition of populations is very revealing. Let us assume that in a given society all newborn babies live until at least 65 years of age—in other words, there is no mortality until 65. What would the age-group distribution curve look like? A glance at Figure 77 shows that such a population would resemble diagrammatically a truncated pyramid. The only reason that the first portion of the line slants upward is because the first age group—B-4—is only half the size of each succeeding interval. Given these particular intervals the distribution is that of a population in which no deaths occur from birth to age 65. In such a society there would be no wars, accidents, epidemics, famines, or other catastrophies; and medical services would be 100 percent effective. Now let us compare

[2] Kraus, B. 1954. *Indian Health in Arizona*. Tucson: University of Arizona Press.

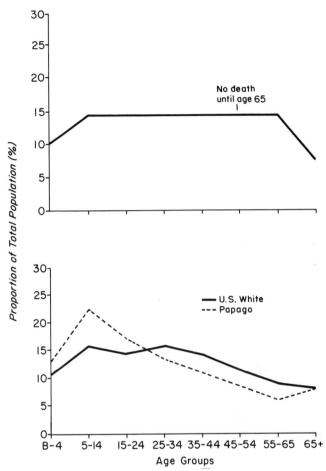

FIGURE 77. *Age-group Composition of an Ideal and an Actual Population*

with this ideal situation the actual case of a population, the Papago, where hospital utilization is low and medical services meager. In the same Figure we see the age-group composition of the American White population represented. It is quite clear that there are two main differences. The peak of the Papago distribution curve is in the teen-age group while the White curve is

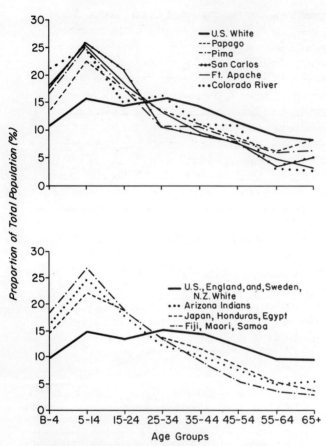

FIGURE 78. *Age-group Composition Curves of Modern Civilized and Primitive Populations*

relatively flat, indicating lack of predominance of any age group. Among the Papago the curve drops rather sharply and steadily from the younger age-group to age 64, then rises slightly after age 65. In the White population there is a gradual downward slope after age 34. That this difference is not a fortuitous one is illustrated in Figure 78A. Here the age-group composition curves of five Southern Arizona Indian populations are compared with the United States White population. In Figure 78B four curves are shown, representing (1) the combined United States, English, Swedish, and New Zealand populations, (2) the combined Southern Arizona Indian populations, (3) the combined populations of Japan, Honduras, and Egypt, and (4) the combined Fiji, Maori, and Samoan populations. The nature of the age-group distribution curve is obviously related to mortality rates and these, in turn, are a reflection of the availability of modern medical services to the general population. Further proof is afforded when we reconstruct the age-group curves for the American White population of 1900, 1920, 1940, and 1950 (Fig. 79). There is a gradual shift from the 1900 curve which resembles those of the modern Indians, Fijians, Samoans, etc. to the 1950 curve which roughly approximates the ideal curve shown in Figure 77A.

From this study we might speculate about the composition of a Paleolithic population where medical knowledge and skills were nonexistent. Infant mortality rates would be extremely high, perhaps reaching 700 per 1000 live births. Exacting tolls would be leveled against the survivors throughout the first 40 years of life, after which the chances of survival past the age of 65 would be almost as good as those in modern societies. In

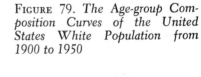

FIGURE 79. *The Age-group Composition Curves of the United States White Population from 1900 to 1950*

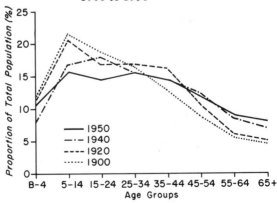

other words, any one in this primitive society who could survive until 40 had to have an iron-clad constitution plus a considerable amount of luck. Contrary to popular ideas about primitive societies, the proportion of people over 65 in Arizona Indian tribes today is very similar to that of the American and European populations. We often hear that the "average" life-expectancy of people of Biblical times was 25 years. This was probably true for all Paleolithic and Neolithic societies if we calculate the average on the basis of all those born alive. However, if the average were calculated without including the first year of life, the life-expectancy figure would rise considerably. This is simply another way of saying that in primitive societies, the individual who reaches ten years of age has a much better chance of becoming an old man than one who is only five years of age. If we divide the life span into socially significant categories, the percentages of the population falling into each for both American Whites and Arizona Indians are as follows:

	Whites	Indians
Pre-adult (B–19)	33.2%	51.3%
Young adult (20–39)	30.8%	25.2%
Middle-age (40–59)	23.5%	15.4%
Old-age (60 and over)	11.0%	8.1%

It is quite likely that in a Paleolithic band or a Neolithic village 90 percent of the group consisted of persons under 40 years of age and 65–70 percent under 20.

The "Load of Mutations"

The population of the world, as is well known, is increasing at such a tremendous rate that the phenomenon is often referred to as the "population explosion." This is the result of greatly lowered mortality rates at all ages and a high birth rate. Inevitably it means that more and more genetically "unfit" individuals can survive and reproduce, thus perpetuating their mutant genes and adding to the genetic "load of mutations" already present in the population. The gene pool of a population might be visualized as a tank full of oil and water. The oil represents all the established alleles of the population and of course

FIGURE 80. *Inflow and Outflow of Mutant Genes in Domestic (Human) and Wild Populations*

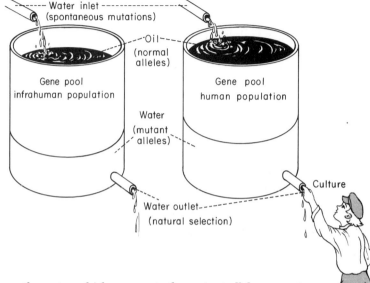

lies above the water, which represents the mutant alleles present. At the bottom of the tank there is a small outlet which continuously drains off the water. Above the tank is a small pipe dripping water into the tank at a constant rate. The rate of water inflow and water outflow is the same. The pipe feeding water into the tank represents the occurrence of spontaneous mutations; the drain represents the action of natural selection in eliminating mutations. In all animal species in the wild state, and presumably in pre-Paleolithic hominids, the elimination of mutations kept pace with the rate of new mutations so that the "level of water" in the tank remained at a fairly constant level (Fig. 80). As culture developed and interceded more and more between the selective forces of the natural environment and the human species, the process of elimination of mutations was slowed down; the "drainpipe" became more and more clogged up, so to speak. The result was that the continuing rate of new mutations began to raise the "water level," since the rate of mutation outflow began to lag behind the rate of mutation inflow. In terms of biological evolution, human culture has played the role of the boy at the dike; it has been jamming a finger into the drain pipe of the human genetic pool.

This is not to say that all the selective forces of Nature have been thus diverted. There is some evidence that natural selection still plays a role in human evolution, but the difficulty that geneticists are now experiencing in detecting and measuring it would seem to be sufficient indication of its relative ineffectiveness. On the other hand, Penrose takes the viewpoint that:

The belief that natural selection in man has been abolished by civilization, socialism, hygiene or whatever it may be, depends upon superficial reasoning. What has happened is that the force has been altered and transferred at certain points from one genotype to another.[3]

He admits, however, that "the main force of natural selection now seems to be directed towards defects present before birth and leading to failure of development or of function." In other words, in the civilized societies natural selection still operates at the prenatal level. As we have indicated earlier, at least 20 percent of all pregnancies terminate before birth and probably a majority of these die because of genetic defects.

On the other hand, natural selection presumably continues to operate at the postnatal level but not primarily upon physical traits. Dobzhansky has defined the modern operational field of natural selection as follows (1956):

Man's environments are decisively influenced by his cultural developments. For good or for ill, natural selection fits man to live in the environments created by his own culture and technology. In these environments, the ability to subsist on uncooked foods is probably now less important than it once was; the ability to resist certain infections prevalent in crowded towns is probably more important than it was. So is the ability to learn, to become educated, and to live in reasonable accommodation with one's neighbors. Natural selection now works in what some may call unnatural conditions, but it is still natural selection.[4]

[3] Penrose, L. Op. cit.
[4] Dobzhansky, T. and Allen, G. 1956. Does Natural Selection Continue to Operate in Modern Mankind? *American Anthropologist*, 58:591–604.

In the final analysis, it is the reproductive fertility of the individual that is the measure of his biological adaptiveness. The reasons for reduced numbers of offspring in some individuals, large numbers in others, and lack of progeny in still others, are multitudinous in human society. They are intermeshed with all aspects of our social and cultural life—religious, economic, psychological, sociological, and political. Whether selective processes are purely cultural or natural, or a combination of both, is a moot point. Our knowledge of our own social and cultural environment is too meager and uncertain to enable us to identify or assess the operation of selective forces or their effects on modern civilized man. The protective shield of culture with its consequent relaxation of stringent demands upon biological fitness has, beyond doubt, led to increased proportions of mutant alleles in the population. This, in turn, has brought about increased phenotypic variability, in physical as well as in behavioral or "mental" traits. It is interesting to speculate about the apparent paradox that this has created.

Differential Biologic and Social Maturity in Man

From the very beginnings of culture, when Man lived in small social groups, there must have been rules of behavior which governed certain aspects of the individual's life and imposed restraints upon his freedom of action. In a primitive band these rules could not have been numerous nor onerous but they were necessary to preserve the cohesion of the group and to maintain its functional efficiency. We know from the study of modern primitive bands that the individual retained a great deal of personal freedom and, in fact, could leave his band to join another if he was unhappy with the leadership. With the development of village life and the establishment of large centers of population, the number and variety of regulations governing the individual's behavior increased rapidly and placed many more restraints upon his personal freedom. Rules were necessary to prevent conflicts between individuals and groups and to maintain social harmony. As the complications of life increased with the advent of more technological advances and larger populations the number of regulations grew at almost a geometrical rate. Specialists did nothing but memorize and administer them. With the invention of writing the oral body of laws became codified. The need for new laws and regulations continually increased so that today special bodies of men exist at all levels of society whose main concern is to draft more and more regulations. Take a single example of a technological advance—the automobile. Its rapid spread necessitated the building of roads, bridges, and underpasses, the regulation of traffic patrolmen, the building of auto parks, parking lots, trailer camps, and service stations, and the establishment of special courts to administer traffic laws. All of these new activities necessitated the formulation of thousands of new regulations—regulations which further restrict the individual's freedom of behavior.

The inroads upon freedom of individual expression are well illustrated by the developments in the field of education. Education is a cultural phenomenon whose function is to indoctrinate the new members of the society into the cultural patterns of the group so that they will be able to assume the roles of adults in an efficient manner. We have observed that for almost one million years there was remarkably little change in the cultural inventory of Man. The rate of accretion was so slow as to be imperceptible to the oldest living persons at any point in time. In other words, parents in a Paleolithic society could be sure that the ways of life which they and their own parents and grandparents had practiced would be precisely what their own children would undergo. This meant that the cultural adaptations which served their generation would be quite adequate for the following generations. Education therefore consisted of teaching the children everything they knew. The process began early in childhood when girls learned from their mothers how to tend camp, cook food, make skin garments, and pack their meager belongings for seasonal treks through the territory. Boys accompanied their fathers on hunting and gathering expeditions, learning how to make weapons, select wood and stone for fashioning various implements, trap and kill game, and select suitable camp sites. By the time boys and girls had reached puberty they at least knew the total content of their culture and each could function as adults, albeit not quite as skillfully. Indeed, among primitive peoples even today the advent of puberty is marked by "rites de passage," indicating the transformation from childhood to adulthood. We in western civilization also celebrate this event with such ceremonies as "confirmation" and "bar mitzvah"; but in our society they are simply vestigial, recalling a former primitive state but now bereft of all functional meaning. Physiologically we still attain puberty at a mean age of 13 years, but socially and culturally we remain children until 21 and over.

In Paleolithic societies the entire educational process must have been assumed by the family, and each individual was indoctrinated into the total culture of the group. With the beginnings of agriculture, village life, and specialization, the cultural inventory soon became too extensive for any one individual to grasp all its aspects. The potter raised his sons to be potters, and the weapon-maker taught his sons to follow his speciality. The individual was indoctrinated by his family into only a segment of the total cultural pattern. Nevertheless, in Neolithic times the pace of cultural advancement was probably still slow and what the older generation knew and practiced sufficed for the younger. With the Age of Metals and the spread of writing, the rate of new inventions was greatly accelerated and culture became increasingly complex. No one family could provide adequate indoctrination to its offspring, so that a group of specialists arose whose sole function was to assume the role of educators. With the advent of the Industrial Revolution and the bewildering development and spread of technology with its attendant effects upon all forms of social life, the family became less and less competent to train its young. The task of education fell upon the corps of teachers, who in turn found it necessary to limit their scope of study and to concentrate upon particular aspects of culture. For proper indoctrination it was necessary for the young member of society to be exposed to several specialists who were now conveniently gathered under one roof to form an institution known as the "school." At first, a few years of such formal indoctrination was generally deemed adequate to equip the child with the necessary knowledge of his society and culture. If he could learn the three "R's" and some fundamental facts about history, literature, politics, and science, he could then apprentice himself to some craftsman and learn a trade or perhaps enter into his family's business or farm life. At most he need attend a formal school only from 6 to 14 years of age. As we all know, today we do not consider even 12 years of formal education adequate. And what is more, there is a distinct tendency to lower the age at which formal, nonparental supervision of the child's education begins. What was once purely a family affair which resulted in a functioning young adult at the age of about 13 years, has now become a community task beginning with nursery and pre-kindergarten children and ending, in the case of some professional training, as late as 30 years of age.

The age at which a new member of our society becomes an adult varies considerably. Physiologically he still makes the transition at about 13 years. His state government usually recognizes his adult status at 16 years—but only as an automobile driver. The federal government considers him to be sufficiently adult to vote at age 21; but he can function as a defender of the society in its armed forces at 18 years. If he wishes to become a physician or dentist he cannot hope to be economically independent and functional until he is at least 25 or 26 years old. If he is to become a professional scientist or medical or dental specialist, then rarely can he finish his parasitic existence before the age of 29 or 30. Nevertheless, many religious groups will formally recognize his "adulthood" with religious rites when he attains the age of 13. This growing disparity between biological and social maturity is a paradox of Man's biological and cultural evolution and no doubt is at the root of many of the ailments that seem to plague our society today.

Biologic Individuality and Social Conformity

The complexities of urban life and the mass production of goods by both industry and agriculture place unprecedented demands upon the individual for behavioral conformity. There are very specific times to awaken, to report on the job, to perform certain tasks, to take a "coffee break," to have lunch, to punch a clock, and to return home. There is a time to relax, to have meals, to attend church, and to take a vacation. This premium on conformity extends to the educational sphere where the child learns very early to suppress his individual desires and behavior. Unwritten but nevertheless very real and very stringent sanctions compel him to dress like his fellows, to talk like them, and to follow the same patterns of conduct both in and out of school. One must like the same music, the same style of dancing, and the same type of food; otherwise the student loses status with his peers and this is the worst kind of punishment he can undergo. We are thus hemmed in by all sorts of restrictions—by the formal laws of our city, county, state, and federal governments, by the regulations of unions and industry, and by the informal sanctions of our churches, clubs, associations, and social groups. For the sake of social euphoria these restrictions upon individual freedom of expression and behavior are necessary and will continue to multiply as the population increases and as life becomes more complicated. Opposed to the increasing demands for behavioral conformity is the trend towards increased biological variability, involving both physical and mental traits. Social misbehavior may well be the inevitable result of the stresses produced by the tendency to place round pegs (biological individuality) into square holes (social conformity). Certainly one of Mankind's most precious possessions is the genetic variability that ensures individuality. In it lies the seeds for future successful adaptation to changing natural and cultural environments. On the other hand, the same culture that has permitted Man to overcome the adverse forces of Nature in the absence of an adequate physical endowment and to survive in spite of an increasing load of mutations, now seeks to suppress the expressions of the very individual variability it continues to foster.

The apparent incompatibility between Man's biological nature and the demands of society for conformity has brought about numerous and varied revolts on the part of individuals. They take many forms, some of which evoke social sanctions while others require medical care. The load of mutations will continue to increase, as will the need for further sublimation of the individual for the good of the society. What implications this paradox bears for the future of Man is a problem that may be even more urgent and significant than that involving the settlement of planets in outer space. Perhaps a serious consideration of the relationship between human biology and human culture in the light of their evolution will give us deeper insight into the causes of our increasing social dysphoria. Our courts, social and welfare agencies, ministers, marriage and family counselors, penologists, and psychiatrists have been treating symptoms. The disease has been untouched because the etiology is unknown. It must be sought for in the very origins of human evolution and cultural development. Like flat feet, hernia, and low back pains, the stresses and strains of life in modern society may be another scar of human evolution.

The Problems of Race and Racial Differences

A final subject awaits our attention. How shall the modern varieties of Man throughout the world be assessed in the light of human evolution? What are the "races of man" and how have they come about? And even more important, what is the significance of racial differences? These questions are of particular interest today because of the revolt of the Negro in the United States, the emergence of the Negro societies of Africa, and the rise to power of the Mongoloid peoples of Communist China. The wars and social upheavals of the past 30 years have generally unfurled the banners of racial hatred and bigotry alongside those of nationalism, social reform, and defense of the fatherland. Racial "purity" has been extolled; race mixture is deplored. The term "race" is applied to Jews, Negroes, Mexicans, Japanese, Nordics, and Hottentots alike. By labeling a particular group of people a "race" the implication follows that all attributes, whether biological or cultural, are thereby hereditary and of long standing, hence immutable and eternal. Race has become a straw man against which unhappy and frustrated societies may vent their spleen. Variability, the fundamental phenomenon by which all species are given the opportunity to adapt to their environments, is incomprehensible to Man. He cannot understand, as Turgenev once wrote, how one man can blow his nose differently from himself. The sight of a darker skin fills him with vague fears. Gestures, dress, hair styles, and ways of eating that are different from his make him uneasy and apprehensive. Yet this same Man looks boldly into the heavens as he prepares to explore the planets and the stars.

From the perspective gained from our contemplation of biological evolution and the immense span of time since the origin of life itself, let us examine our species as it was distributed over the earth before the discovery of the New World by the peoples of Europe. We see, first of all, a communality of characteristics which sets this species apart from all other animals. Its members all have upright posture and bipedal gait, large brains and small faces, sparse body hair, forelimbs freed from locomotion and weight-bearing, and hands that can grasp and manipulate objects. In addition, all the members of this group can and do interbreed, and when they do their offspring are viable and quite fertile. Truly they are one species if we apply this criterion to them as we do to all other forms of life. What is more, we observe that they all possess the ability to communicate with each other by means of writing and systems of sounds issuing from the mouth. They live in organized groups each of which has altered the environment in which it lives in different ways; each has attained a degree of mastery over the ecological niche in which it finds itself. These attributes are characteristic of no other form of life that has ever inhabited this earth.

Now we look more closely at our species. We see that those occupying the continent of Europe exhibit certain bodily traits that distinguish them from the inhabitants of Africa or Asia. The peoples of Africa, in turn, have characteristics which render them distinguishable from the Asiatic members of the species. In North and South America we see groups of people who seem to have certain characteristics which appear to be peculiar to them. And the islands of the Pacific Ocean are occupied by a variety of groups, some of which resemble Europeans, some Africans, and others Asiatics. In general, however, there appear to be three major classes or subspecies of Man. They are referred to as Mongoloids (Asiatics), Caucasoids (Europeans), and Negroids (Africans). The differences in bodily characteristics of these three groups of Mankind are generally well known. Almost anyone who stands on a street corner in Manhattan will be able to sort out most of the people who pass by into the three categories. Every textbook in anthropology has a table listing the diagnostic traits of the three major subspecies of Man. We shall mention only some of the better known ones:

Negroid Traits	Caucasoid Traits	Mongoloid Traits
Dark brown skin color	Light pinkish skin color	Yellowish or coppery skin color
Kinky or frizzly hair	Wavy or curly hair	Straight hair
Long headed	Long or round headed	Round headed
Low nasal bridge	High nasal bridge	Low to moderate nasal bridge
Broad nose	Narrow nose	Moderate to broad nose
Dark brown hair	Blond, red, and brown hair	Dark brown hair
No epicanthic fold	No epicanthic fold	Pronounced epicanthic fold
Relatively long legs	Moderately long legs	Relatively short legs
Absence of shovel-trait	Absence of shovel-trait	Shovel-shaped incisors
Facial prognathism	Orthognathism	Moderate prognathism

Any individual possessing all the traits listed under one of these categories would easily be identifiable as Negroid, Caucasoid, or Mongoloid. Each trait is obviously inherited since it "breeds true," that is, offspring of Mongoloids show the same constellation of bodily characteristics as their parents.

On the other hand it must not be thought that within the Mongoloid, Caucasoid, or Negroid populations there is no variation. Among the Caucasoids, for example, skin color ranges from a light pinkish hue to very dark brown, as is found in the peoples of India. Long-headedness (dolichocephaly) is characteristic of many West African Negroes but the Pygmies of the Congo forests and the Bataan Peninsula in the Philippines are extremely roundheaded (brachycephalic). Many Caucasoids show some degree of shovel-shape in their upper incisor teeth and many American Indian tribes have a rather low frequency of this trait. There is, then, overlap among the major subspecies of Man with respect to any *single* trait. In the total configuration of subspecific traits, however, it would be rare indeed to find among the Mongols of Asia an individual who could "pass" as a Negroid or Caucasoid, or among the Negroes of West Africa a person who would be mistaken for a European Caucasoid.

With the discovery of the New World and the Age of Conquest and Exploration, vast migrations of peoples began to take place. African Negroes were forcibly moved as slaves to many parts of the world. Europeans came in a steady flow to North and South America. Others established colonies in Africa, on the peripheries of Asia, and in the islands of the Pacific. Many Mongoloids left Asia for better opportunities in the Americas. Malaysia attracted peoples from the Near East, India, China, and Japan. Within a relatively short span of time the three major groups of Mankind had representative populations in almost all parts of the world. This led to widespread hybridization. Numerous studies have been made by anthropologists of the effects of such interbreeding on the nature and distribution of subspecific traits in the offspring of these crosses. Davenport and Steggerda in 1929 studied "race" crossing in Jamaica,[5] Williams investigated Spanish-Maya Indian hybrids in Yucatan in 1931,[6] and Boas[7] and Jenks[8] each conducted studies of Indian-White crosses in North America. Anthropologists were stirred by the possibility of physical changes resulting from migrations to new and different environments. Shapiro and Hulse examined anthropometrically the descendants of Japanese migrants to Hawaii.[9] Boas made a classical study of the children of immigrants to the United States from southern Europe.[10] Goldstein worked with descendants of Mexican migrants to the United States[11] and recently Lasker has been conducting similar studies.[12]

[5] Davenport, C. and Steggerda, M. 1929. Race Crossing in Jamaica. *Publications of the Carnegie Institution*, No. 395.

[6] Williams, G. 1931. Maya-Spanish Crosses in Yucatan. *Papers of the Peabody Museum of American Archaeology and Ethnology*, Vol. 13, No. 1.

[7] Boas, F. 1894. The Half-Blood Indian: An Anthropometric Study. *Popular Science Monthly*, (Oct.) pp. 761–770.

[8] Jenks, A. 1916. Indian-White Amalgamation. *Studies in Sociology* (University of Minnesota), No. 6.

[9] Shapiro, H. and Hulse, F. 1939. *Migration and Environment*. London: Oxford University Press.

[10] Boas, F. 1910. Changes in Bodily Form of Descendants of Immigrants. *Senate Document 208*, 61st Congress, 2nd Session, Washington, D.C.

[11] Goldstein, M. 1943. *Demographic and Bodily Changes in Descendants of Mexican Immigrants*. Texas: University of Texas, Institute of Latin American Studies.

[12] Lasker, G. 1952. Environmental Growth Factors and Selective Migration. *Human Biology*, 24:262–289. Also, 1954. The Question of Physical Selection of Mexican Migrants to the U.S.A. *Human Biology*, 26:52–58.

The results of such investigations have been neither consistent nor entirely valid. Inevitably the hybrid offspring of mixed marriages exhibit traits of both parents in degrees and combinations which are generally unpredictable. Primarily the difficulty lies in the fact that the genetic basis for these traits is not known and undoubtedly is complex. Furthermore, each trait exhibits a continuous distribution, making any clear-cut division into categories that correspond to underlying genetic differences almost impossible. Certain traits, it is true, act very much as if the alleles determining them are dominant; they tend to appear in the offspring. For example, it would seem that straight hair is dominant over curly hair, epicanthic fold over absence of fold, thick everted lips over thin lips, and dark eye color over light colored eyes. None of these traits, however, are inherited according to the laws of simple Mendelian dominance.

In recent years attention has been diverted from the study of bodily characteristics to the investigation of subspecific differences in traits whose precise mechanism of inheritance is known. These include primarily the various blood-group antigens as well as certain other biochemical processes such as the formation of abnormal hemoglobins, the excretion of certain substances in the urine, the ability to taste phenylthiocarbamide, the presence of a particular haptoglobin pattern, the frequency and combination of transferrins, and the frequency of the gamma-globulin factor. There is no question that subspecific differences can be better described if put upon a firm genetic basis. Nevertheless, the differences in gene frequencies among various populations as established by serological traits appear to conform with the divisions of Mankind recognized by the anthropologist (and the laymen, too) on the basis of visible physical traits.

Not content with the classification of Mankind into three major subspecies, anthropologists and geneticists have been subdividing each into smaller categories. Often the Mongoloids, Caucasoids, and Negroids are referred to as "subspecies," "stocks," or "varieties." Their respective subgroups are generally known as "races." There is, however, no consistency in the application of these terms either on the part of scholars or the general public. Although no two classifiers "recognize" the same number of races within the three subspecies of *Homo sapiens*, anthropological tradition has more or less entrenched the following as the living races of man:

Caucasoid Races	Location
Mediterranean	Shores of the Mediterranean Sea
Nordic	Scandinavia and Northern Europe
Alpine	Central Europe
Dinaric	Southeastern Europe
Armenoid	The Near East

Mongoloid Races	
Classic Mongoloid	Japan, Mongolia, China
Micronesian	Western Pacific islands
American Indian	North and South America
Malayo-Indonesian	Malay Peninsula, Sumatra, Java, Philippines, etc.

Negroid Races	
Melanesian	New Guinea, Solomon Islands, etc.
Pygmies	Congo, Borneo, Malay Peninsula, Bataan
Bushman	South Africa
Negro	West Africa

Often the Malayo-Polynesian peoples, the Eskimo, the Australian aborigines, Ainu, and the Bushman-Hottentots are given separate ranking rather than included in any of the three major categories.

On the other hand, Boyd, an immunochemist, has constructed a racial classification based on blood groups in which he recognizes 13 races.[13] They are:

European Group
Early European (hypothetical)
Lapps
Northwest Europeans
East and Central Europeans
Mediterraneans

[13] Boyd, W. 1963. Genetics and the Human Race. *Science* 140:1057–1064.

African Group
   African race
   Asian race
   Indo-Dravidian race

American Group
   American Indian race

Pacific Group
   Indonesian race
   Melanesian race
   Polynesian race
   Australian race

We have, then, two basically different ways of partitioning the populations of Mankind. One, the classical method of anthropology, utilizes external morphology and measurements whose genetic basis is only vaguely known. The reader can gain a great deal of insight into the highly tenuous and disputed theories on this subject by consulting Hooton's *Up From the Ape*,[14] Coon's *The Races of Europe*,[15] and Count's *This Is Race*.[16] The other method is that of genetics and relies principally on the frequency distribution of blood group alleles. Its foremost advocate is Boyd, who first locked horns with the anthropologists in 1950 with his book *Genetics and the Races of Man*.[17]

The "Origin of Races"

In 1962 a third concept of the racial subdivisions of *Homo sapiens* was offered by Coon in his book *The Origin of Races*.[18] The basis of his presentation rested heavily upon a somewhat

[14] Hooton, E. 1946. *Up From the Ape*, 2nd ed. New York: The Macmillan Company.
[15] Coon, C. 1939. *The Races of Europe*. New York: The Macmillan Company.
[16] Count, E. (ed.). 1946. *This is Race*. New York: Henry Schuman.
[17] Boyd, W. 1950. *Genetics and the Races of Man*. Boston: D. C. Heath and Company.
[18] Coon, C. 1962. *The Origin of Races*. New York: Alfred A. Knopf, Inc.

original and highly problematical interpretation of human evolution. Coon recognized five major groupings of Mankind: Australoids, Caucasoids, Mongoloids, Capoids, and Congoids. He stated:

> My thesis is, in essence, that at the beginning of our record, over half a million years ago, Man was a single species, *Homo erectus*, perhaps already divided into five geographic races or subspecies. *Homo erectus* then evolved into *Homo sapiens* not once but five times, as each subspecies, living in its own territory, passed a critical threshold from a more brutal to a more *sapient* state.

Coon's stand has evoked widespread comment in the press, some favorable, some highly critical. It is difficult, however, even for the specialist to follow his argument because of the rather confusing use of terminology and disregard of certain fundamental biological principles of evolution. The use of the term *Homo erectus* to designate the early hominids of the period between one million (Coon claims 700,000) and 25,000 years ago has many parallels in the literature. It corresponds with such terms as Archaeanthropic, Protoanthropic, and Palaeanthropic Man, as used by Sergi, Piveteau, and Weidenreich, and recognizes differences of specific ranking between early and modern Man. We have seen that between the earliest of hominids and the most recent there was a series of minor morphological gradations of a continuous nature. The major evolutionary adaptations had already been attained sometime between one million and 500,000 years ago. Any cut-off point in this continuum to designate the boundary between two different species must be purely arbitrary and without demonstrable biological significance. A common paleontological practice, as we have seen, is to bestow specific ranking when there is no longer overlap between the ancestral distribution curve and that of some descendent group. This is manifestly impossible to do in the case of the last one million years of human evolution. The attenuated nature of morphological characters as species criteria in Man is implicitly recognized by Coon when he stated:

> Short-cutting anthropometric details, we have set the boundary between *Homo erectus* and *Homo sapiens* on the basis of brain size, the degrees of curvature of the bones composing the

cranial vault, and, to a lesser extent, on tooth size, particularly as tooth size is related to brain size.[19]

For racial criteria he has selected two which are "particularly easy to follow. These are tooth morphology and degrees of facial flatness."

If there were five subspecies or races of Homo erectus, each of which has survived to the present day, and if Homo erectus evolved into Homo sapiens, then the five races also evolved, "independently," into their present sapiens status. What is more, each made the transition at different times. As Coon claims:

In the case of Man, the subspecies of Homo sapiens are probably of different ages, depending on the times at which regional populations of Homo erectus, in one way or another, crossed the sapiens threshold. But all of them did this before the end of the Pleistocene.[20]

We know of no precedent for this sort of evolutionary phenomenon in the entire paleontological record. The biological cul-de-sac into which Coon maneuvered himself is partially eliminated if the insistence on speciation by succession in the last one million years of hominid evolution is abandoned. Weidenreich, in 1947, first proposed this in the following statement:

I believe that all Primate forms recognized as hominids no matter whether they lived in the past or live today represent morphologically a unity when compared with other Primate forms, and that they can be regarded as one species.[21]

This went a step beyond Simpson, who in 1945 ("The Principles of Classification and a Classification of Mammals") asserted that "almost none of the anthropological 'genera' has any zoological reason for being."[22] Dobzhansky (Mankind Evolving,

[19] Ibid.
[20] Ibid.
[21] Weidenreich, F. 1947. Facts and Speculations Concerning the Origin of Homo Sapiens. American Anthropologist, new series, 49:187–203.
[22] Simpson, G. 1945. The Principles of Classification and a Classification of Mammals. Bulletin of the American Museum of Natural History, Vol. 85.

1962) recognizes two genera among hominids—*Homo* and *Australopithecus*. Within the genus *Homo* he distinguishes, as does Coon, two species, *erectus* and *sapiens*. Among the latter are included both the Neanderthaloids and Rhodesian hominids. His explanation of the transition from *Australopithecus* to *Homo erectus* is as follows:

One of the species of *Australopithecus* (if, indeed, there were several contemporaneous ones) became dependent for survival on tool-making and tool-using. It adopted, thereby, a way of life that no other animal species responded by becoming even more dependent on the invention of better tools that could be used in new ways. The successful response to the challenge, via natural selection, accelerated the tempo of the evolutionary change. The species became classifiable as *Homo*, no longer as *Australopithecus*.[23]

Homo erectus spread into many new areas, according to Dobzhansky, and once established began to differentiate into some six different "races." Dobzhansky is not, however, inclined to accept the thesis that these *erectus* races were necessarily the ancestors of those now in existence, for he states:

. . . we cannot lightly dismiss the possibility that the now-living human species carries in its gene pool genetic elements derived from most or from all the fossil races of *Homo erectus* and *Homo sapiens*, though in very unequal proportions. On the other hand, we may be descended from only one ancient race, all others having petered out.[24]

A somewhat different point of view was advanced by Mayr (in 1950).[25] He included *Australopithecus* along with all other fossil hominids in the single genus *Homo*. The basis for this he explained as follows:

I did not find any morphological characters that would necessitate separating them into several genera. Not even *Australopithecus* has unequivocal claims for separation. This form appears to possess what might be considered the principal generic character of *Homo*, namely, upright posture with its shift to a

---

[23] Dobzhansky, T. 1962. *Mankind Evolving*. New Haven: Yale University Press.

[24] *Ibid.*

[25] Mayr, E. 1950. Taxonomic Categories in Fossil Hominids. *Cold Spring Harbor Symposia on Quantitative Biology*, 15:109–118.

terrestrial mode of living and the freeing of the anterior extremity for new functions which, in turn, have stimulated brain evolution. Within this type there has been phyletic speciation resulting in *Homo sapiens.*

In a more recent publication, however, Mayr reversed his position, stating:

Since it (*Australopithecus*) already has the essential morphological characters of *Homo*, such as upright posture, reduced canines, and bicuspid premolars, I remarked previously that "not even *Australopithecus* has unequivocal claims for (generic) separation" (Mayr, 1950). I now agree with those authors who have since pointed out not only that upright locomotion was still imperfect but also that the tremendous evolution of the brain since *Australopithecus* permitted Man to enter so completely different a niche that generic separation is definitely justified. Here, as in other cases, it is important not only to count characters but also to weigh them. The brain evolution justifies the generic separation of *Australopithecus* from *Homo* no matter how similar they are in other characters.[26]

He thus returned to the taxonomic position held by Dobzhansky and Coon. To Mayr the question of a separate generic status for the Australopithecinae essentially hinges upon the determination of whether or not these earliest hominids of the Pleistocene, with their demonstrably small-sized brains, produced culture. If they did, then it should be evident that from the point of view of biochemistry and physiology they had made the crucial neurological transition from ape to Man.

Mayr recognized three phyletic hominid species, that is, species by succession: *transvaalensis, erectus,* and *sapiens.* However, his reasons for distinguishing them as species are very obscure. On the one hand, he claimed that Mankind "speciated" only once—when it originally branched out from the common hominoid trunk. In this sense of the term "speciation" he meant "the origin of discontinuities through the origin of reproductive isolating mechanisms." On the other hand, Mayr freely admitted that to determine the point in human evolution where the *sapiens* level was attained "is quite impossible." Coon attempted to pinpoint this boundary on the basis of brain size, cranial

[26] Mayr, E. 1963. *Animal Species and Evolution.* Cambridge: Harvard University Press.

vault curvature, and tooth morphology, but Mayr insisted it is "dangerous, in fact, outright misleading" to use brain size as such a criterion. He further minimizes the value of cultural markers since the earliest hominids made stone tools and the first use of fire cannot be dated reliably. As regards cranial contours and tooth morphology, the reader already is acquainted with our assignment of these anatomical details to the order of tertiary effects. The minute and gradual changes in cranial vault contours were most likely responses of bone to the growth in size of the brain. Likewise, the crown morphology of the dentition no longer had selective value after erect posture was achieved. Since, as Mayr (1950) himself pointed out, "it was a very gradual process leading from *erectus* to *sapiens* and no particular form can be singled out as the missing link" and since no one has succeeded in showing a constellation of trait distribution curves wherein *Homo erectus* and *Homo sapiens* overlap by less than 25 percent (Simpson, 1961),[27] it would appear that there really is no firm basis for disputing Weidenreich's thesis that all hominid forms from the beginnings of the Pleistocene to the present represent a single species.

If our thesis holds that all erect, bipedal, culture-producing hominids can properly be subsumed under the single genus *Homo* and the single species *sapiens*, then clearly we have been in error in following the usual practice of giving separate generic and specific ranking to such forms as *Pithecanthropus erectus*, *Sinanthropus pekinensis*, *Australopithecus prometheus*, etc. It would have been much more consistent, although a source of confusion to the novitiate, to label such forms as *Homo sapiens pekinensis*, *Homo sapiens erectus*, *Homo sapiens prometheus*, etc. Unfortunately, the anthropological literature is already saddled with the former terminology and no good purpose would be served by further confounding it. The reader is best advised to consult Cain (1954),[28] Mayr (1963),[29] and Simpson (1961),[30]

[27] Simpson, G. 1961. *Principles of Animal Taxonomy*. New York: Columbia University Press.

[28] Cain, A. 1954. *Animal Species and Their Evolution*. London: Hutchinson.

[29] Mayr, E. 1963. *Animal Species and Evolution*. Cambridge: Harvard University Press.

[30] Simpson, *Op. cit.*

among others before deciding whether he shall approach the fossil evidence for human evolution as a "splitter" or as a "lumper."

Although we have already discussed the species concept at some length, a few concluding remarks may serve to clarify the point of view we are expounding relative to human evolution. Mayr's definition of species is a genetical one: "Species are groups of actually or potentially interbreeding natural populations, which are reproductively isloated from other such groups." For living populations of animals this definition is biologically sound and readily applicable. But how can it be applied to an evolutionary series—"an ancestral-descendant sequence of populations" (Simpson, 1961)—when neither the potentiality of interbreeding nor the degree of isolation can be observed? In such cases an evolutionary definition of species has been proposed by Simpson which he claims is consistent with the genetical definition:

"An evolutionary species is a lineage . . . evolving separately from others and with its own unitary evolutionary role and tendencies."[31]

Roles are definable, according to Simpson, "by their equivalence to niches, using 'niche' for the whole way of life or relationship to the environment of a population of animals . . ." If morphological traits are adaptive they are related to roles. Modern *Homo sapiens* adapts to his environment in a unique way—through culture. His anatomy and physiology do not peculiarly adapt him to his environment; at most they are permissive rather than positive. Only his central nervous system is unique in that it evolved to the point where speech and culture were made possible. If culture is the "role" of the human evolutionary species, then any fossil hominid found in unequivocal association with evidence of culture should be regarded as a member of the evolutionary species *Homo sapiens*. For the moment, at least, the designation of the Australopicinae as *Homo sapiens* must await confirmation of such evidence.

Races Versus Breeding Populations: a Conceptual Dilemma

We have seen that as few as six modern races of Man have been recognized. On the other hand some anthropologists and other

[31] Ibid., p. 153.

interested scholars have delineated as many as 32 races (Coon, Garn, and Birdsell, 1950).[32] There is no argument about either the usefulness or the reality of the species concept; but there is little agreement as to the definition or practicality of subspecies. Simpson (1961)[33] feels that the problem of subspecies can be summed up by two questions: (1) Is there any objective element in subspecies?; and (2) Does the subspecies concept offer any advantage to the student of evolution? There is no clear-cut answer to either question. Nevertheless, we must consider the implications of both as they apply to the human species.

The fundamental unit in biological evolution is, of course, not necessarily the species but the effective breeding population, however small or however large. As we carefully survey the world's population we see not 6 or 32 but thousands of such human units. Some of these breeding populations are partially isolated by geographic factors, others by social barriers such as class and status institutions, religious beliefs, economic ranks, and ethnic affiliation. None are completely isolated, but constantly interbreed with other populations with variable frequency. Let us concentrate on the situation as it exists among the American Indians. It is still thought by most students and certainly by the public that the term "American Indian" refers to a biological and cultural entity, comparable to the Negroes of West Africa or the people of China. The term actually has validity only in the sense that it refers collectively to the inhabitants of North America before the White Man arrived. Nothing else binds them together. They speak many different languages, some as unrelated to each other as Japanese and Hungarian. They represent many different physical types. While they themselves entered into North America via the same route—the Bering Strait—they did so at different times and in many small groups. Their origins in Asia are still only guessed at, but there is no evidence that their migrations began much before 20 or 30 thousand years ago. Culturally they run the gamut from simple hunting and gathering bands to populous villages supported by extensive agricultural practices. Putting them all into

[32] Coon, C., Garn, S., and Birdsell, J. 1950. *Races—A Study of the Problems of Race Formation in Man.* Springfield: C. C. Thomas.
[33] *Op. cit.*

one category—American Indian—and calling them a branch of the Mongoloid peoples of the world, simply obscures the real and meaningful biological fact that the Indians of North America comprise hundreds of breeding populations. These are not necessarily identified with the so-called tribal names. The Apache Indians of Arizona and New Mexico are not a breeding population but rather comprise several breeding groups. They are not distinguishable by locality but by band affiliation. Members of different bands are linguistically, physically, and geographically indistinguishable; nevertheless, they practice band endogamy, that is, marriage takes place only between members of the same band. The fact that the blood group genes show significantly different frequencies between any two such bands is evidence that such bands are relatively isolated reproductively. The usual practice on the part of epidemiologists, geneticists, and even some anthropologists, of sampling tribes or reservations rather than breeding populations has rendered a considerable portion of the reports on differential frequencies of blood group genes and morbidity among "American Indian Tribes" without meaning or validity. As with the Indians, so with the populations of Europe and Africa. Generally a large sample is given preference over a sample selected with regard to actual breeding groups. The studies of Glass on the Dunkers and Witkop on triracial isolates on the Eastern Atlantic Seaboard are sterling examples of how the preliminary determination and definition of the breeding population can yield valid and significant results in both genetics and medicine.[34] Thieme (1952) warned against indiscriminate sampling in his study of the Puerto Rican population,[35] and Sanghvi and Khanolkar (1949) have demonstrated the need for thorough analysis of social forces promoting reproductive isolation in their investigation of endogamous groups in Bombay.[36]

In reality, each breeding population, regardless of size, is

[34] Witkop, C. 1956. A Study of Tri-racial Isolates in Eastern United States. *Acta Genetica et Statistica Medica*, 6:410–412.

[35] Thieme, F. 1952. The Population as a Unit of Study. *American Anthropologist*, 54:504–509.

[36] Sanghvi, L. and Khanolkar, V. 1949. Data Relating to Seven Genetical Characters in Six Endogamous Groups in Bombay. *Annals of Eugenics*, 15:52–64.

potentially a species in the making. In Man, however, this potentiality will probably never be realized. No group is completely isolated today. Geographical barriers have been broken down by modern means of transportation and communication. Social barriers are generally in a state of flux and are constantly being broken down. Physical differences, in spite of their avowed social effect, have never proven to be an effective deterrent to interbreeding. In the past, however, the situation was much different. As Mayr wrote:

There is much indirect evidence that primitive man was much more broken up into small scattered tribes with little contact with each other, intensely subject to local and selective factors.[37]

To what extent the differences now present between local breeding groups reflect a history of reproductive isolation is a question that can only be answered by intensive study of specific cases. The Dunkers showed genetic divergence from their European relatives and the surrounding American population as a result of only three or four generations of isolation, presumably as a consequence of genetic drift. The genetic differences among Apache bands may have come about hundreds of years ago when small, isolated hunting groups of Athabascan speakers migrated southward from Canada into their present location in the Southwest.

The value of linguistic and cultural similarities in determining biological affinity is extremely difficult to assess. Both language and culture can spread over vast areas and affect many populations without biologically significant intercourse between peoples. Conversely, as we know from the frequent invasions of Europe from Asia, there can be considerable interbreeding without significant interchange or substitution of language or culture. As any anthropologist knows, the culture areas of North America do not necessarily embrace peoples of one language or of a single physical type.

Knowing, as we do, the long history of Man during which he lived in small bands, relatively or completely isolated by formidable geographical barriers, it should not be surprising if many differences that arose through selection and genetic drift

[37] Mayr, *Op. cit.*

should be preserved to some extent in modern local groups scattered throughout the world. Isolating mechanisms, however, can work at different levels, from the small territory of the band to the large continental mass. Thus, Europe could have been more or less effectively sealed off from Africa for thousands of years so that the populations of the two continents could diverge to the point where those differences recognizable between Caucasoids and Negroids could become established. Within both populations, however, smaller groups developed minor distinguishing characteristics of their own as a result of both social and geographical isolating mechanisms. The process of evolutionary differentiation was operating both between and within large populations. Its rate, in each case, was a function of the degree and duration of isolation. The picture is further complicated by the fact that constant migrations from one population to another took place. Segments of two large populations could have settled a third area and, by their intermingling, have established a hybrid group that then pursued an independent evolutionary pathway for a period of time sufficient to develop entrenched phenotypic traits of its own. This interpretation, which is in accord both with known biological principles of evolution and with the modifications of these principles by the social and cultural forces peculiar to the hominid line, is consistent with the nature and distribution of the modern human racial groups. It does not seek or demand "racial purity" or "separate evolution of racial lines" when in fact no such entities exist in Man.

It is much more realistic to look at both the obvious and the not-so-obvious genetic and morphologic groupings of modern Man as rivers, streams, and brooks that are represented in a cross-section of a map (Fig. 81). If we drew a straight line across a highland area we would intersect many small streams and brooks. The line would pick up some streams right at their points of origin, others would be shown merging into one stream, while still others would be depicted as independent little brooks. Looking only at this one section we would have no idea of their courses nor could we possibly predict their future fates; which would eventually dry up in some desert area, which would join with others, and which would pursue an independent course

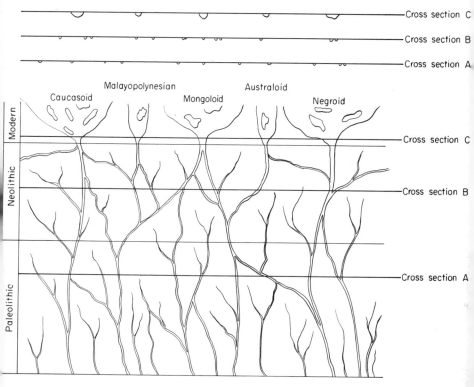

FIGURE 81. *The Segmented View of the Flow of Human Evolution Afforded by Isolated Fossil Remains*

to some sea or lake. Suppose we were to draw our cross-section even farther from the divide. We would be presented with an entirely different picture. Some of the rivers and streams that were shown in cross-section A would have disappeared or be unidentifiable in cross-section B. A few streams would have become enlarged into rivers as a result of previous junctions with other streams. Some new brooks would be represented that had not originated as far back as cross-section A. In another cross-section C, still farther removed from the highlands, we get quite a different view. There are many more rivers of considerable breadth, but the number of small streams has decreased.

Let us designate cross-section A as representing a moment of time during the Paleolithic period. The separate lines represent relatively isolated bands of food gatherers and hunters. Whence they came and whither they are going we cannot say from a single cross-section. Yet this is all we have to go on—the entire map is lacking and only minute unconnected segments will ever be known to us. Cross-section B represents the Neolithic period during which there is an increase in population size (the streams are becoming wider). There are still plenty of more or less isolated small bands but there are more "confluences of rivers" as transportation, communication, and trade increases. The origins and previous evolutionary histories of the populations revealed in cross-section B cannot be easily traced from the few scattered earlier cross-sections that are available to us. Nevertheless, it is quite probable that many bands in cross-section A have "dried-up" and others have "merged" (hybridized) to form some of the populations shown in cross-section B. Finally we look at cross-section C, which slices across the population "streams" at some point in modern times. We note at least three major "rivers" (Caucasoid, Mongoloid, and Negroid) and perhaps a few lesser ones (Australoid, Ainu, Malaysian, Bushmen-Hottentot, etc.). Instead of tiny brooks and rivulets we see "channels" and "eddies" in the main rivers. Such channels of the "Mongoloid river" constitute the various American Indian populations. In the "Caucasoid river" we detect swirls and eddies that we might label Nordic, Mediterranean, Alpine, etc. They are not clearly demarcated from each other but in general one can see that they are different currents in the same river. The great "Negroid stream" likewise shows numerous channels and eddies we can identify as Papuan, Pigmy, Bantu, etc.

The larger a river the more likely it has a relatively longer independent course. This is tantamount to saying that the larger and more phenotypically distinct a modern population is, the more likely it has pursued a *relatively* isolated evolutionary pathway. But we must remember that any river is composed of contributions, at various points in its course, by smaller streams joining it from widely separated and often remote areas. A chemical analysis of a river's contents will probably not disclose the nature of the individual streams that have contributed to them. In similar fashion, the gene frequencies and phenotypic characteristics of a large population, like the Alpine group of the Caucasoid family, will not tell us what smaller bands and tribes have merged to contribute their genes to the larger group. Nor can we determine at what moments in time these "junctures" had occurred.

The "cross-sections" of the streams of hominid evolution are very few and incomplete. They are represented by fragmentary and geographically isolated fossil remains. What is more, our geological and chemical chronometers are not refined enough to permit us to determine contemporaneity of two fossil finds except in terms of thousands of years. Thus some paleontologists refer to the *Tabūn* and *Skhūl* finds as "contemporary" but actually they may be temporally separated by as much as 10 or 20 thousand years. This poses certain difficulties for theories of hybridization taking place on the slopes of Mt. Carmel. Numerous obstacles, therefore, stand in the way of any attempt at tracing the phylogenetic history of modern populations of Man. They include:

1. Chronological inaccuracy
2. Small number of isolated fossil finds
3. Data confined only to the skeletal elements
4. Fragmentary nature of the skeletal evidence
5. Great temporal and geographical discontinuities of the fossil evidence

For these reasons we must regard claims as to the time, place, origin, and course of evolution of the modern human races for what they really are: ofttimes fanciful excursions into the unknown far beyond the limits of the available evidence.

Races and Racial Subdivisions

A final subject must yet be considered: the differences between the boundaries separating subspecies (Caucasoid, Mongoloid, Negroid, etc.) and those demarcating the races or "sub-subspecies" (Nordic, Alpine, Hottentot, Pygmy, Eskimo, etc.). We have already indicated some of the morphological criteria of the major subspecies of Man. Gene frequency differences can be found in the works of Boyd (1963),[38] Race and Sanger,[39] and Mourant.[40] *Almost* any member of one of the subspecies will present the typical bodily characteristics of that subspecies. Almost any African Negro, picked at random, will show everted lips, frizzly hair, broad nose, dark skin, etc. Practically any Caucasoid will show the typical high nasal bridge, narrow nose, thin lips, light colored skin, etc. And the same applies to almost any Mongoloid. On the other hand, it would be a rare case indeed for the blood groups to reveal the subspecific affiliation of an individual. Every type of blood group gene (with the possible exceptions of Di, Ro, Fy, and V) is represented, albeit in different frequencies, in each of the major subdivisions of Man.

When we examine the minor subdivisions or races of Man, we meet with an entirely different problem. There are no clear-cut morphological differences by which all individuals of one race are clearly separated from all members of another. Instead, anthropologists have often described "ideal racial types," each of which possesses the constellation of traits that is supposed to be diagnostic for that race. Unfortunately, very few members of the race can be found who are "typical." We are all familiar with the difficulties Hitler ran into when he postulated the "pure" Nordic type and found that many of his people, including himself, lacked the necessary morphological equipment to qualify for membership. Perhaps one of the most revealing studies of the real status of race criteria was that of Schlaginhaufen. He classified 34,630 Swiss army recruits according to stature, cephalic index, facial index, nasal index, hair color, and eye color. There were 4800 possible categories using all aspects of these criteria and the Swiss army men comprised 1590 of these. The largest number of individuals falling into any one category was 612 or 1.77 percent of the total. Using the accepted anthropological criteria of race, he found that 1.57 percent were Nordics, 0.615 percent were Mediterraneans, and 1.41 percent

[38] Boyd, W. 1963. Genetics and the Human Race. *Op. cit.*

[39] Race, R. and Sanger, R. 1954. *Blood Groups in Man*, 2nd ed. Springfield: C. C. Thomas.

[40] Mourant, A. 1954. *The Distribution of the Blood Groups*. Springfield: C. C. Thomas.

were Alpines.[41] Nevertheless, Coon claims that a "large Nordic element has survived here (in Switzerland) in solution."[42]

The anthropological picture presented by the peoples of Europe is precisely what we should expect. Interbreeding of small Paleolithic bands and, later, of larger Neolithic agricultural populations, have so mixed the genes of these Caucasoid isolates that today there is no possibility of identifying the earlier groups or the extent of their genetic contribution. Nevertheless, anyone crossing Europe from Scandinavia south through Italy gets an impression of a gradual change in the physical types. The impression is reinforced only by statistical analysis of large samples drawn from successive areas. Statistical differences are not meaningful as racial criteria but they do reflect in a vague way the historic existence of ancient widespread population isolates. The central European Alps must have served as a partially effective barrier to interbreeding between bands living in what is now Italy and bands living in Western and Central Europe.

The time-honored but utterly fallacious practice of constructing statistical means or averages and then holding these up as diagnostic of race simply helps to perpetuate the myth of "pure race" and to emphasize "racial differences" which are fraught with social and political overtones and barren of biological significance without intensive analysis. It would be in the nature of a statistical miracle to expect the means of two samples, even if drawn from the same population, to be identical. They may indeed be so different as to be "statistically significant." Nevertheless, such averages, and the differences between them, are used to "demonstrate" the difference in "intelligence" between American Whites and American Negroes. We all know the vicious uses to which these and other racial "facts" are put. The literature on such subjects is truly vast and the reader is cautioned to enter it with the extremely critical attitude that only a background of modern statistics and biology will provide.

[41] Schlaginhaufen, O. 1946. Die Anthropologie der Eidgenossenschaft. Anthropologia Helvetica, I. *Archiv der Julius Klaus-Stiftung.* Vol. 21. Zürich: Art. Institut Orell Füssli A.-G.

[42] Coon, C. 1939. *The Races of Europe.* New York: The Macmillan Company.

The Problem of Adaptiveness of Racial Traits

In the past 15 years there have been increased efforts to explain certain racial characteristics, particularly those related to external bodily shape and proportions, on the basis of their adaptive value. Some of these explanations have been ingenious if not well substantiated. Coon, Garn, and Birdsell (1950) saw adaptive significance in such correlations as:

Rice diet	Reduced body size
Meat diet	Muscularity
Climate	Bodily proportions
Sunlight	Skin pigmentation
Heat	Hair shape
Cold and snow glare	Epicanthic fold
Extreme cold	Low nasal bridge, flat face
Extreme cold	Sparse, coarse, straight hair

These authors call upon mutations with a high selective value to explain the development of the Mongoloid racial type. Such mutations, they claimed, "would have a good chance to produce a new racial type in a small population over the 400 to 500 generations during which the maximum cold reached its peak."[43] The deterrent effects of culture upon the selective forces of Nature were not considered in their hypothesis. It is interesting to note that two of our foremost authorities on evolution are in disagreement about the adaptive significance of racial traits. Dobzhansky (1962) states:

Shocking though this may be, solid and conclusive evidence concerning the adaptive significance of racial traits in Man is scant in the extreme, and the best that can be offered are plausible speculations and surmises![44]

Mayr (1963), on the other hand, claims:

There is no reason why man should be immune to this type of natural selection (of adaptive racial traits), and yet there have been many authors who ascribe the differences between human races to "accidents of variation."[45]

[43] Coon, C., Garn, S., and Birdsell, J., Op. cit.
[44] Dobzhansky, T. 1962. Mankind Evolving. New Haven: Yale University Press.
[45] Mayr, Op. cit.

He considers that Coon, Garn, and Birdsell, among others, have "demonstrated" the adaptive value of racial traits in Man. The fact of the matter is that correlations that may be found between environmental features and human phenotypes do not constitute proof of causal relationship between the two. Until experimental evidence of such relationship is forthcoming, it is perhaps best to hold the question in abeyance, as Dobzhansky seems to suggest.

With this all too brief review of the many topics so pertinent to an understanding of human evolution, we must now turn to the problem of marshalling the various facts, theories, and hypotheses to the end that a consistent and logical story of Man's development will emerge.

PROBLEM X

AN INTERPRETATION
OF HUMAN EVOLUTION

There is no more need to postulate an élan vital *or a guiding purpose to account for evolutionary progress than to account for adaptation, for degeneration or any other form of specialization. . . . The purpose manifested in evolution, whether in adaptation, specialization, or biological progress, is only an apparent purpose. It is just as much a product of blind forces as is the falling of a stone to earth or the ebb and flow of the tides. It is we who have read purpose into evolution, as earlier men projected will and emotion into inorganic phenomena like storm or earthquake.*

JULIAN HUXLEY, *Evolution, the Modern Synthesis,* 1942

My own "hunch" is that all organic evolution is following a pattern which constitutes one portion of the great design of the universe. Of course, I cannot prove that such is the case, any more than those who hold the opposite view can prove their position.

P. A. MOODY, *Introduction to Evolution,* 2nd ed. 1962

It is difficult, to say the least, for the scientist to interpret and evaluate the pathway and meaning of the evolution of a species of which he himself is a member. At every turn his biological and social individuality seeks expression and may color his judgment and point of view almost without his realization that this is the case. Nevertheless, it is encumbent upon him to marshal

345

the facts, weigh the evidence, and produce an interpretation, if only to provide others with food for thought and a stimulant for further contemplation of the subject. Who is in a better position to provide the "mirror for Man"—the perspective in which Man can see from whence he came—the better to formulate a blueprint for his future course? We do no less when we plan a Summer vacation. Our destination and the duration and nature of our trip are conditioned by many factors, each of which we carefully evaluate before setting forth. How much money is available? Where have we previously spent our vacations? In what shape is the car? Do we have the proper clothing? What kind of accommodations are provided? Few of us would embark even on a week's vacation without giving some consideration to such questions.

Yet, now plotting a future course for himself among the stars and planets of this and perhaps other galaxies, Man has already created a technological inventory that will transform life on earth in ways which he cannot even imagine. The creation of life itself and the shaping of the future course of biological evolution will soon be within his grasp. These changes are "for real." There will be no return to the good old familiar "home" life, as when we return from a vacation. Man has set a course for that "undiscover'd country, from whose bourne no traveller returns." Has he prepared himself properly? Does he have the biological, social, and cultural potentialities for surviving such a trip? Can he, unlike all other forms of life on earth, persevere as a species in the face of continual catastrophic changes in his environment—changes which he himself has brought about? Truly Man has set in motion a gigantic force. It is like dislodging a boulder set on the top of a mountain. At first it moves slowly and hesitantly and then it picks up speed until it descends with such momentum that it breaks free other rocks on the way down. Before long an avalanche has developed, uncontrollable and unpredictable. In the case of Man, this first boulder was perhaps the invention of fire and the use of stones and twigs as tools and weapons. At first this little "boulder" of culture traveled slowly and uncertainly down the slopes of Time. On its way it dislodged other "pebbles" of culture—new traditions of stone working, the use of bone for implements, the creation of crude stone or wood shelters. For almost a million years an avalanche of culture was slowly building up, its progress through Time imperceptible to the existent generations. Its true rate of descent can only now be measured by the tools of the geochronologist and archaeologist as he surveys what happened from his vantage point of elapsed time. Finally a tremendous rock outcropping was broken loose—the invention of agriculture, and the avalanche picked up greater speed. Within the past 10,000 years the avalanche of culture has descended with such speed and with such devastating effect that today we can almost measure its progress by the hour. We are swept along with it as with the raging currents of a mountain stream. Every phase of Man's life is involved. The question that faces us is not: Can we stop the flood of culture that we have unwittingly released? What should concern us now is: Can we gain some sort of control over its course? How can we negotiate a "breather" so that we can learn something about the characteristics both of Man himself and the cultural Frankenstein he has created before the latter completely engulfs the former?

The story of human evolution, even though it presents many formidable gaps and areas of argument and doubt, is much more than a subject of academic interest. It can provide us with the perspective that we all need in order to see ourselves in proper relationship to the apparently bewildering world in which we live. To some this story will be disquieting and may clash with many of the beliefs and values which they have culturally acquired and to which they are comfortably adapted. To others it may provide the basis for a new philosophy that is personally satisfying and conducive to the peace of mind we all seek.

In preparation for an interpretation of Man's evolution we have attempted to bring together some of the important pieces of evidence from many different fields of scientific interest. Doubtless some points have been omitted that some might feel would significantly supplement or alter the subsequent interpretation. There is no claim to all-inclusiveness; nor is there any attempt to defend the specific weighting given to a particular bit of evidence. Probably no two students of human evolution would agree on the emphasis or evaluation that should be afforded to any single fossil discovery, or on the significance of a particular biological principle for human phylogenesis. Nevertheless a vast amount of evidence from geology, paleontology, anatomy, embryology, anthropology, physiology, genetics, and biochemistry has been accumulated through the years. Contained therein is an intriguing account of the origin and development of Man. The manipulation of these data so as to bring forth a reasonably reliable picture of human evolution is a formidable task, with every likelihood that certain changes will be required as new evidence and greater knowledge is acquired. There is sufficient material, however, for sketching in the outlines of the picture. Whether the result is realistic or impressionistic only Time will tell.

Some 70 million years ago the vicissitudes of environment brought about an adaptive radiation of a group of small arboreal Mammals called Insectivores. Subsequent branchings of this newly evolving group have been given the name Primates. Primarily these animals were distinguished by a relatively enlarged brain, stereoscopic vision, grasping, prehensile hands and feet, and a tendency for upright position of the trunk when sitting. Several types of locomotion were to be found among them. Some were primarily brachiators; others progressed on all fours, either on the ground or in the trees. A few could even walk along on their hind legs, but this was neither their usual nor most efficient means of locomotion. The first Primates probably originated in North America and Europe whence they spread southward into South America, Asia, and Africa. Those who occupied the western hemisphere remained completely isolated from their eastern relatives and as a result evolved in somewhat different, but relatively minor, ways. They played no role in the evolution of those later Primate forms which included Man.

The Prosimians, as these earliest of Primates are called, included lemurs and tarsiers, whose descendants now inhabit southeastern Asia and Madagascar. It is most likely that the tarsier line gave rise to the Old World monkeys or Cercopithecoidea, on the one hand, and the Hominoidea on the other. Another important center of radiation developed in East Africa during the early part of the Miocene epoch. Here groups of primitive Cercopithecoidea underwent rapid evolution into a series of ape-like creatures who ultimately gave rise to the Pongidae and the

Hominidae. Undoubtedly there were other such centers, perhaps in Europe and in Egypt, but the East African events are the best documented. From these centers such forms as the Dryopithecinae migrated in all directions. Some found their way into Europe while others moved north to Egypt and thence across southern Asia into India and China. Another group may have moved into South Africa. From the paleontological record we have no inkling of the ultimate fate of the European and Chinese migrants, but there is ample evidence that a relatively large number of these Dryopithecinae thrived in the Siwalik Hills region of India, developing into a variety of local forms which might very well have been the precursors of the later hominids. Beyond teeth and fragments of jaws we have no clues as to the bodily characteristics of the widespread Dryopithecinae.

We can only postulate that there was a migration of these East African hominoids into South Africa on the basis of the fact that the remains of the earliest ancestors of Man have been found here. The Australopithecine fossils probably pertain to the beginning of the Pleistocene epoch, about one million years ago. A gap, therefore, of perhaps as much as 20 million years separates the East African Dryopithecinae from their presumed descendants, the Australopithecinae. This is surely an ample period of time for the development of the quantitative changes in both skeleton and central nervous system that led to the upright posture and bipedalism as well as the culture-producing brain of the Australopithecinae. The South African hominids of the early Pleistocene did walk erect and if there is not yet direct evidence that they produced fire and fashioned crude implements, there is the distinct possibility that such evidence will eventually be found. It does not seem likely that the attainment of a brain capable of producing culture and permitting articulate speech could have lagged far behind the assumption of erect posture. As certain ape-like creatures gradually rose from all fours to assume an upright position they suffered a concurrent and progressive loss of their customary weapons of attack and defense. Their teeth and jaws were rendered "hors de combat." The elimination of the forelimbs from the usual role of locomotion reduced their speed, both in pursuit and in flight. The important olfactory senses were no longer as acute. In order to survive, these animals had to be able to think, to remember, and to communicate with each other more precisely than ever before. The need for these properties set the stage for the selection of the adaptive qualities of the brain. If the Australopithecinae did not have the rudiments of simple culture—the knowledge of fire, the use of stones as weapons and implements, and the fashioning of tree limbs as clubs and piercing tools—how could they and their ancestors have survived? Were such critical developments as the hominid-type brain and the beginnings of culture suddenly achieved after the appearance of the Australopithecinae and before the time of *Pithecanthropus*—in other words, at some time between one million and 500,000 years ago? Probably the origin of the potentialities of the human brain for thought and speech will forever be shrouded in mystery, but we can speculate that the selective forces that initiated and developed it were at work during that long stretch of time when groups of Dryopithecine apes were evolving into bipedal Australopithecines.

The Australopithecinae must have lived in small relatively isolated groups. The cranial fragments thus far recovered reveal a rather wide range of morphological types. Which, if any, of these South African bands survived to become the direct ancestors of modern Man we shall probably never know. It is not a particularly important point. What is important is that the morphological stage they represent is one through which the human evolutionary line must have passed. It is quite possible that a similar hominid phase of development was attained by advanced Dryopithecine groups in India and China, but of this there is no evidence. As matters stand, it would appear that Man, as an upright brainy Primate, first appeared on the world's scene about a million years ago in South Africa.

For the next 500,000 years the fossil record is almost nonexistent and our geological timepieces are somewhat unreliable. Both a morphological and a geographical gap exist between the Australopithecinae and the more advanced hominid forms such as *Sinanthropus*, *Pithecanthropus*, and the Olduvai hominine fossils. In the mid-Pleistocene, culture-bearing hominid populations lived in China, Java, and Africa. In addition, artifacts of a similar age, but without a trace of the skeletons of their makers, with the single exception of Swanscombe Man, are found throughout Europe and Asia. Evidently hominids were widespread in the Old World by the middle of the Pleistocene. Had they all originated from a single center, or had they evolved independently in the areas in which they now lived? If the former, where was this center located and at what morphological stage of evolutionary development had the migrations taken place? If polycentrism is the explanation then we must ask how and at what point of hominoid development such centers began. If Pleistocene hominids evolved separately and independently from European, Asiatic, and African groups of Dryopithecinae, then certainly there would have been sufficient time (perhaps 10 to 20 million years) for evolutionary divergence to have resulted in different species of Man. Yet today there is but one species. What is more, the differences between *Sinanthropus*, *Pithecanthropus*, and such African hominids as Saldanha and Rhodesian Man are not such as to suggest that these forms represent different species. It would seem more logical to postulate that from a single center in South Africa between early and mid-Pleistocene times a series of migrations took place. The migrants were morphologically more hominid than the Australopithecinae who were their forebears and culturally somewhat more advanced. They drifted northward through Africa and spread into Europe and Asia. In Asia some groups continued into what is now China. They are represented by the *Sinanthropus* fossils recovered from a cave near Peking. Others turned southward, crossing from the Malay Peninsula over a landbridge into Indonesia. The *Pithecanthropus* fossils of Java represent this southern migrant group. The European migrants left plenty of evidence of their tool-making proclivities but thus far, except for Swanscombe and Heidelberg, there have been no undoubted fossils of their skeletons.

If we subscribe to the hypothesis of a monocentric early Pleistocene origin of mid-Pleistocene hominids of the Old World, then two unwieldy problems are resolved. By this time these hominids must have developed articulate speech and hence communication between scattered bands was rendered possible and even probable. With a means of communication complete biological isolation for any one group over an extended period of time was highly unlikely. What is more, even without inter-communication and interbreeding it would be improbable that speciation could have taken place in the relatively brief span of two or three hundred thousand years representing but 10,000 generations. The archaeology of this period indicates a wide-spread community of stone-working traditions, mute testimony to the fact that there was considerable intercourse in ideas, hence undoubtedly in genes, amongst the many scattered groups of mid-Pleistocene men.

Though few bands were completely biologically isolated most of them tended to be largely endogamous so that differences in gene frequencies constantly developed. Genetic drift played a large role in effecting these differences in small population groups. In addition, mutations could easily become established at a low rate of equilibrium in some bands while failing to arise in others. These interpopulational genetic differences were often expressed in phenotypic traits observable in the skeleton. An-thropologists often seize upon such morphological differences as indicative of specific and even generic separation of fossil hominids. It is unlikely that such relatively minor variations reflect anything but the slight shifts in gene frequencies brought about by genetic drift operating in small groups that were only partially isolated for brief periods of time. If we grant specific rank to every fossil collection found, we would be placed in the untenable position of relegating all such early hominid popula-tions except one to the limbo of "dead-ends" or abortive at-tempts of Nature to produce Man.

The present day races or subspecies of Man could hardly have originated before the three continents were populated by hominids of mid-Pleistocene times. The Negroids could well have been the first hominids to differentiate inasmuch as they were closest to the Australopithecine center in Africa. The Caucasoids probably began to develop their characteristic geno-types once they had established themselves in Europe. The Mongoloids had already acquired certain skeletal characteristics in mid-Pleistocene times as is apparent in the *Sinanthropus* material. Within each of these major subspecies, however, nu-merous small populations existed in relative isolation through-out most of the Pleistocene. They acquired, within the larger framework of the racial genotype, minor genetic peculiarities of their own. The boundaries of subspecific distinction were the continents, while those of racial criteria were geographical, social, and cultural barriers within each continent. Even if Man had remained to the present day in a Paleolithic stage of cultural development, it is doubtful, in view of his inquisitive nature and gregarious proclivities, if the continental barriers to subspecific intermixture would have remained intact. With the advent of agriculture, however, the walls between hominid populations began to crumble and the unity of Man as a single species was assured.

The advent of culture was possibly the most profound event that ever happened in some three billion years of organic evolution. It changed the rules of the game not only for Man but for all other animals on earth. It made Man the dominant form of life and placed the destiny of all other animals potentially under his control. In fact, it began to replace the natural environment as the principle selecting agent in human evolution. Culture has even placed in Man's hands the distinct possibility of either promoting or terminating his own evolution.

For almost the first million years of his existence as an upright thinking animal, Man had to be in prime physical condition in order to subsist, to find a mate, to raise a family, and to protect it against the onslaughts of both Nature and his fellow men. Because he had fire, clothing, shelter, and weapons, certain of his bodily structures lost adaptive value. The condition of his teeth was not critical for his survival. Whether or not he had profuse body hair was unimportant, for he could keep warm in other ways. The genes that control these traits could vary with a certain amount of impunity. But should a mutation arise that affected his eyesight, neuromuscular coordination, or skeleton, then a stringent natural selection would very likely eliminate him before he could reproduce and transmit such genes to his offspring. With the rapid increase in the cultural inventory brought about by plant and animal domestication, the physical prowess so necessary in a Paleolithic condition of life was rendered less important. The Industrial Revolution and its results in science, medicine, communication, and technology made it possible for any man to survive, reproduce, and compete economically with all other men in spite of many kinds of physical weaknesses and disabilities. The selective forces now are focused upon the attributes of the brain—intelligence, temperament, personality, talent, and adaptability. What is more, it is primarily culture, not the natural environment, that is doing the selecting. Man need not adapt to cold, heat, drought, infectious agents, and other conditions that beset his Paleolithic ancestors. Instead he must adjust to the rules of a society, to the complexities of modern factory or business life, to the pressures of urban life, and to the vagaries of economic fluctuations (Fig. 82).

If the environment still plays a direct role in natural selection for the human species, it is exceedingly difficult to identify or describe what this role is. True, geneticists have found a handful of conditions where in it has been convincingly demonstrated

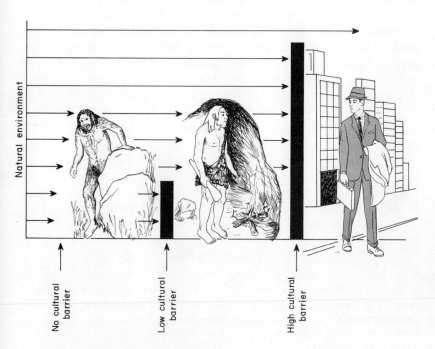

FIGURE 82. *The Interceptive Role of Culture in the Evolution of Man*

that natural selection is operating in Man, but these conditions pertain almost entirely to populations which are still in a primitive stage of civilization. The vast increase in size of the civilized populations make it improbable that selection either on the part of culture or Nature now plays a significant role in human evolution. But whether or not selective forces are at work, it would be an almost Herculean task to sort out the multitudinous cultural factors involved, categorize segments of the population into different fertility groups, and then to attempt to find meaningful associations between these groups and particular cultural and social forces.

For the human species today the term adaptation properly refers to Man's cultural rather than to his natural environment. Culture has pulled most of the teeth out of natural environment but has bared certain of its own fangs instead. In thwarting the selective forces of nature with advances in medicine, nutrition, drugs, and other ameliorative and preventive measures, culture has permitted both an explosive increase in the human population and a greater load of mutations. The result has inevitably been to broaden the range of variation not only in physical traits but in characters that are manifestations of the central nervous system. This trend can be regarded in two different ways from the standpoint of the future evolution of the human species. In the words of one geneticist the variability of the species is being "mobilized" so that Man has the potentiality of moving in any one of several directions that future selection might dictate. On the other hand we have the alternative possibility, painted in rather stark terms, by Muller:

If the attempt were made to continue indefinitely to substitute a more remote equilibrium for f_t (total frequency of manifestation of mutant genes) by ameliorative practices it would mean an even greater heaping up of mutant genes. There would be no limit to this short of the complete loss of all of the genes or their degradation into utterly unrecognizable forms, differing chaotically from one individual of the population to another. Our descendants' natural biological organization would in fact have disintegrated and have been replaced by complete disorder. Their only connections with Mankind would then be the historical one that we ourselves had after all been their ancestors and sponsors, and the fact that their once-human material was still used for the purpose of converting it, artificially, into some semblance of Man . . . For all of them would differ inordinately from one another, and each would present a whole series of most intricate research problems, before the treatments suitable for its own unique set of vagaries could be decided upon.[1]

The demise of Man, should it come about, is not apt to be the product of his genetic deterioration, however. It is much more likely that he will bring about his own destruction by the very tools which culture itself has placed in his hands. Since the environment of primary importance for Man is Culture rather than Nature, he must adapt more rapidly than ever before. The natural environment generally changes very slowly, permitting the genetic adaptive mechanism of a species to adjust to its demands. But culture changes dramatically in many ways within the lifetime of a single generation. The usual biological methods of adaptation are rendered inadequate. This being so, the question arises: How can Man adapt to an environment which he himself created but no longer controls, and which is constantly changing in ways that are hardly predictable? We have observed that for a long period of cultural history children were indoctrinated into the ways of their society by their parents with the assurance that the customs they would practice and the situations they would meet would be like those familiar to their parents, grandparents, and great-grandparents. In turn they would pass on the same knowledge to their own children, secure in the belief that this would adequately equip them to cope with the problems of life.

Today the responsibility of education has come to be held by society itself. The cultural inventory has become too vast and the burdens of making a living too time-consuming to entrust the indoctrination process to individual parents. Nevertheless, the cultural environment in which our children must live and function will be much different from that in which our generation has operated. The culture that they are learning to adapt to will exist only in history books by the time they reach adulthood. We suspect that the problems of future society will revolve about automation, space travel, underground dwellings, a

[1] Muller, H. J. 1950. Our Load of Mutations. *American Journal of Human Genetics*, 2:111–176.

ten-hour work week, and week-end trips to Europe. But how can we educate our children to cope with this kind of living when we ourselves have not experienced it? We know that racial prejudice has existed in all human societies from the beginning of recorded history, but we also are becoming aware that all races seek and demand equal treatment and opportunity. Biologically Mankind is one species. It cannot survive if its essential unity is not socially and culturally recognized. The problem of race is here now. It must be met and solved. What are we doing to help our children understand the meaning of race, of racial differences, and, more important, of racial similarities?

In education, not in genetic change, lie the potentialities for future adaptation of the species. In a world that is changing so rapidly in so many ways it is alarming to find that education remains so resistant to innovation and experimentation. Must we rely upon transitory threats of catastrophe, such as Sputnik, to jar us into making, almost blindly, a few onslaughts on the educational curriculum? Is hysteria the basis for revising the system of indoctrination of our children into the problems of tomorrow? It is hard to believe that teaching calculus and chemistry to junior high school students will make them anything but technicians, unless they learn also the meaning of technology in the modern world. When shall we begin to instruct them about Man, his society, and his culture? Why are evolution and anthropology absent from the curricula of practically all our primary and secondary schools? Perhaps religion, or rather the effects of religion, lies at the core of our apparent resistance to the teaching of evolution. There seems to be a fear, sometimes latent, sometimes quite explicit, as at the Scopes trial, that evolution denies the existence of God. It is proper that we conclude with a discussion of this subject.

It was pointed out in a previous Problem that Paleolithic and Neolithic societies "invented" superorganic beings in order to achieve some measure of control over the unpredictable vagaries of the natural environment. Lacking true knowledge of the causes of such events as floods, drought, scarcity of game, and other natural phenomena that might spell disaster for an entire band or village, the need for controlling these events was nonetheless imperative. It was fulfilled by all early human societies in much the same way. Deities were invented who presumably "owned" or controlled the various forces of Nature. By properly approaching such deities they could be influenced to withhold catastrophes and to bring about desirable conditions and occurrences. The world of primitive Man was heavily populated by such superorganic beings and spirits since there was much in his environment that he neither understood nor could regulate.

As time went on and greater comprehension of the natural world was achieved, there was less need for a large pantheon. Whereas hunting and gathering peoples were apt to spend much of their time soliciting and propitiating the deities, the more settled agricultural societies had gained a greater measure of control over their environment. A larger segment of their world had become "profane," with a corresponding reduction in the number of supernatural spirits. It is noteworthy that the concept of a single supreme deity never arose in a hunting and gathering society, if we may judge from a survey of recent populations of this primitive level.

Today science and technology have pierced much of the mystery of the world we live in. We have, collectively, an impressive understanding of Nature and many of its phenomena. We can often predict, if not control, its forces. There is no longer need for a god of wind, of rain, or of pestilence. Nevertheless there are still some areas in which we are beset by doubts and fears. In these areas we still turn to a supreme being for help. The phenomena of birth and death, of marriage and of the after-life, of war and of natural holocausts—these events we neither understand fully nor can control. It is in connection with such matters that we still look to a supernatural being for solace if not for a satisfactory solution. As with primitive Man, our approach to the deity is varied. It may be in the form of propitiation, prayer, pleas, or even bribery. The place of communication may be in the privacy of the home or in the more formal atmosphere of a religious edifice. The approach may be accompanied by much ritual and pageantry, or be extremely simple and spontaneous. The method by which one seeks the attention of the supreme being is conditioned by the society and culture in which he lives and reflects a tradition that goes far back into the past.

This interpretation of the nature and origin of the concept of the superorganic implies that supreme beings are the invention of Man for the purpose of gaining ascendancy over his environment. This is far from saying that there exists no need for such a concept. The fact that there is widespread belief in at least one deity is ample testimony to Man's need for guidance and protection. However, the universality of Man's need for supreme beings does not prove their existence. Religion is a part of culture and, like it, is the product of human intelligence. Religion may be defined as that aspect of culture concerned with the manner in which Man and his society organize and adapt to the supernatural elements of the environment as they are conventionally conceived in that society.

The social roles that religion plays, including the promotion of harmonious relations between men and between societies, are too well known to require reiteration here. Religion is based upon belief, as distinct from evidence. Belief is simply an emotional identification with a concept and as such is not open to question or challenge. The belief that Man was specially created by a divine being, or that his "soul" was a divine gift breathed into his body ignores the evidence of human evolution that is steadily accumulating. Is the kind of emotional thrill that we experience in a beautiful church or before a spectacular sunset denied us as we contemplate the long tortuous path trod by thousands of generations of fish, reptiles, mammals, and monkeys that led to our present pinnacle of achievement? What can be more wondrous and inspiring than the knowledge that the spark of life kindled three billion years ago still burns within each of us?

As we survey the evolutionary history of life we are struck by the multitudes of forms which failed to "make the grade." We have learned about some of the biological principles and "laws" that have governed the success or failure of so many species that lived in the past. Our lineage was one that survived because environmental circumstances dictated that the central nervous system would, by its peculiar development, play the key adaptive role. The specialized brain of Man invented a new environment —culture—which soon put Man in a position to dominate the natural environment and to become the architect of his own evolutionary destiny. Are we to deny that human intelligence, which has brought us so far, has the potentialities for steering a safe and peaceful course for the future?

The recognition that Man's brain has, apparently, unlimited capabilities and that the horizons of human culture cannot yet be perceived is not to deny his need for a belief in some superorganic being. Until we have established direct control over all aspects of life and have come to accept the inevitability of organic death, we apparently must turn, as have all men in the past, to some concept of divine supremacy. The nature of this concept should be a matter for each individual to decide, according to his emotional and intellectual requirements. Some may feel that the unfolding of life on earth and the manifold evolutionary radiations in response to an integrated system of biological principles reflect the existence of a supreme law or force that pervades the universe, and may call it God. To them it may seem ignoble to turn to a personalized primitive deity for guidance. Others may find that they have no need for a supernatural explanation of the universe and prefer to hold in abeyance any judgments about cause and effect in matters that still defy our understanding. The vast majority of people, however, will continue to hold firm in their emotional attachment to the concept of a divine being who has breathed the spark of humanity into Man and continues to watch over the daily activities of each one of us.

Our goal has been to place before the reader the facts, the theories, and the speculations about Man's emergence from a lower form of life, that he might better understand himself and his role in human society and culture. How he integrates this knowledge with his own need for peace of mind in an increasingly complex world is his own prerogative. That he does this in a way that will offer him the greatest motivation towards a meaningful life as a member of the species *Homo sapiens* is our sincere wish.

SUGGESTED READINGS

Problem I. Man's Kinship with the Animal Kingdom

Hickman, C. 1955. *Integrated Principles of Zoology*. St. Louis: C. V. Mosby Company.

Buchsbaum, R. 1938. *Animals Without Backbones*. Chicago: University of Chicago Press.

Hooton, E. 1946. *Man's Poor Relations*. New York: Doubleday and Company, Inc.

Le Gros Clark, W. 1949. *History of the Primates*. London: British Museum (Natural History).

Walter, H. and L. Sayles. 1949. *Biology of the Vertebrates*, 3rd ed. New York: The Macmillan Company.

Bishop, D., Brown, F., Jahn, T., Prosser, C. and Wulff, V. 1950. *Comparative Animal Physiology*. Philadelphia: W. B. Saunders Company.

Oparin, A. 1962. *Life: Its Nature, Origin, and Development*. New York: Academic Press Inc.

Wiener, A. and Gordon, E. 1960. The Blood Groups of Chimpanzees. The A-B-O Groups and M-N Types. *American Journal of Physical Anthropology*.

Bender, M. and Mettler, L. 1958. Chromosome Studies of Primates. *Science*, 128: 186–190.

Schultz, A. 1950. Origin of the Human Stock: the Specializations of Man and His Place Among the Catarrhine Primates. *Cold Spring Harbor Symposia on Quantitative Biology*, 15: 37–53.

Problem II. Perspectives in Space and Time

Libby, W. F. 1956. Radiocarbon Dating. *American Scientist*, 44:98–112.

Kulp, J. L. 1961. Geologic Time Scale. *Science*, 133:1105–1114.

Douglass, A. E. 1929. The Secret of the Southwest Solved by the Talkative Tree-rings. *National Geographic Magazine*, 54:737–770.

De Vries, H. and K. P. Oakley, 1959. Radiocarbon Dating of the Piltdown Skull and Jaw. *Nature*, 184:224–226.

Oakley, K. P. 1958. Application of Fluorine, Uranium, and Nitrogen Analysis to the Relative Dating of the Rhünda Skull. *Neues Jahrbuch für Geologie und Paläontologie*, Monatshefte 3–4, pp. 130–136.

Montagu, M. 1951. An Introduction to Physical Anthropology, 2nd ed. Springfield: C. C. Thomas.

Clark, W. 1949. History of the Primates. London: British Museum (Natural History).

Oakley, K. 1948. The Fluorine-Dating Method. *Yearbook of Physical Anthropology*, 4:44–52.

Simons, E. 1963. Some Fallacies in the Study of Hominid Phylogeny. *Science*, 141:879–889.

Oakley, K. 1961. Dating Man's Emergence. *Nature*, 191:988–989.

Problem III. Foundations of the Theory of Evolution

Mendel, G. *Experiments in Plant Hybridization*. Cambridge: Harvard University Press, 1946.

Iltis, H. *The Life of Mendel*. New York: W. W. Norton and Company. 1932.

Dodson, E. 1956. *Genetics*. Philadelphia: W. B. Saunders Company.

Osborn, H. 1894. *From the Greeks to Darwin*, 2nd ed. New York: The Macmillan Company.

Problem IV. The Mechanism of Evolution

Allison, A. 1961. Genetic Factors in Resistance to Malaria. In *Genetic Perspectives in Disease Resistance and Susceptibility, Annals of the New York Academy of Sciences*, 91:710–729.

Harnden, D. 1961. The Chromosomes. *Recent Advances in Human Genetics*. Edited by L. S. Penrose. 1–18.

Schneider, H. 1961. Genetic Resistance and Susceptibility to Infectious Disease: A Synthesis. In *Genetic Perspectives in Disease Resistance and Susceptibility, Annals of the New York Academy of Sciences*, 91:758–760.

Dodson, E. 1956. *Genetics*. Philadelphia: W. B. Saunders Company.

Steinberg, A. 1961. *Progress in Medical Genetics*. New York: Grune and Stratton.

Zamenhof, 1959. *The Chemistry of Heredity*. Springfield: C. C. Thomas.

Stevenson, A. (editor). 1961. Human Genetics. *British Medical Bulletin*, 17:177–259.

Gerald, P. 1961. The Abnormal Haemoglobins. In *Recent Advances in Human Genetics*. Edited by L. Penrose.

Problem V. Principles of Evolution

Ross, H. 1962. *A Synthesis of Evolutionary Theory*. Englewood Cliffs, New Jersey: Prentice-Hall, Inc.

Simpson, G. 1953. *The Major Features of Evolution*. New York: Columbia University Press.

Dobzhansky, T. 1955. *Evolution, Genetics, and Man*. New York: John Wiley and Sons, Inc.

Simpson, G. 1949. *The Meaning of Evolution*. New Haven: Yale University Press.

Blum, H. 1962. *Time's Arrow and Evolution*, 2nd ed., revised. New York: Harper and Row.

Patterson, J. and Stone, W. 1952. *Evolution in the Genus Drosophila*. New York: The Macmillan Company.

Jepsen, G. 1948. Selection, "Orthogenesis," and the Fossil Record. *Yearbook of Physical Anthropology*, 4:158–179.

Gregory, W. 1936. On the Meaning and Limits of Irreversibility of Evolution. *American Naturalist*, 70:517–528.

Dobzhansky, T. 1961. Adaptation in Man and Animals: A Synthesis. In Genetic Perspectives in Disease Resistance and Susceptibility. *Annals of the New York Academy of Sciences*, 91:634–636.

Roberts, D. and Harrison, G. (editors). 1959. *Natural Selection in Human Populations*. London: Pergamon Press.

Schultz, A. 1948. Ontogenetic Specializations of Man. *Yearbook of Physical Anthropology*, 4:200–219.

Problem VI. The Nature of the Evidence: Bones and Teeth

Colbert, E. 1961. *Evolution of the Vertebrates*. New York: Science Editions, Inc.

Romer, A. 1961. Synapsid Evolution and Dentition. In *The Evolution of Lower and Non-Specialized Mammals*, 2:9–56. Brussels: Paleis der Academien-Hertogsstraar.

Butler, P. 1955. The Ontogeny of Molar Pattern. *Biological Reviews*, 31:30–70.

Goodrich, E. 1958. *Studies on the Structure and Development of Vertebrates*. New York: Dover Publications, Inc. 2 Vol.

Edinger, T. 1942. Evolution of the Horse Brain. *Memoirs of the Geological Society of America*, No. 25.

Problem VII. The Fossil Evidence for Human Evolution

Howell, F. 1952. Pleistocene Glacial Ecology and the Evolution of "Classic Neanderthal" Man. *Southwestern Journal of Anthropology*, 8:377–404.

——. 1951. The Place of Neanderthal Man in Human Evolution. *American Journal of Physical Anthropology*, 9:379–412.

Le Gros Clark, W. 1955. The Os Innominatum of the Recent Ponginae with Special Reference to that of the Australopithecinae. *American Journal of Physical Anthropology*, 13:19–27.

Broom, R. and Schepers, G. 1946. The South African Fossil Ape-Men, the Australopithecinae. Pretoria: Transvaal Museum.

Robinson, J. 1954. The Genera and Species of the Australopithecinae. *American Journal of Physical Anthropology*, 12:181–199.

——. 1953. Telanthropus and Its Phylogenetic Significance. *American Journal of Physical Anthropology*, 11:445–500.

Weidenreich, F. 1940. The "Neanderthal Man" and the Ancestors of "Homo Sapiens." *American Anthropologist*, 42:125–134.

——. 1945. Giant Early Man from Java and South China. *Anthropological Papers*, American Museum of Natural History, Vol. 40, Part I.

——. 1946. *Apes, Giants and Man.* Chicago: University of Chicago Press.

Dart, R. 1955. *Australopithecus prometheus* and *Telanthropus capensis.* American Journal of Physical Anthropology, 13:67–96.

Problem VIII. The Development of Human Culture and Its Biological Implications

Hughes, A. 1954. Hyaenas Versus Australopithecines as Agents of Bone Accumulation. *American Journal of Physical Anthropology*, 12:467–485.

Blum, H. 1963. On the Origin and Evolution of Human Culture. *American Scientist*, 51:32–47.

Oakley, K. 1958. *Man the Toolmaker*, 4th ed. Norwich: Jarrold and Sons Ltd.

Washburn, S. (editor). 1961. *The Social Life of Early Man.* Chicago: Aldine Publishing Co.

Tax, S. (editor). 1962. *Anthropology Today: Selections.* Chicago: University of Chicago Press.

Birdsell, J. 1957. Some Population Problems Involving Pleistocene Man. *Cold Spring Harbor Symposia on Quantitative
Biology*, 22:47–68.

Childe, G. 1950. *What Happened in History*. Great Britain:
Penguin Books.

Problem IX. Biological and Cultural Status of Modern Man

Krogman, W. 1945. The Concept of Race. In R. Linton (ed.),
The Science of Man in the World Crisis, pp. 38–62. New
York: Columbia University Press.

Klineberg, O. 1945. Racial Psychology. In R. Linton (ed.), *ibid.*

Crow, J., Levine, P., Coon, C., and Neel, J. 1958. *Natural Selection in Man*. Detroit: Wayne State University Press and
the American Anthropological Association.

Chung, C. and Morton, N. 1961. Selection at the ABO Locus.
American Journal of Human Genetics, 13:9–23.

Sanghvi, L., Crow, J., and Li, C. 1963. Genetic Load: Three
Views. *American Journal of Human Genetics*, 15:298–321.

Goldschmidt, E. (editor). 1963. *The Genetics of Migrant and
Isolate Populations*. Baltimore: Williams and Wilkins Company.

INDEX

138

42518

COLLEGE LIBRARY
Date Due
UNIVERSITY COLLEGE

Due   Retur